ALAN ROGERS SEL

EUROPE

over 400 of the best campsites across Europe

alan
rogers

full page listings
comprehensive writeups
useful travel information

Compiled by: Alan Rogers Travel Ltd

Cover photo: FR62030 (page 94)

Editorial & Production
Editor: Robin Fearn – enquiries@alanrogers.com
Editorial Assistant: Florrie Wood, Russell Wheldon
Production & Cartography: Robert Baker
Visual Design: Ben Tully

Advertising Agencies
France: ICCS International Tourism Promotions - info@iccsfrance.com
Spain: Servicios Turisticos Heinze Latzke S.A. - info@servitur-heinze.com
Portugal: Roteiro Lda - info@roteiro-campista.pt
UK: Space Marketing - davidh@spacemarketing.co.uk
Switzerland: Spatz Camping & Tourist Service AG - nicole.jugenheimer@scts.ch
Austria, Germany, Italy Croatia & Slovenia: IGL Werbedienst GmbH - k.perner@igl.at
Other Countries: trafficking@alanrogers.com

Alan Rogers Travel
Chief Operating Officer: Chris Newey
Finance Manager: Alison Harris
IT Manager: Roland Greenstreet

Special thanks to our Campsite Assessors
John & Margaret Corrall
Pete Lowen & Ann Cazenave
Martin & Cheryle Cawley
Mike & Anita Winks
Mike Annan
Ken Elborn
Paul Johnson

Published by: Alan Rogers Travel Ltd,
Spelmonden Old Oast, Goudhurst, Kent TN17 1HE
www.alanrogers.com

55th edition - February 2023
ISBN 978-1-909057-96-8

Printed in Great Britain by S&G

Stay in touch alanrogers.com/signup
Contact us alanrogers.com/contact

 facebook.com/alanrogerstravel

 twitter.com/alanrogers

 instagram.com/alanrogerstravel

Contents & map

Norway (368)

Sweden (452)

Great Britain (206)

Ireland (282)

Belgium (26)

Luxembourg (330)

Switzerland & Liechtenstein (462)

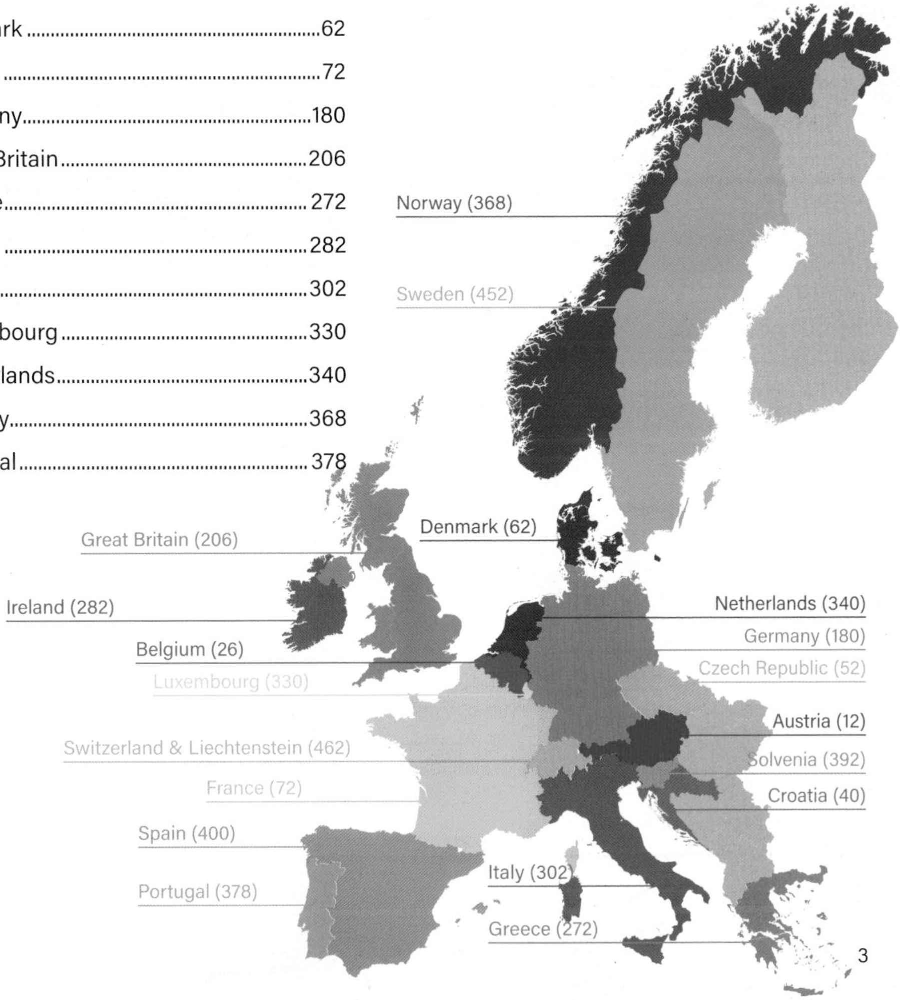

France (72)

Spain (400)

Portugal (378)

Denmark (62)

Netherlands (340)

Germany (180)

Czech Republic (52)

Austria (12)

Slovenia (392)

Croatia (40)

Italy (302)

Greece (272)

3

Our top travel tips

EU travel

If you're a UK resident, travel to the EU, Switzerland and Norway has changed. Make sure you familiarise yourself with any new processes that have come into effect due to the UK's withdrawal from the European Union.

For the most up to date information, visit **gov.uk/brexit**

· ·

Top tip GB stickers are no longer valid. If you have one, you should remove it. You will need a UK sticker if your number plate doesn't include a UK identifier. See page 11.

Low emissions

Countries across Europe, including the UK, have enforced Low Emission Zones to help reduce urban pollution. It means some vehicles are prohibited from entering city centres or must pay to enter the zones.

Find out more at **ar.camp/low-emissions**

Accessibilty

We firmly believe that travel should be accessible to everyone. But for some, it can be challenging.

With the help of Karla (more on page 10), a friend, member of the Caravan and Motorhome Club, writer and wheelchair user, we've rated each country featured in this guide.

· ·

The score given is out of five and rated against our criteria, considering things like ease of movement, transport, facilities, inclusivity laws etc. You can find out more by visiting the link below.

· ·

To find out more and to download our free mini-guide to accessible travel in Europe, visit **ar.camp/open-to-all**

Public holidays

We've listed all public holidays; some have fixed dates, and others change from year to year. Research public holidays before you travel, as they could affect your plans.

Foreign travel advice

The UK Foreign & Commonwealth Office provides advice about travelling abroad, including the latest information on coronavirus, safety and security, entry requirements and travel warnings.

We recommend you read the advice before you travel at **gov.travel** or your local government travel website.

Driving on the continent

Driving overseas can be daunting for both experienced tourers and newcomers because of the road's differing laws and regulations. Whilst the EU has meant that some rules are uniform across the continent, others remain specific to certain countries.

Avoid unnecessary stress and read more at **ar.camp/driving-tips**

Welcome to the 55th edition

Alan Rogers Guides were first published over 55 years ago. Since Alan Rogers published the first campsite guide that bore his name, the nature of European campsites has changed immeasurably.

Back in 1968, many campsites, though well established, were still works in progress, having been converted from farms and orchards in the post-war years. Of course, there were fewer to choose from than today, and the quality levels varied hugely.

Over the 55 years since the first edition of the Alan Rogers guide, the quality of most campsites has evolved in leaps and bounds. In terms of today's facilities, infrastructure, technology and accommodation types, there is very little comparison with what was on offer half a century ago.

Since 1968 we at Alan Rogers have developed longstanding relationships with many campsites. We have worked with different generations of campsite owners and shared the trials and tribulations along the way with many of them. Typically, campsite owners are a hardy breed, passionate about their campsite, and keen to show it and their region off to every visitor.

The Alan Rogers guides have always aimed to celebrate the variety, recognise the quality and salute the unique. So read on and find the perfect campsite for your next holiday, whatever type of campsite that may be.

1968

Alan Rogers launched his first guide. It contained over 50 "really good sites" personally recommended by Alan.

1970s

1975 Our first guide to Britain is published

1980s

1985 Our first guide to France is published.

1986 After 18 years of development, Alan Rogers retires. The company is purchased by Clive and Lois Edwards.

1990s

1993 We celebrated our 25th anniversary.

1998 Our first guide to Rented Accommodation in France is published.

2000s

2001 Mark Hammerton buys the business.

2003 Dutch language guides are published.

2010s

2013 The company is acquired by the Caravan and Motorhome Club.

2018 We celebrated our 50th anniversary.

2019 Venturing further than ever before, worldwide caravan holidays are launched.

2020s

2022 Welcome to our 55th year!

Founder of Selected ▶
Sites in Europe
Guide, Alan Rogers

▼ Our first guide,
  published in 1968

ALAN ROGERS'
**selected sites
for caravanning
and camping
in Europe** 1968

Detailed reports on over 50 really good sites
personally recommended by Alan Rogers

'only the best'   4/-

1918   Alan Rogers is born in Warwickshire.

1939   Rogers works as a wireless telegrapher for the RAF during
World War Two.

1948   After the war, Rogers devoted much of his leisure time to
his twin passions of rallying and caravanning. He spent
long periods over the summer with his wife Ruth exploring
newly-founded continental campsites and collecting
information on these sites.

1968   Alan's first official guide to camping goes on sale. Work on
compiling information and reviews began a year earlier.

1986   Rogers retires. He continues inspecting campsites until the
mid 1990s.

2001   Aged 81, Alan passes away. His legacy lives on through the
annual guides that bear his name.

Alan Rogers: in search of 'only the best'

There are many thousands of campsites across Europe of varying quality: this guide contains impartially written reports on over 400, including many of the very finest, in 19 countries. Are there more? Yes, of course, and in countries not included in this book. Online at alanrogers.com, you'll find details of many more - over 8,000 campsites.

Put simply, a guide like this can never be exhaustive. We have had to make difficult editorial decisions to provide you with a selection of the best, rather than information on all – in short, a more selective approach.

We are mindful that people want different things from their choice of campsite, so we try to include a range of campsite 'styles' to cater for a wide variety of preferences.

Those with more specific interests, such as sporting facilities, cultural events or historical attractions, are also catered for. Whether it's part of a chain or privately owned, the size of the site should make

no difference in terms of quality. The key is that it should be 'fit for purpose' in order to shine and stand out.

If a campsite can identify and understand what kind of campsite it sets out to be and who it wants to attract, it can enhance its kerb appeal by developing with that in mind.

By way of example, a lakeside campsite with credentials as a serious windsurfing centre should probably offer equipment for hire, secure storage for customers' own kit, courses and tuition, meteorological feeds and so on.

A campsite in the heart of the Loire Valley might offer guided excursions to local châteaux, weekly tastings of regional wine and cheese, suggested walking or cycling itineraries to local châteaux with entry discounts and so on.

Whatever style of campsite you're seeking, we hope you'll find some inspiration here.

Alan Rogers believes strongly that there is no point in camping uncomfortably when, with a little planning, you can do so in quite reasonable comfort.

He considers too that the greatest degree of comfort is obtained by using organised camping sites and, more especially, by using **only the best** of these sites. Alan Rogers' Selected Sites for Caravanning and Camping in Europe 1968 enables you to do just this.

◀ Taken from our very first guide, Alan coins the 'only the best' term.

Alan Rogers, 1968

Read our first edition guide at **ar.camp/1968** or scan the QR code

Country

Alan Rogers reference code and on-site information including accommodation count, pitch count, GPS coordinates, Postcode and campsite address.

Campsite Name

Campsite contact information

Opening dates

A description of the site in which we try to give an idea of its general features – its size, situation, strengths and weaknesses. This section should provide a picture of the site itself with reference to the provided facilities and if they impact its appearance or character. We include details on approximate pitch numbers, electricity (with amperage), hardstandings etc., in this section as pitch design, planning and terracing affect the site's overall appearance. Similarly, we include a reference to pitches used for caravan holiday homes, chalets, and the like.

Lists more specific information on the site's facilities and amenities and, where available, the dates when these facilities are open (if not for the whole season).

Below we list 'Key Feautres'. These are features we think are important and make the site individual.

 Beach nearby

 Dogs allowed

 Open all year

 Fishing

 Watersports

 Golf

This is a QR code. You can scan it with your smartphone and it will take you directly to the campsite listing on our website. Newer phones have the ability to scan these codes using the camera, but you can download an app and try it.

How to best use this guide

The layout of this edition is similar to our previous 'new-style' Europe guides but different from our pre-2018 editions. We still aim to provide comprehensive information, written in plain English in an easy to use format, but a few words of explanation regarding the content may be helpful.

Toilet blocks Typically, toilet blocks will be equipped with WCs, washbasins with hot and cold water and hot shower cubicles. They will have all the necessary shelves, hooks, plugs and mirrors. There will be a chemical toilet disposal point, and the campsite will provide water and waste-water drainage points and bin areas.

Shop Basic or fully supplied, and opening dates.

Bar, restaurant, takeaway facilities and entertainment We try hard to supply opening and closing dates (if other than the campsite opening dates).

Swimming pools These might vary from a simple, conventional swimming pool to an elaborate complex with multiple pools and waterslides. Opening dates and levels of supervision are provided where we have been notified. There is a regulation whereby Bermuda shorts may not be worn in swimming pools (for health and hygiene reasons). It is worth ensuring that you take 'proper' swimming trunks with you.

Leisure facilities For example, playing fields, bicycle hire, organised activities and entertainment.

Dogs If dogs are not accepted, or restrictions apply, we state it here. If planning to take a dog or other pet, we recommend you check in advance.

Opening dates Campsites can and sometimes do alter these dates before the start of the season, often for good reasons. If you intend to visit shortly after a published opening date or shortly before the closing date, it is wise to check that it will be open at the time required. Similarly, some sites operate a restricted service during the low season, only opening some of their facilities (e.g. swimming pools) during the main season. It is always wise to check.

Sometimes, campsite amenities may be dependent on there being enough customers on-site to justify their opening. Some campsites may not be fully ready by their stated opening dates. They also tend to close down some facilities at the end of the season and generally wind things down.

We usually give an overview of the pitches, including an approximate quantity. This figure may vary year on year, so it is rarely absolute.

> **HANDY TIP**
>
> **Campsite numbers** All campsites listed on the Alan Rogers website have a unique reference number. This makes it easier for us to identify sites, but also for you to find them on our website.

Useful information

The Schengen Area

The Schengen Area is an area of 26 European countries that have relaxed internal border controls, allowing for free movement. Not all countries in the European Union are part of this agreement, so it's worth checking before you embark on your journey.

- Schengen Member States
- Not yet Schengen Member States
- UK & Ireland Common Travel Area (CTA)

Member States Austria; Belgium; Czech Republic; Denmark; Estonia; Finland; France; Germany; Greece; Hungary; Iceland (non-EU); Italy; Latvia; Liechtenstein (non-EU); Lithuania; Luxembourg; Norway (non-EU); Poland; Portugal; Slovakia; Slovenia; Spain; Sweden; Switzerland (non-EU).

Monaco, San Marino and Vatican City all operate open borders but are not part of the Schengen Area.

The Republic of Ireland is not a member of the Area.

CROATIA HAS OFFICIALLY JOINED THE EUROZONE On 1 January 2023, Croatia became the 20th member of the Eurozone, adopting the Euro. Croatian Kuna notes can be exchanged for the equivalent value in Euros at the Croatian National Bank until January 2026.

Dashcams and Sat navs

Dashcams and sat navs are useful equipment for keeping us safe and on track. But laws on their use differ across Europe, so it's worth knowing the rules before travelling.

 Dashcams These are something of a grey area in some parts of Europe as they potentially break privacy laws, especially if the footage captured is shared online or with your insurance company without the consent of those in the video. Because of this, using dashcams in parts of continental Europe is illegal.

 Sat navs The use of sat navs to give directions isn't the issue here. Some models, however, warn of static and mobile speed cameras which, in some countries, is prohibited. This feature should be turned off when driving in countries where it is illegal.

Do I need a UK car sticker?

If you plan to drive in Europe, you must display a UK sticker if your vehicle doesn't already have a UK identifier. GB car stickers are no longer valid. See below to find out if you need a sticker.

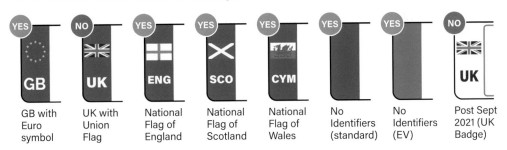

YES	NO	YES	YES	YES	YES	YES	NO
GB with Euro symbol	UK with Union Flag	National Flag of England	National Flag of Scotland	National Flag of Wales	No Identifiers (standard)	No Identifiers (EV)	Post Sept 2021 (UK Badge)

Recycling abroad

It's just as important to be as environmentally friendly on holiday as it is at home. We've introduced a traffic light system to make it easier to know what to and how to recycle abroad.

Green Recycling is widespread and similar, if not better, than in the UK. Glass, plastic, aluminium and paper/cardboard recycled via public bins, deposit schemes or other initiatives.

Amber Recycling is a little hit-and-miss. Some materials are recycled, and others are not, or rules differ from region to region.

Red Recycling is not widespread, and/or rules are complex or unclear.

LEAVE NO TRACE Leave your pitch how you found it. What you leave behind can impact nature, no matter how small. And while it might not be realistic to go waste free, it's important to be mindful of leaving as little a trace as possible during your stay.

Accessible Travel

We firmly believe that travel should be accessible to everyone. It's a wonderful thing to explore a place, journey somewhere new, instil a sense of adventure in the little ones, discover new cultures, learn, experience, and stimulate. But for some, travel can be challenging.

Say hello to Karla She has Spinal Muscular Atrophy, a condition characterised by weak muscles and problems with movement. Both her and her partner Stephen, have a passion for travel and being outdoors, so when they got their first caravan in 2017, it was one of the best decisions they ever made!

Get social AdventureWheelsUK @adventurewheelsuk

Capital Vienna
Currency Euro (€)
Language German
Time Zone CET (GMT+1)
Telephone Code +43

Shops Larger stores are open 8am to 8pm weekdays, smaller shops open later and close earlier. Many close early on Sat and stay closed on Sun. Bakeries open Sun morning.

Money ATMs are widespread, accessible 24hrs a day and have multilingual instructions. Cards accepted at transport hubs and some restaurants; expect to pay cash elsewhere. Daily withdrawal limit of €400.

Travelling with children Programs are usually organised for children over the summer period. Many lakes have supervised beach areas. Many museums in Vienna are free for under 18s. Restaurants will have children's menus or prepare smaller portions.

Public Holidays 1 Jan New Year's Day; 6 Jan Epiphany; Mar/Apr Easter Monday; 1 May Labour Day; May Ascension; May/Jun Whit Monday; Jun Corpos Christi; 15 Aug Assumption; 26 Oct National Day; 1 Nov All Saints; 8 Dec Conception; 25 Dec Christmas Day; 26 Dec Boxing Day

Low Emissions Zones in major cities, currently only applies to HGVs.

● EU Member | ● Schengen Area

Tourism website austria.info/uk

●●●●○ **Accessible Travel Score**

Generally well catered for in cities and larger towns, especially Vienna. Most, but not all, attractions and public services offer assistance.

Driving in Austria All vehicles must pay a toll to use motorways in Austria. You must display a sticker in your windscreen to show you have paid. All vehicles above 3.5t max permitted laden weight are required to use a GO Box. It is legal to overtake a tram (at slow speed), providing passengers are not endangered. At traffic lights, a green flashing light means the green phase is ending, and drivers should prepare to stop.

 Dashcams are **illegal**

 Speed camera detectors are legal

Austria

View all campsites in Austria
alanrogers.com/austria

See campsite map page 472

Climate Moderately hot summers, cold winters and snow in the mountains.

Emergency services Call 112 for the police, ambulance and fire and rescue.

Units Austria uses the metric system. To convert km to miles, multiply by 0.6.

Austria is primarily known for two contrasting attractions: the capital Vienna with its cathedral, wine bars and musical events, and the skiing and hiking resorts of the Alps. It is an ideal place to visit all year round, for the Easter markets, winter sports and the many cultural and historical attractions, as well as the breathtaking scenery.

The charming Tirol region in the west is easily accessible and popular with tourists who flock to its ski resorts in winter. It is transformed into a verdant landscape of picturesque valleys dotted with wildflowers, a paradise for walkers in the summer.

Situated in the centre is the Lake District and Salzburg, the city of Mozart, with its wealth of gardens, churches and palaces. Vienna's iconic Ferris wheel is a must for taking in the beautiful parks and architecture from a height of 200ft.

The neighbouring provinces of Lower Austria, Burgenland and Styria, land of vineyards, mountains and farmland, are off the tourist routes but provide good walking territory. Further south, Carinthia enjoys a mild, sunny climate dominated by crystal clear lakes and soaring mountains. There are numerous monasteries and churches, and the cities of Villach and Klagenfurt, known for its old square and attractive Renaissance buildings.

Scan QR code to browse more campsites on our website

Alan Rogers Code: AU0010
12 accommodations
150 pitches
GPS: 47.18233, 9.68227
Post Code: A-6710

Nenzing, Vorarlberg

Alpencamping Nenzing

www.alanrogers.com/au0010
office@alpencamping.at
Tel: +43 5525 62491
www.alpencamping.at/en

Open (Touring Pitches):
All year excl. week after Easter -
Start May.

Only a short drive from the A14 autobahn, Alpencamping is a well-run and comfortable, all-year-round site set in a natural bowl with splendid mountain views. All 150-level pitches are for touring with 16A electricity; all have fresh, wastewater, and TV connections. Most are set on neat terraces.

At the centre of the site are two restaurant options – traditional Austrian cuisine and a fish and steak option - built in a traditional wooden style with lots of atmosphere, its tables are lit by lamps hanging on metre-long ropes attached to beams in the massive wooden roof. With its bar and terrace, the restaurant understandably attracts many local customers and can be quite busy at weekends. A member of the Leading Campings group.

Key Features

 Pets Accepted

 Disabled Facilities

 Swimming Pool

 Play Area

 Bar/Restaurant

 Bike Hire

 Horse Riding

The newer facilities are state of the art and contain 20 private bathrooms (some free, others for rent). Excellent washroom for children and a baby room. There are plans to renew the older sanitary house in winter 22/23, which will reopen in February 23 as an "Earth sanitary building". Facilities for disabled visitors. Motorhome services. Small shop. Bar. Restaurant with terrace. New heated indoor and outdoor swimming complex (all year) and a bathing lake for adults only. Small play area with another larger one on the top terrace. Kids playhouse and indoor climbing wall with kids cinema. A wellness area on two floors with 6 saunas, infrared cabins and 2 relaxation rooms and massage. WiFi all site (charged).

Scan me for
more information.

Alan Rogers Code: AU0060
50 accommodations
200 pitches
GPS: 47.23755, 11.34201
Post Code: A-6161

Natters, Tirol

Ferienparadies Natterer See

www.alanrogers.com/au0060
info@natterersee.com
Tel: +43 5125 46732
www.natterersee.com

Open (Touring Pitches):
All year.

In a quiet location arranged around two lakes and set amidst beautiful alpine scenery, this site, founded in 1930, is renowned as one of Austria's top sites. Over the last few years, many improvements have been carried out, and pride of place goes to the innovative, award-winning, multifunctional building at the entrance to the site. This contains all the sanitary facilities expected of a top site, including a special section for children, private bathrooms to rent, and a dog bath.

The reception, shop and café/bar/bistro are on the ground floor, and a panoramic lounge and cinema are on the upper floor. Almost all of the 200 generous pitches are for tourers. They are terraced, set on gravel/grass, and all have electricity; most have water and drainage. Most offer a splendid view of the mountains.

Two modern sanitary blocks with underfloor heating, private cabins, and facilities for children & disabled visitors. Laundry facilities. Motorhome services. Fridge box hire. Restaurant, Pizzeria and takeaway (open Easter-September). Mini market. Playgrounds. Children's activity programme and child minding (seasonal). Sports field. Archery. Outdoor gym. Cinema. Mountain bike hire. Bathing lake. Aquapark. Canoes & pedaloes (charged). Daily entertainment programme (seasonal). WiFi (charged). Glamping and accommodations. Bus service to Innsbruck.

Key Features

 Book Online

 Open All Year

 Pets Accepted

 Disabled Facilities

 Play Area

 Bar/Restaurant

 Bike Hire

 Fishing

Scan me for more information.

Alan Rogers Code: AU0110
4 accommodations
240 pitches
GPS: 47.46837, 12.55474
Post Code: A-6391

Fieberbrunn, Tirol

Tirol Camp

www.alanrogers.com/au0110
office@tirol-camp.at
Tel: +43 5354 56666
www.tirol-camp.at/en

Open (Touring Pitches):
Mid May - Early Nov. and Start Dec.
- Late April.

This is one of many Tirol campsites that cater equally for summer and winter (here seemingly more for winter when a reservation is essential). Tirol Camp is in a quiet and attractive mountain situation on sloping ground and has 240 touring pitches, all on wide flat terraces, plus 26 deluxe pitches with their own bathroom at the pitch. Marked out mainly by the electricity boxes or low hedges, they are 80-100 sq.m. and all have 10A electricity, gas, water/drainage, TV and telephone connections.

There is a fitness and wellness centre (free to campers) with an indoor/outdoor pool complex, sauna, steam room, solarium and aromatherapy massage. The site is very close to a ski lift centre, and a ski and snowboard school for winter stays. In addition, horse-drawn sledge rides, floodlit tobogganing runs and langlauf skiing are available.

Key Features

 Pets Accepted

 Disabled Facilities

 Swimming Pool

 Play Area

 Bar/Restaurant

The upgraded toilet block in the main building is excellent with some washbasins in cabins and some private bathrooms on payment. A modern heated block at the top end of the site has spacious showers and washbasins in cabins. Facilities for disabled visitors. Washing machines, dryers and drying room. Motorhome services. Shop and snacks. Restaurant (closed Oct, Nov and May). Separate general room. Outdoor swimming pool (12x8 m). Indoor pool and wellness centre. Sauna. Fitness centre. Outdoor chess. Playground. Entertainment and activity programmes (July/Aug). Internet point. WiFi (charged).

Scan me for more information.

Alan Rogers Code: AU0265
10 accommodations
200 pitches
GPS: 47.57427, 12.70602
Post Code: A-5092

St Martin bei Lofer, Salzburg

www.alanrogers.com/au0265
home@grubhof.com
Tel: +43 6588 82370
www.grubhof.com

Open (Touring Pitches):
All year.

Camping Grubhof

Camping Grubhof is a beautifully laid out, level and spacious site set in the former riding and hunting park of the 14th-century Schloss Grubhof. The 200 touring pitches have been carefully divided into separate areas for different types of visitors – dog owners, young people, families and groups, and a quiet area. All the generous XXL pitches (at least 180 sq.m) provide electricity (16A), water and drainage (also in winter), many along the bank of the Saalach river.

Although new, the central building has been built in traditional Tirolean style using, in part, materials hundreds of years old reclaimed from old farmhouses. The result is most attractive. On the ground floor, you will find the reception, a cosy café/bar, a restaurant and a small shop, and on the first floor, a deluxe sauna, a beauty and wellness suite, two apartments and a relaxation room.

Three attractive, modern sanitary units constructed of concrete, wood and glass provide excellent facilities. XXL-family bathrooms (free for guests on XXL-pitches, to rent in winter). Washing machine, dryer and drying gallery. Gym upstairs (€10 membership per pitch/week). Recreation and conference room and a small library. Saunas, steam bath and massage. Ski and canoe storage room. Motorhome services. Luxury dog shower. Shop, restaurant and bar. Adventure-style playground. Youth room. Playroom. Watersports. Cabins to rent. Hotel and B&B accommodation. Free WiFi hotspots, on pitches against fee.

Key Features

 Book Online

 Open All Year

 Pets Accepted

 Disabled Facilities

 Play Area

 Bar/Restaurant

 Skiing

 Bike Hire

Scan me for more information.

Alan Rogers Code: AU0180
40 accommodations
300 pitches
GPS: 47.28372, 12.81695
Post Code: A-5671

Bruck an der Glocknerstraße, Salzburg

www.alanrogers.com/au0180
info@sportcamp.at
Tel: +43 6545 73030
www.sportcamp.at

Open (Touring Pitches):
All year.

Sportcamp Woferlgut

Sportcamp Woferlgut, a family-run site, is one of the best in Austria. It lies in the village of Bruck at the northern end of the Großglocknerstrasse mountain road in the Hohe Tauern National Park, near the Zeller See. The level grass pitches are marked out by shrubs, and each has 16A metered electricity, water, drainage, cable TV socket and a gas point.

The site's own lake is popular for swimming and sunbathing and has an adventure timber ropeway and playground. A free entertainment programme for kids of all ages is provided during the peak periods. The first-class toilet and shower facilities, as well as a wellness centre and 5 pools, has everything you need for a relaxing stay in the Austrian mountains.

Three modern sanitary blocks have excellent facilities, including private cabins and underfloor heating. Washing machines and dryers. Facilities for disabled visitors. Family bathrooms for hire (some with bathtubs). Motorhome services. Shop, bar, restaurant and takeaway. Heated outdoor pool and children's pool as well as a swimming lake with rope garden. TV rooms and lounge with a library. Gym with bathing house and adventure centre with sauna. Three playgrounds, indoor playroom and children's cinema. Fun train. Tennis and horses' meadow for Pony rides. Bicycle hire. Watersports and lake swimming. Crazy golf course. WiFi over site (charged).

Key Features

 Book Online

 Open All Year

 Pets Accepted

 Disabled Facilities

 Swimming Pool

 Play Area

 Bar/Restaurant

 Skiing

Scan me for more information.

19

Alan Rogers Code: AU0139
24 accommodations
162 pitches
GPS: 47.14278, 13.66556
Post Code: A-5570

Hammer, Tirol

Camping Mauterndorf

www.alanrogers.com/au0139
info@camping-mauterndorf.at
Tel: +43 6472 72023
camping-mauterndorf.at

Open (Touring Pitches):
All year.

The pitches at Camping Mauterndorf are a great size and surrounded by mountains from all angles, and the staff are helpful and efficient. One of the greatest benefits of this site is that for the duration of your stay, you get a Lungau Card which entitles you to a series of free and discounted activities within the area, such as Großeckbahn Cable Car, which normal price would set you back €16 per person for a return journey - with your card you get a one-time free trip. Panoramic views await you at the top, with hikes galore and Austrian hospitality at its best.

This is a fabulous place to stay and is highly recommended. The site has around 160 grass/hardstanding touring pitches with 12amp hook-up points. There are also Mobile homes, bungalows and apartments available to hire.

The heated toilet block has showers, washbasins and WCs. Baby room. Facility for visitors who are disabled. Laundry washing machine and dryer. Chemical toilet point. Motorhome service point. Dishwashing area. Wellness centre. Heated outdoor swimming pool. Dogs allowed. BBQs allowed. Bike and ski hire. Twin axle caravans are allowed. Shop. Bar. Restaurant. Bread to order. Takeaway. Freezer for ice packs. Children's play area. Games room. TV room. Trampoline. Ski bus at the entrance.

Key Features

 Open All Year

 Pets Accepted

 Disabled Facilities

 Play Area

 Skiing

 Bike Hire

Scan me for more information.

Alan Rogers Code: AU0530
10 accommodations
42 pitches
GPS: 47.55499, 13.92256
Post Code: A-8983

Bad Mitterndorf, Steiermark

www.alanrogers.com/au0530
camping@grimmingsicht.at
Tel: +43 3623 2985
www.grimmingsicht.at

Open (Touring Pitches):
All year.

Camping Grimmingsicht

Kur Camping Grimmingsicht is located in the enchanted landscape of the Ausseerland in the Styrian Salzkammergut. A site where Austrian hospitality is offered by the Dutch management. The site is quietly located, about 500 meters from the village, and has a beautiful panorama of various mountains such as the Grimming and the Avalanche Stone. The ground is natural grass. The campsite has 42 grass pitches, of which 31 are for touring units with electric hook-up point 16amp. There is also an apartment and a caravan available to hire.

Camping Grimmingsicht is run by its owners, who are themselves enthusiastic campers. This is a true hiking and cycling paradise in summer, ideal for sun worshippers or swimmers. The nearby beautiful Alpen lido in the centre of Bad Mitterndorf or the surrounding Salzkammergut lakes are ideal. Around Bad Mitterndorf, you will still find beautiful meadows and air that smells of firs and field flowers, rural peace, the splashing of streams with clear water, quiet wide forests, and a hiking experience for every taste level of difficulty. In the winter, it is close to the ski slopes.

The heated toilet block has showers, washbasins and wc's. Laundry with washing machine and dryer. Chemical toilet point. Dish washing area. Dogs allowed. BBQ's allowed Twin axle caravans allowed. Bread to order. Freezer for ice packs. Ski hire. Children's play area. Boules. Crazy golf. Public transport nearby.

Key Features

 Open All Year

 Pets Accepted

 Play Area

 Fishing

Scan me for more information.

Alan Rogers Code: AU0281
2 accommodations
50 pitches
GPS: 48.05702, 15.12972
Post Code: A-3251

Purgstall an der Erlauf, Lower Austria

Camp Purgstall

www.alanrogers.com/au0281
info@topcamp.at
Tel: +43 7489 2015
www.topcamp.at

Open (Touring Pitches):
End March- Mid October.

A warm welcome, friendly vibe, spectacular views, and lauded 'exceptional' amenities are all yours at Austria's Aktiv Camp Purgstall Camping und Ferienpark, a family-friendly site on a small Scheibbs farm on the edge of the mountainous Ötscherland region.

There are loads to do in this lovely location without having to step outside the site: the grounds include a pond for swimming and paddling; a petting zoo so the kids can look at chickens and rabbits; a roomy canine exercise area for dogs to run around in, and not just a playground but a play meadow too.

You will want to spend significant time at the central guesthouse when back at the base, as it houses the Aktiv restaurant (with the wine-tasting area), the guest kitchen and a common room with a TV and internet connection. If you want to cook your own dinner, barbecues and campfires are allowed so that you can spend significant time should you wish to tuck into supper under the stars.

Amenities in the main guesthouse are well-kept; the bathrooms are kitted out with mirrors and hairdryers. A baby room with a bath, changing table and bottle warmers is available.

Key Features

 Book Online

 Pets Accepted

 Disabled Facilities

 Play Area

 Bar/Restaurant

 Bike Hire

Disabled sanitary Facilities, Baby room, Restaurant, Bar, Shop, BBQ allowed, Small farm, Children's playground, Lake swimming, Bicycle hire, TV room, Multisport field, WiFi, Pets allowed.

Scan me for more information.

Alan Rogers Code: AU0320
2 accommodations
100 pitches
GPS: 48.31078, 16.32812
Post Code: A-3400

Klosterneuburg, Lower Austria

www.alanrogers.com/au0320
campklosterneuburg@oeamtc.at
Tel: +43 2 2432 5877
www.campingklosterneuburg.at

Open (Touring Pitches):
Mid March - Early November.

Donaupark Klosterneuburg

Klosterneuburg lies just to the north of Vienna on the Danube. It is outside the city boundary, away from the noise and bustle of the famous city but only minutes away by train. Owned and run by the Austrian Motor Club (OAMTC), this site is in a park-like situation, surrounded by trees but with little shade. The 100 pitches are on the small side. However, all are accessed from hard roads, and all have 6A electricity. Alongside the site is Happyland, an amusement park with a large swimming pool (discounts for campers).

This is a good spot for families with the glories of historic Vienna easily reached and Happyland for the children. Donaupark Camping is only a few hundred metres from the river, a walk away from Klosterneuburg, its well-known Baroque abbey, and the Wienerwald.

Two modern sanitary units, one at reception and the other by the pitches (may be under pressure when busy). Facilities for disabled visitors. Motorhome services. Washing machines and dryer. Electric cooking rings. Freezer for ice packs. Restaurant/snack bar incl. small shop for basics (High season). Play area. Bicycle hire. WiFi (free).

Key Features

 Pets Accepted

 Disabled Facilities

 Play Area

 Bike Hire

Scan me for more information.

Alan Rogers Code: AU0385
30 accommodations
40 pitches
GPS: 46.55841, 14.75147
Post Code: A-9143

Pirkdorf, Carinthia

www.alanrogers.com/au0385
office@pirkdorfersee.at
Tel: +43 4230 321
www.pirkdorfersee.at

Open (Touring Pitches):
Start May - Late September.

Pirkdorfer See

Set in the open countryside and bordering a small lake in southern Austria close to the Slovenian border, Pirkdorfer See is part of a hotel/restaurant complex. The 40 touring pitches are located close to the site's main building, housing the reception, a restaurant and sanitary facilities. They are open, level, and on grass, with 12A electricity connections. There are views across the lake from the pitches to the adjoining woodland and the mountains beyond. The grassed area surrounding the lake is ideal for sunbathing, and the traditional restaurant serves a daily menu and homemade Austrian dishes. In the adjacent fun park, sporting and other activities are available.

The site's location makes it an ideal base from which to tour southern Austria. For a change of language and culture (but not currency), a trip across the border to Slovenia is well worth the effort. There are numerous places to visit in the region after a cable car trip to 1,700 m. above sea level, you can appreciate the scenery at its best. There are entertainment programmes for younger children on-site during the high season to supplement the wide range of sports facilities.

Modern heated sanitary building. Showers are controllable and free. Facilities for disabled visitors. Baby room. Washing machines and dryer. Shop (July/Aug). Bar. Comfortable restaurant with a terrace offering a daily menu and traditional meals (high season). Play area. Adjoining fun park with beach volleyball, skate park, basketball and a small climbing wall. Entertainment programme for children (high season). WiFi (charged).

Key Features

 Pets Accepted

 Disabled Facilities

 Play Area

 Bar/Restaurant

 Fishing

Scan me for more information.

Alan Rogers Code: AU0400
400 pitches
GPS: 46.57768, 13.93775
Post Code: A-9583

Faak am See, Carinthia

Camping Arneitz

www.alanrogers.com/au0400
camping@arneitz.at
Tel: +43 4254 2137
www.arneitz.at

Open (Touring Pitches):
Mid April - Late September.

Directly on Faakersee, Camping Arneitz is one of the best sites in this area, central for the region's attractions, watersports and walking. Family run, Arneitz leads the way with good quality and comprehensive facilities. A newly built reception building at the entrance reflects the site's quality and, separate from reception facilities, has a good collection of tourist literature and two desks with computers for guests to use.

The 400 level, marked pitches are mainly of gravel, off hard roads, all with 16A electricity, TV, water and wastewater connections. Some have good shade from mature trees. There is a delightfully appointed restaurant at the entrance with entertainment in the high season. Day trips can be made to Venice and many other parts of northern Italy and the surrounding countryside.

Key Features

 Pets Accepted

 Disabled Facilities

 Play Area

 Bar/Restaurant

 Fishing

 Sailing

Splendid family washroom, large, heated and airy, with family cubicles around the walls and in the centre, washbasins at child height in a circle with a working carousel in the middle. Extra, small toilet block nearer the lake. Laundry facilities. Motorhome services. Supermarket. Self-service restaurant, bar and terrace. General room with TV. Small cinema for children's films. Beauty salon. Well equipped indoor playground. Fishing. Dogs are not accepted in July/Aug. WiFi throughout (charged).

Scan me for
more information.

Capital Brussels
Currency Euro (€)
Language French, Flemish and German
Time Zone CET (GMT+1)
Telephone Code +32

Shops Most shops are open 10am to 6pm weekdays or until 7pm/8pm on Sat. Some shops open on Sun and close on Mon morning but check before visiting. Some close for an hour at lunchtime.

Money ATMs are widespread, accessible 24hrs a day and have multilingual instructions. Credit/debit cards are widely accepted, although some shops may only accept cash.

Travelling with Children Many cities have museums and other attractions that run activity days and programs for children. Entrance fees for many attractions are reduced for those under 12.

Public Holidays 1 Jan New Year's Day; Mar/Apr Easter Monday; 1 May Labour Day; May Ascension; May/Jun Whit Monday; 21 Jul National Day; 15 Aug Assumption; 1 Nov All Saints; 11 Nov Armistice Day; 25 Dec Christmas Day

♲ **LEZ** Low Emissions Zones in major cities. Registration required for entry.

● **EU Member** | ● **Schengen Area**

Tourism website visitbelgium.com

●●●●○ **Accessible Travel Score**

Most public areas and services are suitable for wheelchair users and less able individuals. Transport is well-equipped.

Driving in Belgium Motorways are toll-free for all vehicles except those over 3.5t. Drink-driving and using your mobile whilst driving are illegal. Trams always have priority. If you are stationary, you should switch off the engine. Blue Zone parking areas exist in most major cities. Parking discs can be obtained from police stations, garages and some shops. Discs should not be used inside Blue Zone areas unless the parking meter is out of use.

 Dashcams are legal

 Speed camera detectors are legal

Belgium

View all campsites in Belgium
alanrogers.com/belgium

See campsite map page 473

Climate Temperate, similar to Britain. Cool, damp winters and mild summers.

Emergency services Call 112 for the police, ambulance and fire and rescue.

Units Belgium uses the metric system. To convert km to miles, multiply by 0.6.

A small country divided into three regions, Flanders in the north, Wallonia in the south and Brussels the capital. Belgium is rich in scenic countryside, culture and history, notably the great forest of Ardennes, the historical cities of Bruges and Ghent, and the western coastline with its long sandy beaches.

Brussels is at the very heart of Europe. It is a must-see destination with its heady mix of shops, bars, exhibitions and festivals – a multicultural and multilingual city that is a focal point of art, fashion and culture.

In the French-speaking region of Wallonia lies the mountainous Ardennes, home to picturesque villages rich in tradition and folklore. It is a favourite of nature-lovers and walkers who enjoy exploring its many castles and forts. The safe, sandy beaches on the west coast run for forty miles. The cosmopolitan resort of Ostend, with its yacht basin and harbour, offers year-round attractions, including a carnival weekend and a Christmas market, and the myriad seafood restaurants will suit every taste. Bruges is Europe's best-preserved medieval city, crisscrossed by willow-lined canals, where tiny cobbled streets open onto pretty squares. After visiting the many museums and art galleries, why not sample some of the delicious chocolate for which the city is famous.

Scan QR code to browse more campsites on our website

Alan Rogers Code: BE0794
270 accommodations
30 pitches
GPS: 51.07910, 5.39550
Post Code: B-3530

Limburg, Flanders

www.alanrogers.com/be0794
info@molenheide.be
Tel: +32 11 52 10 44
www.molenheide.be

Open (Touring Pitches):
All year.

Camping Molenheide

In the centre of a naturally beautiful area, Park Molenheide is a great base for exploring this peaceful area: perhaps cycling or walking through the lush pastures, along the trails that run along the idyllic waterways and through the low, wooded hills, or visiting Belgium's oldest town, dating from Roman times. This is predominantly a bungalow park but has 30 large touring pitches located in a flat, grassy field with easy access. All the pitches have 6/10A electricity.

What sets this site aside from others in the area is its amazing range of activities and high-class facilities. All manner of recreational activities are housed indoors with a large tropical-style 'Aquapolis' swimming pool with slides and an excellent themed children's pool, all supervised. There are numerous high-quality bars and restaurants housed under the same roof.

One single well-equipped, modern toilet block (bring your own paper) with large free controllable showers. Fully equipped en-suite unit for disabled visitors. Excellent bars and restaurants. Outstanding leisure facilities include tropical indoor heated swimming pool, bowling, incredible children's indoor play area, and a unique crazy golf course. Bicycle hire. Max. 1 dog – allowed on the campsite but not in the facilities. WiFi (charged).

Key Features

 Open All Year

 Pets Accepted

 Disabled Facilities

 Swimming Pool

 Play Area

 Bar/Restaurant

 Bike Hire

Fishing

Scan me for more information.

Alan Rogers Code: BE0781
3 accommodations
100 pitches
GPS: 51.13726, 5.56830
Post Code: B-3960

Limburg, Flanders

www.alanrogers.com/be0781
info@campingkempenheuvel.be
Tel: +32 89 46 21 35
www.campingkempenheuvel.com

Open (Touring Pitches):
Start March - End October.

Camping De Kempenheuvel

Kempenheuvel is located around 2 km from the bustling Limburg town of Bree, a relaxed place with a central square, some attractive historic buildings and useful shops (also an excellent Friday morning market which dates back to the 13th century).

This is a friendly, family site with a heated outdoor swimming pool and a children's pool. It is popular with anglers, thanks to a large well-stocked carp pond. Other amenities include a tennis court and a boules pitch. Cycling is popular, and Kempenheuvel is linked to the Limburg cycling route network, which offers easy-going routes meandering through the idyllic countryside. Pitches are of a good size and are supplied with 6A electricity. Plenty of activities are available in peak season, including darts tournaments and line dancing.

Two toilet blocks, both with good, clean facilities, including free, preset showers and facilities for babies. The older one has facilities for disabled visitors; the modern prefabricated unit is on the touring field. Bar/restaurant. Takeaway. Outdoor heated swimming pool and paddling pool (May-Sept). Tennis. Play area. Fishing lake. Activity and entertainment programme. WiFi over site (charged). Mobile homes to rent.

Key Features

 Pets Accepted

 Disabled Facilities

 Swimming Pool

 Play Area

 Bar/Restaurant

 Fishing

Scan me for more information.

Alan Rogers Code: BE0703
100 accommodations
119 pitches
GPS: 50.53151, 5.86301
Post Code: B-4910

Liège, Wallonia

www.alanrogers.com/be0703
info@campingpolleur.be
Tel: +32 87 54 10 33
www.campingpolleur.be

Open (Touring Pitches):
Start April - Late October.

Camping Polleur

Set in the heart of the idyllic countryside, Camping Polleur is a real family campsite in the Belgian Ardennes. Lying in the valley of the river Hoëgne, on the edge of the woods near the village of Polleur, it's a peaceful spot.

There's plenty of interest in the area, including the historic town of Spa, 10 minutes drive away and famous for its health-giving mineral waters. Elegant Liège and historic Theux (5 km), with its ruined medieval castle, are nearby too.

With an outdoor adventure centre on the doorstep, there is something for everyone with hiking, kayaking, quad biking and mountain biking. Various hiking and biking trails start from the campsite itself and meander through the glorious countryside and the wooded slopes.

Key Features

 Pets Accepted

 Swimming Pool

 Play Area

 Bike Hire

Two modern toilet blocks with free showers and baby/toddler washing facilities. Swimming pool (10m x 15m) with waterslide, children's pool (40cm deep) and toddlers' pool (15 cm deep). Small shop (High season), bar/snack bar/restaurant (restricted outside high season). Laundrette, dishwashers. Three playgrounds. Bike rental, quad bikes, kayaking nearby, fishing lake, table tennis, boules. Entertainment (High season). WiFi.

Scan me for more information.

Alan Rogers Code: BE0670
251 accommodations
235 pitches
GPS: 50.09647, 5.28570
Post Code: B-6927

Luxembourg, Wallonia

www.alanrogers.com/be0670
vacances@sandaya.fr
Tel: +32 84 36 00 50
www.sandaya.co.uk

Open (Touring Pitches):
End March - Late September.

Camping Parc la Clusure

A friendly and very well-run site, Camping Sandaya Parc la Clusure is highly recommended. Set in a river valley in the lovely wooded uplands of the Ardennes, known as the l'Homme Valley touring area, the site has around 500 large, marked, grassy pitches (around 250 for touring). All have access to electricity, cable TV and water taps, mostly in avenues off a central, tarmac road. There is some noise from the nearby railway. There is a very pleasant riverside walk; the river is shallow in summer and popular with children (caution in winter). The site's heated swimming pool and children's pool have a poolside bar and terrace. You will also find over 200 rental accommodations.

The famous Grottoes of Han are nearby, also the Euro Space Center, Château de Lavaux-Sainte-Anne and the Bastogne War Museum. Those preferring quieter entertainment might enjoy the Topiary Park at Durbuy.

Three excellent sanitary units, one heated in winter, include some washbasins in cubicles; facilities for babies and children. Facilities for disabled campers. Motorhome services. Well-stocked shop, bar, restaurant, snack bar and takeaway (seasonal). Swimming pools (seasonal). Bicycle hire. Tennis. New playgrounds. Organised activity programme including canoeing, archery, abseiling, mountain biking and climbing (summer). Caving. Fishing (licence essential). WiFi over site (free). Max. 1 dog in July/Aug.

Key Features

 Book Online

 Pets Accepted

 Disabled Facilities

 Swimming Pool

 Play Area

 Bar/Restaurant

 Bike Hire

 Fishing

Scan me for more information.

Alan Rogers Code: BE0684
80 pitches
GPS: 49.70201, 5.80677
Post Code: B-6700

Luxembourg, Wallonia

www.alanrogers.com/be0684
campingofficiel@skynet.be
Tel: +32 63 22 65 82
www.campingofficielarlon.be

Open (Touring Pitches):
Start March - End October.

Camping Officiel Arlon

Camping Officiel Arlon is an attractive, well-maintained, family-owned site situated close to Belgium's largest forest and surrounded by rolling hills and nature trails, perfect for keen cyclists and walkers. Lying just northwest of Luxembourg, it's an ideal stopover site when travelling north or south, with good access from the E411, and merits a longer stay if possible. The Roman city of Arlon has many interesting sights, and a large flea market is held on the first Sunday of the month from March until October, so you may be tempted to linger.

There are 80 grassy touring pitches (100 sq.m) with 6A electricity. The excellent on-site amenities include a clean sanitary block, bedecked with colourful flowers during the summer, a bar and restaurant and a pleasant terrace.

One clean, well-maintained sanitary block by the entrance has free, controllable hot showers and some washbasins in cubicles. Facilities for disabled visitors (key access). Dishwashing area and washing machine. Motorhome services. Bar/restaurant/takeaway (April-Oct; limited menu). Free WiFi over the site.

Key Features

 Pets Accepted

 Disabled Facilities

 Bar/Restaurant

Scan me for more information.

Alan Rogers Code: BE0712
4 accommodations
130 pitches
GPS: 49.81605, 5.01567
Post Code: B-6830

Luxembourg, Wallonia

Camping Ile de Faigneul

www.alanrogers.com/be0712
iledefaigneul@belgacom.net
Tel: +32 61 46 68 94
www.iledefaigneul.com

Open (Touring Pitches):
Start April - End September.

Few campsites are in sole possession of an island, and when that island lies in a beautiful valley flanked by steep slopes carpeted with trees, the site is likely to be something special. Camping Ile de Faigneul is! This peaceful site, a real family campsite in summer, is surrounded by the River Semois and is near the small village of Poupehan in the picturesque Belgian Ardennes and close to the French border.

The 130 level pitches, all with 6A electricity (Europlug), on this grass-covered island are all for touring units. The site's friendly owners, Alouis and Daniella van Zon-Berkes, who speak good English, took over the site a few years ago and have worked hard to return it to its present state of natural beauty. Photographs in the bar will testify to their achievements. With its terrace, the homely bar/snack bar is entirely in keeping with this comfortable, natural site.

The well appointed, well maintained sanitary block is ultra modern. Preset showers operated by key (deposit € 25) and some washbasins in cabins. Facilities for disabled visitors, family shower room, baby changing area. Laundry room. Shop. Bar/snack bar. Canoe rental. Fishing. Playground (unfenced and near the river). Special area beside river for campfires. Max. 2 dogs. WiFi throughout.

Key Features

 Pets Accepted

 Disabled Facilities

 Play Area

 Fishing

Scan me for more information.

Alan Rogers Code: BE0801
105 pitches
GPS: 50.27756, 4.89717
Post Code: B-5500

Namur, Wallonia

Camping Devant Bouvignes

www.alanrogers.com/be0801
camping.communal@dinant.be
Tel: +32 82 22 40 02
dinant.be/tourisme/campings/
camping-devant-bouvignes

Open (Touring Pitches):
Mid March - Mid November.

Well located beside the River Meuse, Camping Communal De Devant Bouvignes is about a 20-minute walk into the town of Dinant, or an unmarked cycle path is available on the western bank. It's an attractive town with a picturesque waterfront backed by toy-like houses dwarfed by the onion-domed church and the massive cliffs topped by the imposing citadel. Nearby are castles, abbeys and pleasant gardens to visit.

Sanitary facilities are modern and well-kept, with a token system operating for showers. The touring pitches are all on grass, and several permanent pitches are located on the site's river side; these are allocated to seasonal or longer-term rentals. There can be some road noise and freight traffic on the railway on the opposite side of the river.

When visiting Dinant, a cable car trip to the citadel is worth a visit, and you should also keep your eyes open for one of the several statues around the town commemorating the birth of Adolph Sax, the inventor of the Saxophone who was born in the town. Don't miss the Leffe Maison tour if you're a beer fan.

Key Features

 Pets Accepted

 Disabled Facilities

Fishing. Ideally located for the nearby city of Dinant. Wifi Available. Pets allowed (Max 2 dogs). Showers are token operated.

Scan me for more information.

Alan Rogers Code: BE0540
50 pitches
GPS: 50.59988, 3.41377
Post Code: B-7500

Hainaut, Wallonia

www.alanrogers.com/be0540
tourisme@tournai.be
Tel: +32 69 22 26 35
walloniabelgiumtourism.co.uk/en-gb/
content/lorient-camping-tournai

Open (Touring Pitches):
All year.

Camping de Tournai

Previously known as Camping de L'Orient, Camping de Tournai is an attractive, good-quality municipal site in a quiet, green location close to the historic town of Tournai and convenient for the E42. It is immaculately kept by its manager. The 50 level, grassy, individual pitches (all for touring units) are separated by laurel hedges and have shade in some parts and 16A electricity. Adjoining the site is an attractive restaurant and bar with a superb terrace overlooking the lake where campers can fish and hire pedalos. There is also a new, high-quality pool complex with a cafeteria, an indoor pool with spectator seating and an outdoor pool with water slides.

Tournai centre should not be missed. It boasts the oldest belfry in Europe, and there's the cathedral and various museums dedicated to decorative arts, folklore, tapestry and military history. Get to know the surroundings via the excellent network of cycleways and footpaths which weave around the town. Many details are in the brochure given to visitors on arrival at the site.

Two modern sanitary units are of high quality, spotlessly clean and heated in cool weather. They include some washbasins in cubicles and roomy showers on payment. Washing machine and dryer. Facilities for disabled campers (but no ramped access). Basic provisions are available from reception (bread can be ordered).

Key Features

 Open All Year

 Pets Accepted

 Disabled Facilities

 Swimming Pool

 Play Area

 Bar/Restaurant

 Fishing

 Sailing

Scan me for
more information.

Alan Rogers Code: BE0570
3 accommodations
66 pitches
GPS: 50.84682, 2.89748
Post Code: B-8900

West Flanders, Flanders

www.alanrogers.com/be0570
info@jeugdstadion.be
Tel: +32 57 21 72 82
www.jeugdstadion.be

Open (Touring Pitches):
Start March - Mid November (All year
for motorhomes).

Camping Jeugdstadion

Lying on the southern fringe of medieval Ypres, this is a convenient spot from which to explore the town's history, inextricably linked to the Great War, perhaps starting at the elegant central square with its Cloth Hall, largely rebuilt after 1918, and the moving In Flanders Fields Museum. A footpath leads you straight into the town.

Camping Jeugdstadion is a small municipal site that has had a substantial facelift in recent years. It is well maintained, clean and neat and has 40 touring pitches, 18 of which are hardstands, all with 10A electricity, plus a separate grassy area for 70 tents. There's an adjacent small nature reserve, and trees are dotted around, providing shade in high summer. The site entrance barrier links to the automated booking system, so even when there are no staff on-site, it is still possible to gain access at the 24-hour reception. This also allows all-year use by motorhomes.

The heated sanitary block has some washbasins in cubicles and free hot showers. One toilet for disabled campers. Three sinks for dishwashing outside. Motorhome services. Bicycle hire. Free WiFi in reception.

Key Features

🐾 Pets Accepted

♿ Disabled Facilities

Play Area

🚲 Bike Hire

Scan me for more information.

Alan Rogers Code: BE0565
100 accommodations
170 pitches
GPS: 51.15787, 2.76060
Post Code: B-8434

West Flanders, Flanders

www.alanrogers.com/be0565
westende@kompascamping.be
Tel: +32 58 22 30 25
www.campingwestende.be

Open (Touring Pitches):
End March - Mid November.

Camping Westende

Set about 20 km up the coast from Dunkirk, Kompas Camping Westende is a large holiday site near the sea. The vast sandy beach is only a short walk away, and there is easy access to the coastal tram service. Of the 435 pitches, half are taken by seasonal caravans plus 43 rental units, leaving some 100 touring pitches on grass with 10A electricity, plus a group of 77 large (150 sq.m) serviced pitches with water and electricity.

The site is well cared for, with a range of amenities for children, including a play barn. The shop, bar and restaurant are grouped around the reception. One end of the site is leased to a firm providing rental accommodation in mobile homes.

Four toilet blocks are modern, recently renovated, and very clean. One block is due for refurbishment. Good facilities for children and disabled visitors in one block. Shop, bar, restaurant and takeaway (high season and w/ends). Adventure playground. Play barn. Sports area. Boules. Entertainment and activities programme for children (July/Aug). Bicycle hire. WiFi throughout (charged).

Key Features

 Book Online

 Pets Accepted

 Disabled Facilities

 Beach Access

 Play Area

 Bar/Restaurant

 Bike Hire

Scan me for more information.

Alan Rogers Code: BE0546
40 pitches
GPS: 51.31168, 3.15354
Post Code: B-8370

West Flanders, Flanders

Camping Bonanza 1

www.alanrogers.com/be0546
info@bonanza1.be
Tel: +32 50 41 66 58
www.bonanza1.be

Open (Touring Pitches):
Late March - Late September.

Camping Bonanza 1 is a modern, family site within walking distance of a good beach and close to the centre of the important resort of Blankenberge, home to Belgium's only sea pier. Pitches here are grassy and are generally without shade. All have 10A electrical connections. A separate area for tents is available at the rear of the site. The centrally located toilet blocks are well maintained (a small charge is made for hot showers). On-site amenities include the friendly Azura bar/bistro, with a terrace overlooking the well-appointed playground for children.

Blankenberge is undeniably one of Belgium's premier seaside resorts. It is lively with a popular casino and plenty of cafés, restaurants and many other amenities. By way of contrast, the small city of Bruges is just 13 km. away and easily reached by train.

A clean and well maintained central sanitary unit has facilities for disabled visitors (key access). Laundry with washing machines and dryer. Motorhome services. Bar/bistro with varied menu and takeaway meals. Play areas. Pétanque. WiFi (charged).

Key Features

 Pets Accepted

 Disabled Facilities

 Beach Access

 Play Area

 Bar/Restaurant

 Bike Hire

Scan me for more information.

Alan Rogers Code: BE0652
370 accommodations
125 pitches
GPS: 51.07905, 4.81868
Post Code: B-2260

Antwerp, Flanders

www.alanrogers.com/be0652
info@hofvaneeden.be
Tel: +32 16 69 83 72
www.hofvaneeden.be

Open (Touring Pitches):
All year.

Camping Hof Van Eeden

Hof van Eeden is a cosy, quiet and child-friendly family site located in a green area in Westerlo also called the 'Pearl of the Kempen'. It is a great base to explore the surrounding region. You will find it to be an ideal walking and cycling environment.

The Kempen-Hageland route passes next to the campsite (take Junction 85). The ideal place to spend your holidays or as an overnight stop site. The site is within a wood and by a lake/recreational pond. The site has pitches with shade and others without shade. located close to a sandy beach. It is possible to rent mobile homes and hikers' cabins.

The 4 toilet blocks provide showers, wash basins and wc's. Facility for visitors who are disabled. Laundry with washing machine and dryer. Dish washing area. Motorhome service point. Chemical toilet point. Shop. Children's play area. Pets allowed. Entertainment programme. Outdoor swimming pool and a toddlers' pool. You can also swim in the nearby lake/recreational pond. Snack bar. Restaurant. Take away. Ice pack freezer. Gas sales. Wi-Fi partial site. Defibrillator. BBQ's allowed, all types. Table tennis. Boules area. Multi sports pitch. Games room. Public transport and Supermarket nearby.

Key Features

 Open All Year

 Pets Accepted

 Swimming Pool

 Play Area

 Bike Hire

 Fishing

Scan me for more information.

Capital Zagreb
Currency Euro (€) (officially adopted January 2023)
Language Croatian
Time Zone CET (GMT+1)
Telephone Code +385

Shops 8am to 8pm weekdays, until 2pm or 3pm on Sat and closed on Sun. Some shops shorten their hours or shut down in the summer months.

Money ATMs are widespread, accessible 24hrs a day, and some have multilingual instructions. Smaller restaurants and shops often only accept cash. Amex isn't as widely accepted as Visa and Mastercard.

Travelling with Children Beaches are safe. Many museums and historical attractions run activity trails. Child fees are applicable for under 9s. The dining scene is relaxed, and many restaurants will offer a kids menu.

Public Holidays 1 Jan New Year's Day; 6 Jan Epiphany; Mar/Apr Easter Monday; 1 May Labour Day; 30 May Statehood Day; May/Jun Corpus Christi; 22 Jun Anti-Fascist Struggle Day; 5 Aug Victory Day; 15 Aug Assumption; 1 Nov All Saints; 18 Nov Remembrance Day; 25 Dec Christmas Day; 26 Dec Boxing Day

There are no Low Emissions Zones currently in place.

● **EU Member** | ○ **Schengen Area**

Tourism website croatia.hr

●●○○○ **Accessible Travel Score**

Largely unequipped for less able travellers but improving. Public transport in larger cities is generally good.

Driving in Croatia Tolls are present on some roads. Euros are sometimes accepted as payment. Roads along the coast can become congested in summer and queues are possible at border crossings. Children under 12 cannot sit in the front of a vehicle. Parking is illegal on or near a bend, intersection, brow of a hill or bus/tram or taxi stop. Drink-driving and using your mobile whilst driving are illegal.

 Dashcams are legal

 Speed camera detectors are legal

Croatia

View all campsites in Croatia
alanrogers.com/croatia

See campsite map page 474

Climate Warm, dry summers and wet, long winters. Warmer along the coast.

Emergency services Call 112 for the police, ambulance and fire and rescue.

Units Croatia uses the metric system. To convert km to miles, multiply by 0.6.

Croatia has developed into a lively and friendly tourist destination while retaining its coastal ports' unspoilt beauty and character, traditional towns and tiny islands with their secluded coves. Its rich history is reflected in its Baroque architecture, traditional festivals and two UNESCO World Heritage sites.

The most developed tourist regions in Croatia include the peninsula of Istria, where you will find the preserved Roman amphitheatre in Pula, the beautiful town of Rovinj with cobbled streets and wooded hills, and the resort of Umag, with a busy marina, charming old town and an international tennis centre. The coast is dotted with islands, making it a mecca for watersports enthusiasts, and there is an abundance of campsites in the area.

Further south, in the province of Dalmatia, Split is Croatia's second-largest city and lies on the Adriatic coast. It is home to the impressive Diocletian's Palace and a starting point for ferry trips to the islands of Brac, Hvar, Vis and Korcula, with their lively fishing villages and pristine beaches. The old walled city of Dubrovnik is 150 km. south. A favourite of George Bernard Shaw, who described it as 'the pearl of the Adriatic', it has a lively summer festival, numerous historical sights and a newly restored cable car to the top of Mount Srd.

Scan QR code to browse more campsites on our website

Alan Rogers Code: CR6605
4 accommodations
50 pitches
GPS: 45.80235, 15.82708
Post Code: HR-10437

Rakitje, Zagreb

Camp Zagreb

www.alanrogers.com/cr6605
info@campzagreb.com
Tel: +385 133 245 67
www.campzagreb.com

Open (Touring Pitches):
All year.

Lying west of the capital of Zagreb, one of Central Europe's oldest cities, this is a useful location for those who want a short stopover or a longer stay to explore this attractive region. The campsite is located in the village of Rakitje beside a lake fringed with inviting trails. The pitches here are laid out in a circular arrangement, linked by pathways.

As well as offering 50 camping pitches in 2 sizes (38 x 75m2 and 10 x 100m2), Camp Zagreb also has accommodation in 4 modern wooden bungalows suitable for 2-4 people and one glamping tent.

The wellness suite, which overlooks the lake, features a water bed, jacuzzi, Finnish sauna and large sun terrace with a lake view. Activities include kayak rental (included in the rental price of the glamping accommodation.) The on-site pizza restaurant, with views over the lake, Pizzeria Jezero is highly recommended.

Pizzeria, Cafe Bar, Wellness apartment (with sauna, jacuzzi, terrace, and water bed), Wooden bungalows, Glamping tent, Massage studio, Beach, Pet Shower, Laundry room, Dishwashing room, Chemical Toilet Disposal Point, Kayak hire and Bike hire.

Key Features

 Open All Year

  Pets Accepted

  Disabled Facilities

  Play Area

  Bar/Restaurant

  Bike Hire

Scan me for
more information.

Alan Rogers Code: CR6749
40 accommodations
280 pitches
GPS: 45.27075, 14.26881
Post Code: HR-51415

Medveja, Kvarner

www.alanrogers.com/cr6749
reservations@liburnia.hr
Tel: +385 051 710 444
liburnia.hr/en/campsite-and-holiday-resort-medveja

Open (Touring Pitches):
All year.

Campsite Medveja

Campsite & Holiday Resort Medveja is located close to a long pebble beach on the Opatija Riviera. Surrounded by Mediterranean greenery at the foot of the Ucka Mountains, it is a good base from which to explore the wide range of leisure facilities along the coast, with its warm, clear blue sea. A range of walking trails thread through the countryside and along the coast, with the enticing waters of the Adriatic to cool off in after a hike.

Medveja has 280 stony pitches, with 200 having electricity and 96 having water as well. In addition, Medveja Holiday Resort includes apartments and rooms in bungalows, rooms in the Villa Medvejica, and 40 new premium mobile homes that are equipped with air-conditioning, satellite TV and an outdoor terrace with a grill.

Three adequate sanitary blocks. Toilet for disabled visitors. Private sanitary facilities available, Washing machine and dryer. Bar, snack bar, takeaway, restaurant (from May). Children's play area, children's club (high season). Barbecues are not permitted. WiFi throughout. Pets allowed.

Key Features

 Book Online

 Open All Year

 Pets Accepted

 Disabled Facilities

 Beach Access

 Play Area

 Bar/Restaurant

 Fishing

Scan me for more information.

Alan Rogers Code: CR6722
80 accommodations
540 pitches
GPS: 45.19529, 13.58927
Post Code: HR-52440

Porec, Istria

Camping Zelena Laguna

www.alanrogers.com/cr6722
mail@plavalaguna.hr
Tel: +385 052 410 101
istracamping.com/en/camping/
zelena-laguna

Open (Touring Pitches):
Early April - Early October.

Camping Zelena Laguna is situated just outside the popular resort of Poreč (just 15 minutes on the convenient tourist train). On the Istrian coast, this is a well run and long established site with 540 touring pitches, all with 10A electricity, 42 being fully serviced. Access to the pitches is by hard surfaced roads with gravel side roads. There are many mature trees providing plenty of shade and hedges separate most pitches.

Part of the site is on a peninsula with terraced pitches and the remainder are either on level or slightly sloping ground. A path circles the peninsula, below which are paved waterside sunbathing areas. Those to the right of the site are within easy reach of the cocktail bar. Further to the right is a small harbour, attractive restaurant and swimming pool.

Six modern and well maintained sanitary blocks. The washbasins have hot water and there are free hot controllable showers. Toilets are mostly British style and there are facilities for disabled visitors. Supermarket and shop. Several restaurants and snack bars. Swimming pool. Tennis (instruction available). Bicycle hire. Boat hire (motor and sailing). Boat launching. Riding. Entertainment programme for the family. Free WiFi throughout.

Key Features

 Book Online

 Pets Accepted

 Disabled Facilities

 Beach Access

 Swimming Pool

 Play Area

 Bar/Restaurant

 Bike Hire

Scan me for
more information.

Alan Rogers Code: CR6745
650 accommodations
1100 pitches
GPS: 44.91717, 13.81105
Post Code: HR-52212

Fazana, Istria

Camping Bi-Village

www.alanrogers.com/cr6745
info@bivillage.com
Tel: +385 052 300 300
www.bivillage.com

Open (Touring Pitches):
End April - Late October.

Camping Bi-Village is a large holiday village in an attractive location close to Pula's historic town and opposite the Brioni National Park islands. From the beach, superb sunsets can be observed as the sun sinks below the sea's horizon. The site is landscaped with many flowers, shrubs and rock walls and offers over 1,000 pitches for touring units (the remainder taken by bungalows and chalets).

The campsite is separated from the holiday bungalows by the main site road, which runs from the entrance to the beach. Pitches are set in long rows accessed by gravel lanes, slightly sloping towards the sea, with only the bottom rows having shade from mature trees and good views over the Adriatic.

Four modern toilet blocks with toilets, open plan washbasins and controllable hot showers. Child size washbasins. Baby room. Facilities for disabled visitors. Washing machine. Shopping centre (High season). Bars (High season) and restaurants. Bazaar. Gelateria. Pastry shop. Three swimming pools. Playground. Playing field. Trampolines. Motorboats and pedalos for hire. Boat launching. Games hall. Sports tournaments and entertainment. Massage. WiFi in some areas (charged). Dogs are not permitted on the beach.

Key Features

 Book Online

 Pets Accepted

 Disabled Facilities

 Beach Access

 Swimming Pool

 Play Area

 Bar/Restaurant

 Bike Hire

Scan me for more information.

45

Alan Rogers Code: CR6650
47 accommodations
550 pitches
GPS: 44.95043, 15.64114
Post Code: HR-47245

Rakovica, Karlovac

Camping Korana

www.alanrogers.com/cr6650
info@np-plitvicka-jezera.hr
Tel: +385 053 751 888
np-plitvicka-jezera.hr/en/plan-your-visit/hotels-and-camps/camp-korana

Open (Touring Pitches):
Start April - End October.

This is the perfect site for a visit to the Plitvice Lakes National Park (a UNESCO World Heritage Site of over 100 sq. km), just 6 km away and deservedly one of Croatia's most famous attractions with its waterfalls, lush vegetation and lakes. This 35-hectare site has a large, park-like environment and 550 unmarked pitches amid a naturally wooded landscape which offers plenty of activities for lovers of the great outdoors.

Tourers can choose between the tarmac hardstandings close to the entrance and open grassy plots with spectacular views towards the rear of the site. All have 16A electricity. The site has a good information centre, and planning a visit to the park is a must for most visitors with stunning scenery all around. Tour E leads walkers down to the gorgeous waterfalls, a trail that takes two and a half hours. A large restaurant provides a good choice of reasonably priced meals and a separate welcoming bar and shop selling various basic items.

The well-maintained toilet blocks include facilities for disabled visitors. Washing machines. Motorhome services. Large restaurant. The shop is open in the morning and afternoon, and a dedicated information office with details about the National Park is open all day. No charcoal barbecues. WiFi (free in the information office). 47 furnished cabins for hire.

Key Features

 Book Online

 Pets Accepted

 Disabled Facilities

 Bar/Restaurant

Scan me for more information.

Alan Rogers Code: CR6772
100 accommodations
500 pitches
GPS: 44.55555, 14.44166
Post Code: HR-51550

Mali Losinj, Kvarner

Camping Poljana

www.alanrogers.com/cr6772
info@poljana.com
Tel: +385 051 231 726
www.campingpoljana.com

Open (Touring Pitches):
Start April - End October.

Camping Poljana lies on the narrow strip of land in the southern part of Losinj island, just north of the pleasant town of Mali Losinj, and in a fantastic location for exceptional boat trips and excursions along the coast - perhaps some dolphin spotting? There's plenty to do and a superb sandy beach which is the focal point of this sunny, attractive campsite.

With 780 pitches (500 for touring), this site is bigger than it looks. The camping area has been newly laid out with some flat areas and some terraces. The pitches are marked with flowers and shrubs. There are some mature trees for shade and 500 electricity connections. Campers may be able to experience both sunset and sunrise from the same pitch! The toilet facilities are new and well maintained, while a shop and a series of bars and restaurants are available close by.

On the far and quiet side of the island is a private strip of shore (rock and concrete). A cocktail bar is available here. A marina for campers' boats has recently been refurbished.

Toilet blocks, including solar panels for hot water, are entirely up to date and adequate. Family room. Facilities for disabled visitors. Baby rooms. Motorhome services. Washing machine. Daily entertainment programmes. Bicycle hire. WiFi throughout (charged). Rock beach with cocktail bar. Marina. Kayaks.

Key Features

 Book Online

 Pets Accepted

 Disabled Facilities

 Beach Access

 Play Area

 Bar/Restaurant

 Bike Hire

 Fishing

Scan me for
more information.

Alan Rogers Code: CR6781
8 accommodations
12 pitches
GPS: 44.24127, 15.13876
Post Code: HR-23233

Privlaka, Dalmatia

www.alanrogers.com/cr6781
info@campingarcadia.com
Tel: +385 912 000 887
www.campingarcadia.com

Open (Touring Pitches):
Start April - End October.

Camp Arcadia

Camp Arcadia is located close to a sandy beach and small marina on the outskirts of Privlaka, near the town of Zadar. The attractive promenade and sea are accessed from the site by a couple of stairs. In the high season, a cocktail bar/ cafe provides drinks next to the small, unfenced, heated infinity pool.

The site has 12 hardstanding touring pitches with a 16 amp electric hook-up and free WiFi. Pitches are a mixture of standard (x8) or large pitches (x4) and are about 7m deep. The standard pitches are small by UK standards (approximately 4m wide) and more suitable for campervans and smaller motorhomes. Around 7m wide, the large pitches are more suited to caravans with awnings. The eight pitches nearest the pool and bar have now been given over to accommodation units that are operated by a third party.

The modern toilet block has showers, washbasins & WCs. Facility for visitors who are disabled. Bar. Outdoor heated swimming pool. BBQ's allowed, charcoal, gas & electric. Beach adjacent. Dogs allowed. Wi-Fi free. Earliest arrival time 13:00. There is no motorhome disposal point, other than a manhole that can be used by arrangement with the manager. A domestic style washing machine is available and is free to use.

Key Features

 Book Online

 Pets Accepted

 Disabled Facilities

 Beach Access

 Swimming Pool

 Bar/Restaurant

Scan me for
more information.

Alan Rogers Code: CR6844
40 pitches
GPS: 43.80063, 15.94210
Post Code: HR-22221

Lozovac, Dalmatia

www.alanrogers.com/cr6844
goran.skocic@si.t-com.hr
Tel: +385 022 778 495
www.camp-krka.hr

Open (Touring Pitches):
Start March - End October.

Camp Krka

This campsite lies about 15 km from Sibenik, the oldest Croatian town on the Adriatic coast, with narrow little streets and ancient monuments brimming with a colourful heritage. If you wish to experience genuine Croatian hospitality, you cannot afford to miss the opportunity to visit this small, rural site located just 2.5 km from the entrance to the Krka National Park. There's a huge wealth of stunning scenery in the park, with cascading waterfalls, a Roman amphitheatre and the iconic Franciscan monastery set on the tiny island of Visovac.

The site is owned and enthusiastically run by the Skocic family, and they will do all they can to ensure that your stay with them is enjoyable and memorable. There is space for 40 touring units, all on flat grass. Most have good shade, and all have 16A electricity and some tree shade.

The small, rustic restaurant and bar at the site entrance provides a good selection of homemade and reasonably priced dishes. Many incorporate fresh ingredients from the family garden, together with homemade cheese, cured ham, fresh bread and the family's own excellent wine. Two minibuses are used by the family for trips to the nearby Krka National Park.

Two small toilet blocks, recently renovated, have good hot showers. No facilities for disabled visitors. Washing machine. No shop but bread and milk available. Bicycle hire. Play area. Restaurant/bar and takeaway. Pétanque area. WiFi throughout (free).

Key Features

 Book Online

 Pets Accepted

 Beach Access

 Play Area

 Bar/Restaurant

Scan me for more information.

Alan Rogers Code: CR6885
10 pitches
GPS: 43.39746, 17.04865
Post Code: HR-21270

Zagvozd, Dalmatia

www.alanrogers.com/cr6885
camp.biokovo@yahoo.com
Tel: +385 981 733 318
www.campingbiokovo.hr

Open (Touring Pitches):
Start May - End October.

Camping Biokovo

Camping Biokovo is a new, small, family-run site set peacefully away from the coast at the foot of the eponymous mountain and nature park beside Zagvozd village. It's ideal for travellers who want to explore the undiscovered part of central Dalmatia; sample the homemade wine and rakija, organic fruits and vegetables. It's also a great location for visiting the historic towns of Dubrovnik and Split, the national parks of Biokovo, Krka and Plitvice and generally immersing yourself in this ancient landscape of real beauty and heritage.

The close proximity to the 60 km long Makarska Riviera, with its crystal clear sea and lovely stretches of beach, plus the imposing mountain, nature park and easy access to major roads, makes this a popular destination. The coastline is simply magnificent. There are 10 pitches with electricity (10A) and internet connections. The village centre is a 10-minute walk and has a shop, restaurant and café.

Sanitary facilities with showers, toilets and private cabin. Washing machine. Chemical disposal. Motorhome service point. Dogs accepted (max. 1) and dog washing area. WiFi throughout (free).

Key Features

 Pets Accepted

Scan me for more information.

Alan Rogers Code: CR6890
38 accommodations
300 pitches
GPS: 42.66188, 18.07135
Post Code: HR-20000

Dubrovnik, Dalmatia

www.alanrogers.com/cr6890
camping@valamar.com
Tel: +385 020 448 686
camping-adriatic.com/solitudo-camp-dubrovnik

Open (Touring Pitches):
Early April - End October.

Solitudo Sunny Camping

Solitudo is located on the north side of Dubrovnik. There are 21 mobile homes, 17 cabins and 300 pitches for touring units, all with 10-16A electricity and 30 with water, arranged on four large fields that are opened according to demand. Field A is mainly used for tents, and pitches here are small. Field D has pitches of up to 120m sq and takes many motorhomes (long leads required) from some pitches here. There are beautiful views of the mountains and the impressive Dr Franjo Tudman Bridge.

 Access around field D can be awkward for larger units, due to tight bends and trees, so many drivers go the wrong way on some stretches of the one-way system, trying to avoid this. To gain access to the two sanitary blocks and Reception from field D there is a flight of over 30 steps to climb without the aid of handrails. To avoid the steps, you effectively leave the site and travel up the road for 100m, where access can be achieved via one short ramp.

Key Features

 Book Online

 Pets Accepted

 Disabled Facilities

 Beach Access

 Play Area

 Bar/Restaurant

Two attractively decorated, clean and modern sanitary blocks have British-style toilets, open washbasins and controllable, hot showers. Good facilities for disabled visitors. Laundry. Motorhome services. Shop. Attached restaurant/bar. Tennis. Minigolf. Fishing. Bicycle hire. Beach with pedalo, beach chair, kayak and jet ski hire. Excursions organised to the Elafiti Islands. WiFi (free).

Scan me for
more information.

Capital Prague
Currency Czech Koruna (CZK)
Language Czech
Time Zone CET (GMT+1)
Telephone Code +420

Shops Hours can vary but generally shops are open 9am to 6pm weekdays, 9am to 1pm Sat and closed Sun. Shopping centres and tourist areas operate longer hours.

Money ATMs are widespread, accessible 24hrs a day and have multilingual instructions. Credit/debit cards are accepted in most restaurants.

Travelling with Children The country is becoming more child-friendly however, baby facilities remain rare. More often than not, restaurants will cater for children. Historical sights and attractions are partly geared towards kids. Child rates apply up to the age of 18.

Public Holidays 1 Jan New Year's Day; Mar/Apr Good Friday; Mar/Apr Easter Monday; 1 May May Day; 8 May Liberation Day; 5 Jul St Cyril & St Methodius Day; 6 Jul Jan Hus Day; 28 Sep Statehood Day; 28 Oct Independence Day; 17 Nov Freedom & Democracy Day; 24 Dec Christmas Eve; 25 Dec Christmas Day; 26 Dec Boxing Day

There are no Low Emissions Zones currently in place.

● EU Member | ● Schengen Area

Tourism website visitczechrepublic.com

●●○○○ **Accessible Travel Score**

Behind when it comes to accessibility. Older buildings, including museums, are not well equipped. Transport in cities is improving.

Driving in Czech Republic The road network is well-signposted throughout the country. To use motorways, you will need a vignette which can be purchased at border points, post offices and some petrol stations. Drink-driving and using your mobile whilst driving are illegal. Dipped headlights should be used at all times. Winter tyres are compulsory between November and April. Give way to trams and buses.

 Dashcams are legal

 Speed camera detectors are legal

Czech Republic

View all campsites in Czech Republic
alanrogers.com/czech-republic

See campsite map page 472

Climate Summers are warm and dry and winters are cold, sometimes snowy.

Emergency services Call 112 for the police, ambulance and fire and rescue.

Units Czechia uses the metric system. To convert km to miles, multiply by 0.6.

Once known as Bohemia, the Czech Republic is a land of fascinating castles, romantic lakes and valleys, picturesque medieval squares, and famous spas. It is divided into two main regions, Bohemia to the west and Moravia in the east.

Although small, the Czech Republic has a wealth of attractive places to explore. The historic city of Prague is the hub of tourist activity and a treasure trove of museums, historic architecture, art galleries and theatres, and the annual 17-day beer festival!

The beautiful region of Bohemia, known for its Giant Mountains, is popular for hiking, skiing and other sports. West Bohemia is home to three renowned spas: Karlovy Vary, Mariánské Lázne and Františkovy Lázne, which have developed around the hundreds of mineral springs which rise in this area and offer a wide variety of restorative treatments.

Brno is the capital of Moravia in the east, lying midway between Prague, Vienna and Budapest. Visitors will admire its beautiful architecture, notably Mies van der Rohe's Villa Tugendhat. North of Brno is the Moravian Karst. The underground Punkya River has carved out a network of caves, some open to the public and connecting with boat trips along the river.

Scan QR code to browse more campsites on our website

Alan Rogers Code: CZ4815
20 accommodations
70 pitches
GPS: 50.15228, 14.45032
Post Code: CZ-18400

Prague, Central Bohemia

Triocamp Praha

www.alanrogers.com/cz4815
info@trio.camp
Tel: +420 283 850 795
www.triocamp.cz

Open (Touring Pitches):
All year.

This neat, well-maintained site offers a pleasant respite from the bustle of the city. Situated on the northern edge of Prague, it's a great place to stay for a few days, with public transport whisking you into the city in under 30 minutes (buy tickets at reception). Start at the Old Town Square and the extraordinary 15th-century clock before strolling over the 14th-century Charles Bridge.

It has 70 pitches (all for touring units) with electricity (6/15A, half with Europlugs). Most are in the shade of mature trees, which can be very welcoming after a hard day sightseeing. The ground is slightly sloping, but most pitches are level, and access is off one circular, tarmac road with cabins and pitches on both sides. There is one hardstanding for a motorhome. Triocamp has a bar/restaurant with a comprehensive menu and a covered terrace attractively decorated with various flowers.

Key Features

  Book Online

  Open All Year

  Pets Accepted

  Disabled Facilities

  Swimming Pool

  Play Area

Modern, comfortable toilet facilities provide British-style toilets, open washbasins and free, preset hot showers. Facilities for disabled campers. Laundry with washing machine. Motorhome services. Shop. Attractive bar/restaurant. Play area and children's pool.

Scan me for more information.

Alan Rogers Code: CZ4700
50 accommodations
130 pitches
GPS: 50.78417, 15.04260
Post Code: CZ-46001

Severocesky, North Bohemia

www.alanrogers.com/cz4700
info@autokempliberec.cz
Tel: +420 485 123 468
www.autokempliberec.cz

Open (Touring Pitches):
All year.

Autocamp Liberec

Autocamp Liberec is situated 100 km or so north of Prague, on the edge of the town near the sports ground. It's a suburban environment but the camping area offers grassy pitches set among the birch and pine trees and backing onto an open field and woods. The distant Jizera mountains form a dramatic backdrop to the town, and the Jested mountain ski slopes at 1,012 m. dominating the distant skyline. Take the cable car and explore the wooded slopes in summer or visit the 16th-century Grabstejn castle with exceptional views from the tower.

This is a relaxed, informal campsite with its own small restaurant offering Czech specialities and an outdoor terrace. There are 130 touring pitches, 80 with electricity (10A), dotted between the rental accommodation units. Some caravan pitches are divided by low hedges on the edge of the site with views across open countryside.

The single sanitary block has toilets, washbasins, hot showers (on payment), and a kitchen with electric rings. Restaurant with café, snack bar and raised terrace. Good size swimming pool (July/Aug). Tennis. Playground. WiFi in the restaurant.

Key Features

 Open All Year

 Pets Accepted

 Beach Access

 Swimming Pool

 Play Area

 Bar/Restaurant

Scan me for
more information.

Alan Rogers Code: CZ4891
3 accommodations
48 pitches
GPS: 50.52363, 16.35216
Post Code: CZ-54974

Jihomoravsky, South Moravia

www.alanrogers.com/cz4891
info@bozanov.nl
Tel: +420 602 36 13 50
www.bozanov.nl

Open (Touring Pitches):
Start May - Mid September.

Camping Bozanov

Camping Bozanov is located in a very wooded area among the mountains of the Broumovské Steny, excellent for hiking and cycling. The marked trails lead through the beautiful hilly landscape with fields and extensive forests. Nearby is the Adrspach National Park with its bizarre and rugged sandstone rock formations and azure lake surrounded by steep cliffs.

For those looking for a challenge, there is the option of tackling the mountains by mountain bike, with a fantastic descent as a reward. In addition, there are plenty of opportunities for horse riding, mountain climbing, swimming, canoeing and fishing. There are 48 touring pitches, each with a 16amp electric hook-up point and 3 brick-built holiday homes available for hire.

2 toilet blocks with showers, washbasins and WCs. Baby room with a changing table and baby bath. Family room. Clothes and dishwashing facilities. Motorhome service area. Chemical toilet point. Bar with outdoor terrace. Library. Tourist information. Recreation room, table tennis, table football, darts and billiards. Children's farm. Trampoline. Seesaw, wooden playhouse with slide and swing and a sandpit. Multi-sports field, volleyball, badminton and football. Outdoor swimming pool. Fresh bread is available to order. Fire pits. Free Wi-Fi.

Key Features

 Pets Accepted

 Swimming Pool

 Play Area

 Bar/Restaurant

Scan me for more information.

Alan Rogers Code: CZ4885
15 accommodations
132 pitches
GPS: 50.17453, 17.16825
Post Code: CZ-79061

Severomoravsky, North Moravia

www.alanrogers.com/cz4885
camp@bobrovnik.cz
Tel: +420 584 411 145
www.bobrovnik.cz

Open (Touring Pitches):
All year.

Autocamping Bobrovnik

Lipova Lazne is on the northern edge of the Hruby Jesenik area, a protected landscape in the shadow of Praded, Moravia's highest mountain (1,491 m). On a clear day, you can see both the Krkonose of eastern Bohemia and the Tatras of central Slovakia from its peak. The area is great for walking, and waymarked trails abound, threading through rolling wooded hills with spectacular views at regular intervals. From the Cervenohorske Sedio Pass, you can take the cable car down to Ramzova or walk the red trail.

Set in a wooded area and beside a lake, the pitches are grassy and level, with plenty of mature trees dotted among them and providing shade. This quiet and pleasant campsite has 132 level and numbered pitches, 32 with 6A electricity. Facilities are basic, but it will suit active people interested in a holiday surrounded by idyllic scenery and the chance to explore this glorious hilly terrain.

The toilet block is dated but has clean toilets, hot showers and washbasins. Washing machine and dryer. Kitchen and dishwashing. Motorhome drain facility. Bar. Small restaurant. TV/ games room. WiFi (free).

Key Features

 Open All Year

 Pets Accepted

 Bar/Restaurant

Scan me for more information.

Alan Rogers Code: CZ4880
100 accommodations
200 pitches
GPS: 49.46628, 18.16400
Post Code: CZ-75661

Severomoravsky, North Moravia

Camping Roznov

www.alanrogers.com/cz4880
info@camproznov.cz
Tel: +420 571 648 001
www.camproznov.cz

Open (Touring Pitches):
All year.

Roznov pod Radhostem is halfway up the Roznovska Becva valley amidst the scenic Beskydy hills, which extend from North Moravia into Poland in the extreme east of the Republic. It is a busy tourist centre which attracts visitors to the Wallachian open-air museum and those who enjoy hill walking and cycling along the various trails.

This is a well-laid-out site, benefitting from regular investment and innovation. There are 300 pitches (200 for touring units), and 120 have an electrical connection (16A). Some pitches are rather small, although there are some recently landscaped pitches of 90-100 sq.m. They are mostly level and grassy, with a sprinkling of mature trees that add character and shade. A children's mini-zoo with farmyard animals is popular with youngsters.

The good-quality central toilet block has hot water in showers, washbasins and sinks. Facilities for disabled visitors. This block also has a large, comfortable TV lounge/meeting room. A further well-equipped toilet block has washbasins and WCs en-suite for ladies and a washing machine. Shop with basics and fresh bread (High season). Restaurant (High season). Swimming pool (High season). Tennis. Trampolines.

Key Features

 Open All Year

 Pets Accepted

 Swimming Pool

 Play Area

Scan me for more information.

Czech Republic

Alan Rogers Code: CZ4705
4 accommodations
20 pitches
GPS: 48.83964, 14.37518
Post Code: CZ-38101

Jihocesky, South Bohemia

www.alanrogers.com/cz4705
jana.eremiasova@centrum.cz
Tel: +420 776 898 022
www.camping-paradijs.eu

Open (Touring Pitches):
Mid April - Mid October.

Camping Paradijs

Camping Paradijs is a small, quiet, family-run site in a natural setting beside the River Vltava. It has several stone-ringed fireplaces for campfires (wood available at reception), a fairly large building with tables and benches, and an open fireplace, which is useful in bad weather. It's a secluded spot on a bend in the river and promises a relaxed stay amidst some stunning scenery.

The campsite is well run and has grassy pitches, mostly open and sunny, with low, wooded hillsides all around. There are 60 pitches on grass (20 for touring) near or bordering the tree-lined river, with a separate area of 12 pitches with electricity (6A). The reception and sanitary facilities are housed together in one building raised above the site level. This is essentially a site for those who enjoy getting out into nature and exploring the lush, verdant countryside.

The very limited number (2 each) of toilets and showers, with changing/shower compartments separated by a sliding door, are well maintained and very clean. Reception stocks essential items, drinks and tourist information. Bar. Play area. Fishing. Bicycle hire. Free WiFi.

Key Features

 Pets Accepted

 Play Area

 Bar/Restaurant

 Bike Hire

 Fishing

Scan me for
more information.

59

Alan Rogers Code: CZ4645
4 accommodations
140 pitches
GPS: 50.04997, 12.41183
Post Code: CZ-35002

Zapadocesky, West Bohemia

Camping Václav

www.alanrogers.com/cz4645
info@kempvaclav.cz
Tel: +420 354 435 653
www.kempvaclav.cz

Open (Touring Pitches):
Mid May - Mid September.

Camping Václav is situated on the country's western edge, close to the German border on the banks of the Jesenice Lake. The lake is safe for swimming and sailing, cycle trails start from the campsite, and the Soos nature reserve is nearby. Václav is in the 'spa triangle', giving visitors a choice of three different spas – Karlovy Vary, Mariánské Lázné and Frantiskovy Lázné. Guests at Camping Václav can take advantage of discounts for Frantiskovy Lázné.

The site is on two levels – the lower one, which is slightly sloping, has beautiful views over the lake and to the wooded hills beyond. The upper level, which is newer and has an excellent new toilet block, offers less shade. The 140 grassy touring pitches are generous (100-150 sq.m), open and sunny, all with 10A electricity. There is water and drainage on 10 pitches.

Key Features

 Pets Accepted

 Disabled Facilities

 Play Area

 Bar/Restaurant

 Fishing

Two new modern sanitary blocks with open style washbasins, controllable hot showers and facilities for disabled visitors. Washing machine and dryer. Motorhome services. Small shop for drinks and ice-creams. Bar/restaurant. Football field. Tennis. Fishing. Play area. Lake for swimming and boating. Communal barbecue. Internet access. WiFi (free).

Scan me for
more information.

Alan Rogers Code: CZ4745
40 pitches
GPS: 49.28177, 13.24003
Post Code: CZ-34021

Zapadocesky, West Bohemia

Camping U Dvou Orechu

www.alanrogers.com/cz4745
info@camping-tsjechie.nl
Tel: +420 376 382 421
www.camping-tsjechie.nl

Open (Touring Pitches):
Early May - Mid September.

This is a truly idyllic spot, tucked away among fields and wildflower meadows with far-reaching views of wooded hills in the distance. At an altitude of 1,700 feet, this small, quiet site sits in the centre of a beautiful green valley on the doorstep of the Sumava National Park, the Bohemian Forest. This vast area is a UNESCO Biosphere Reserve and, with Bavaria, it is the largest forest in Central Europe, home to otters, lynx and kingfishers. Nature abounds here, the only sound is from the birds, and you can hike or cycle for miles in any direction.

The Dutch owners, Hans and Freda Neuteboom, are painstakingly developing the site to the highest possible standards, and it is clearly one of the best in the Czech Republic. There are 40 large grass pitches, all with 6/10A electricity. Some are terraced next to the owners' house. There are ample opportunities for long walks, cycle rides, or just sitting back and watching the rural scene change as the day progresses.

The sanitary facilities provide showers and toilets, but maintenance can be variable. Washing machine and spin dryer. Sinks and hot water for dishwashing. Bar and snack bar. Play area. WiFi.

Key Features

 Adults Only

 Bar/Restaurant

Scan me for more information.

Capital Copenhagen
Currency Danish Krone (DKK)
Language Danish
Time Zone CET (GMT+1)
Telephone Code +45

Shops 10am to 6pm weekdays, until 4pm on Sat. Larger stores may be open Sun. Supermarkets open from 8am to 9pm. Bakeries (including in-store supermarket bakeries) may open earlier.

Money ATMs are widespread and are accessible 24hrs a day, some have multilingual instructions. Visa/Mastercard accepted widely. Amex less so.

Travelling with Children
Very child-friendly with many attractions from theme parks and zoos to family-friendly beaches. Entry to most museums is free. Many campsites have special programs for children during peak season.

Public Holidays 1 Jan New Year's Day; Mar/Apr Maundy Thursday; Mar/Apr Good Friday; Mar/Apr Easter Sunday; Mar/Apr Easter Monday; Apr/May Prayer Day; May Ascension; May/Jun Whit Sunday; May/Jun Whit Monday; 25 Dec Christmas Day; 26 Dec Boxing Day

There are no Low Emissions Zones currently in place.

● **EU Member** | ● **Schengen Area**

Tourism website visitdenmark.com

●●●●○ **Accessible Travel Score**

Access to buildings, transport and rural areas is improving but some areas are certainly not universally accessible yet.

Driving in Denmark Driving is much easier than at home as roads are much quieter. There are no tolls in Denmark except the Oresund Bridge that links the country with Sweden. Dipped headlights are compulsory at all times. There are no emergency phones on motorways, so make sure you have a mobile phone. Drink-driving and using your mobile whilst driving are illegal.

 Dashcams are legal

 Speed camera detectors are legal

Denmark

View all campsites in Denmark
alanrogers.com/denmark

See campsite map page 475

Climate Generally mild although changeable throughout the year.

Emergency services Call 112 for the police, ambulance and fire and rescue.

Units Denmark uses the metric system. To convert km to miles, multiply by 0.6.

Denmark offers a diverse landscape, all within a relatively short distance. The countryside is green and varied with flat plains, rolling hills, fertile farmland, many lakes and fjords, wild moors and long beaches, interspersed with pretty villages and towns.

It is the easiest of the Scandinavian countries to visit, and distances are short, so it is easy to combine the faster pace of the city with the tranquillity of the countryside and the beaches. It comprises the peninsula of Jutland and the larger islands of Zeeland and Funen, and hundreds of smaller islands, many uninhabited.

Zeeland is home to the climate-friendly capital city, Copenhagen, with its relaxing waterside cafés, vibrant nightlife, Michelin star restaurants and the stunning Frederiksborg castle. Funen is Denmark's second-largest island, linked to Zeeland by the Great Belt Bridge.

Known as the Garden of Denmark, its gentle landscape is dotted with orchards and pretty thatched, half-timbered houses. It also has plenty of safe, sandy beaches. Jutland's flat terrain makes it ideal for cycling, and its long beaches are popular with windsurfers.

Scan QR code to browse more campsites on our website

Denmark

Alan Rogers Code: DK2358
18 accommodations
350 pitches
GPS: 57.55491, 9.93279
Post Code: DK-9850

Nordjylland, Jutland

www.alanrogers.com/dk2358
mail@tornbystrand.dk
Tel: +45 98 97 78 77
www.tornbystrandcamping.dk

Open (Touring Pitches):
All year.

Camping Tornby Strand

Lying right on the northern edge of Denmark, Tornby Strand Camping is a wonderful location for superb sandy beaches. It is near the many exciting attractions of North Jutland. The site has 250 touring pitches, most with electric hook-up point 10amp. Fårup Summerland theme park and Skagen, Denmark's most northerly town, are only a 35–45-minute drive away. Even closer is the North Sea Oceanarium in Hirtshals, northern Europe's largest aquarium.

Further down the west coast lies the Rubjerg Knude disused lighthouse, one of Denmark's most iconic landmarks, standing on the edge of the west coast. Stroll along these magnificent beaches, enjoying the unique natural surroundings and the epic seascapes.

Three toilet blocks provide showers, washbasins and WCs. Facility for visitors who are disabled. Laundry with washing machine and dryer. Chemical toilet. Baby room. Family room. Chemical toilet point. Motorhome service point. Indoor and outdoor swimming pool. Defibrillator. Air hockey. Table football. TV room. Camp kitchen. BBQ area. Children's play area. Bouncy castle. Pets welcome. Dog walk. Volleyball. Badminton. Security barrier. Table tennis. Mini golf. Tourist information.

Key Features

 Open All Year

 Pets Accepted

 Disabled Facilities

 Beach Access

 Swimming Pool

 Play Area

Scan me for more information.

Alan Rogers Code: DK2353
15 accommodations
90 pitches
GPS: 56.75749, 9.24264
Post Code: DK-9640

Nordjylland, Jutland

www.alanrogers.com/dk2353
info@farso-fjordcamping.dk
Tel: +45 98 63 61 76
www.farso-fjordcamping.dk

Open (Touring Pitches):
End March - End September.

Farsø Fjord Camping

On the edge of Limfjord and just a few metres from the sandy beach, this is a friendly, family-run site in the heart of the country in northern Jutland. Set in a rural environment of lush fields and woodland, the natural surroundings are peaceful.

There are 152 pitches, with 90 available for touring, all with electricity and access to shared water points. The site has a range of good-quality accommodations available to rent. The space and range of play areas for children are good, and there are plenty of pedal vehicles that can be freely used by children of all ages. The site boasts the only 30-metre water slide in the area and a terrace with solar-heated swimming and paddling pools.

Two unisex sanitary units with en-suite family showers (coin-operated) and baby rooms. The unit for disabled visitors is accessed by a step. Kitchens and dishwashing facilities. Laundry. Motorhome services. Well-stocked shop. Cafeteria with takeaway service. Swimming pool with water slide and paddling pool. Free use of pedal cars and tricycles. Minigolf. Several playgrounds with trampolines and inflatable trampolines. Adventure play area with zip wire. Fishing. Featured sunken fire and barbecue area with arena seating.

Key Features

 Pets Accepted

 Disabled Facilities

 Beach Access

 Swimming Pool

 Play Area

 Fishing

Scan me for more information.

Alan Rogers Code: DK2085
22 accommodations
365 pitches
GPS: 56.11062, 10.23240
Post Code: DK-8270

Århus, Jutland

Camping Aarhus

www.alanrogers.com/dk2085
blommehaven@dcu.dk
Tel: +45 86 27 02 07
www.dcu.dk

Open (Touring Pitches):
Mid May - Late October.

DCU-Camping Aarhus is an attractive terraced campsite that overlooks the Bay of Aarhus, set right on the beach in the Marselisborg forest that fringes the coastline.

The city centre is about 8 km away, with good transport links in the high season (the bus journey takes around 15 minutes and cycling is a good option). Here you can wander through the old town, the Latin Quarter, and visit the Moesgard museum and the ARoS art museum, one of Scandinavia's largest.

The campsite makes a convenient and pleasant base, a peaceful environment where everyone can relax. The kids make friends easily and enjoy swimming from the beach or the small jetty. Away from the site, enjoy the magnificent views from the summit of Himmelbjerget, visit the Randers Rainforestor take a boat trip out to Samsø.

Key Features

 Pets Accepted

 Beach Access

 Play Area

Pitches are grassy and mostly level with plenty of mature trees adding shade and character to the site. Some of the gravel tracks can be steep and some care must be taken whilst manoeuvring. A small shop at the reception offers sandwiches. Showers. Baby nursing room. Laundry. Play area. Bouncy castle. Climbing wall. Area for ball games. Shop nearby. Bike hire 1 km. Minigolf 1 km. Windsurfing, golf, indoor swimming pool 5 km. BBQ area. WiFi.

Scan me for more information.

Alan Rogers Code: DK2090
4 accommodations
120 pitches
GPS: 55.93430, 10.25729
Post Code: DK-8300

Århus, Jutland

www.alanrogers.com/dk2090
info@hyggestrandcamping.dk
Tel: +45 88 44 83 83
www.hyggestrandcamping.dk

Open (Touring Pitches):
Start April - Mid September.

Camping Hygge Strand

This region of Jutland is deservedly well known for the splendid white beaches that shelve gradually down into the sea. This campsite is just 100 metres from such a beach and, being a Blue Flag beach; it's a good choice for a family holiday. Children will love to splash and jump off the small jetty. This site may particularly appeal to families with younger children, with many attractive play facilities, both indoors and outdoors. The surrounding countryside is peaceful and rural, with quiet country lanes being ideal for walking and cycling.

Arhus, the second city of Denmark, is 30 km. to the north and has great interest, especially around the charming old town and Latin Quarter. This is also a great place from which to make a boat trip to Copenhagen. To the south, Horsens has a large indoor pool complex and a fascinating industrial museum.

Pitches are grassy and level, mostly open but dotted with mature trees and demarcated with hedging. Supermarket (High season). Snack bar. Takeaway (High season). Fresh bread. Swimming from beach. Playground. Entertainment in high season. TV room (all big sporting events). Table tennis. BBQ area. Multi sports field.

Key Features

 Book Online

 Beach Access

 Play Area

Scan me for more information.

Alan Rogers Code: DK2040
61 accommodations
150 pitches
GPS: 55.83116, 9.30076
Post Code: DK-7323

Vejle, Jutland

Riis Feriepark

www.alanrogers.com/dk2040
info@riisferiepark.dk
Tel: +45 75 73 14 33
www.riisferiepark.dk

Open (Touring Pitches):
Early March - Late September.

Riis Feriepark is a good quality touring site ideal for visiting Legoland and Lalandia Billund (18 km), and Givskov Zoo (3 km). It is a friendly, family run site with 150 large level, grass touring pitches which are sheltered and surrounded by trees and shrubs. Electricity (13A) is available to all pitches, and 15 comfort pitches also have water and drainage.

The outdoor heated pool and water slide complex, and the bar that serves beer, ice cream, soft drinks and snacks, are open all season. There is a small, well stocked shop. The excellent indoor kitchen facilities and an attractive, covered barbecue area are very useful. This is a high-class site suitable for long or short stays in this very attractive part of Denmark.

Key Features

 Book Online

 Pets Accepted

 Disabled Facilities

 Beach Access

 Swimming Pool

 Play Area

 Bar/Restaurant

 Bike Hire

Two very good sanitary units include washbasins with divider/curtain and controllable showers (on payment). Suites for babies and disabled visitors, family bathrooms (one with whirlpool bath, on payment) and solarium. Laundry. Motorhome services. Campers' kitchen. Large sitting room with TV, plus barbecue grill house. Shop. Café. Pool complex (High season). Minigolf. Three playgrounds. Trampolines. Outdoor chess. Zip wire. Go-kart track. Train ride for children. Animal farm. Bicycle hire. Cabins to rent. WiFi (charged).

Scan me for more information.

Alan Rogers Code: DK2022
29 accommodations
210 pitches
GPS: 55.15029, 9.49690
Post Code: DK-6100

Sønderjylland, Jutland

Vikær Strand Camping

www.alanrogers.com/dk2022
info@vikaercamp.dk
Tel: +45 74 57 54 64
www.vikaercamp.dk

Open (Touring Pitches):
Start April - Late September.

Vikær Strand Camping in Southern Jutland lies in beautiful surroundings right on the white sandy Diernæs Bugt beach. This is a prime spot on a sheltered sweep of a bay, backed by rolling dunes and, behind them an idyllic countryside crisscrossed by quiet country lanes.

There are 390 grass pitches (210 for touring units), off long gravel lanes, all with 10/16A electricity, some separated by low hedges. There are pitches with sea views and direct access to the beach. Forty newly developed, fully serviced pitches have electricity, water, drainage, TV aerial point and Internet. From these, and from the front pitches on the lower fields, there are marvellous views over the Diernæs Bugt.

Three modern toilet blocks with washbasins in cabins and controllable hot showers. Family shower rooms. Section for children. Baby room. En-suite facilities for disabled visitors. Laundry. Campers' kitchen. Motorhome services. Shop (all season). Playground. Minigolf. Fishing. Archery. Watersports and boat launching. Pétanque. TV room. Playhouse with Lego and Play Station. Daily activities for children in high season. WiFi (charged). Torch useful. English is spoken.

Key Features

 Pets Accepted

 Disabled Facilities

 Beach Access

 Play Area

 Fishing

 Sailing

Scan me for more information.

Alan Rogers Code: DK2250
18 accommodations
107 pitches
GPS: 55.92414, 12.29452
Post Code: DK-3400

Sjælland, Islands

Hillerød Camping

www.alanrogers.com/dk2250
info@hillerodcamping.dk
Tel: +45 48 26 48 54
www.hillerodcamping.dk

Open (Touring Pitches):
Early April - Mid September.

Hillerød is a well-maintained, neat campsite in a residential neighbourhood. Shops, cafés, and restaurants are within walking distance, not to mention the 17th-century Frederiksborg Castle and the magnificent Baroque Gardens. This is also a fine base for visiting Copenhagen and is only 25 km. from the ferries at Helsingør and the crossing to Sweden. Centrally situated, the town is a hub of main roads from all directions.

The campsite has a park-like setting with five acres of well-kept grass, colourful flowers and some attractive trees. There are 107 pitches for tourers, of which 90 have electricity (13A), and these are marked. Most are level and grassy, and there is shade to some. You are assured of a warm welcome here by an enthusiastic couple, Annette and Taco.

The smart, new toilet block behind reception includes washbasins in cabins, free hot showers, facilities for disabled visitors and a baby room. The campers' kitchen adjoins the club room and includes free electric hot plates and coffee making machine. Laundry room (free iron). Motorhome services. Small shop. Comfortable club room with TV. Play area. Bicycle hire. WiFi over site (charged).

Key Features

 Pets Accepted

 Disabled Facilities

 Beach Access

 Play Area

 Bike Hire

Scan me for more information.

Alan Rogers Code: DK2266
27 accommodations
130 pitches
GPS: 54.65427, 11.73171
Post Code: DK-4880

Sjælland, Islands

Nysted Camping

www.alanrogers.com/dk2266
info@nystedcamping.dk
Tel: +45 54 87 09 17
www.nystedcamping.dk

Open (Touring Pitches):
All year.

Nysted Strand Camping is set on the southern edge of Lolland island and prides itself on its natural, unspoilt surroundings. It is a restful, serene spot with mature beech trees, birdsong, clear waters and wonderful sea views. The beach is one of Denmark's most beautiful child-friendly beaches, being safe and great for shrimping. With Nysted bay on one side and the Baltic Sea on the other side, the campsite is an ideal location for a relaxing, fun holiday.

Take a kayak and potter about on the shoreline, or rent bikes from the campsite, then head out onto the sleepy little country lanes, following the coast or exploring the forests and picturesque villages. The little harbour town of Nysted is within walking distance, with a good range of shops, eateries, and its own lovely beach - look out for seals in summer. Kids enjoy pony rides, the trampoline and pedal cars.

Grocery store/kiosk, restaurant, playground, TV room, internet cafe, wireless internet, miniature golf course, football, billiards, table tennis, chess, bathing jetty, communal grill area, toilets for the handicapped, bathing facilities for children, family room, communal kitchen etc.

Key Features

 Book Online

 Open All Year

 Pets Accepted

 Beach Access

 Play Area

 Bar/Restaurant

 Bike Hire

 Fishing

Scan me for
more information.

Capital Paris
Currency Euro (€)
Language French
Time Zone CET (GMT+1)
Telephone Code +33

Shops Hours vary throughout the year, often opening for shorter hours during low and shoulder seasons. In high season shops are open 10am to noon and 2pm-7pm weekdays and Sat. Longer hours, including Sun for shops in tourist zones.

Money ATMs are widespread, accessible 24hrs a day and have multilingual instructions. Credit/debit cards are widely accepted, but don't assume everywhere. Take cash for emergencies.

Travelling with Children
One of the most child-friendly countries in Europe, France has a good mix of cultural sights, historical monuments and other attractions. Most museums are free for under 18s.

Public Holidays 1 Jan New Year's Day; Mar/Apr Easter Monday; 1 May Labour Day; 8 May Victory Day; May Ascension; May/Jun Whit Sunday; May/Jun Whit Monday; 14 Jul Bastille Day; 15 Aug Assumption; 1 Nov All Saints; 11 Nov Armistice Day; 25 Dec Christmas Day

LEZ Low Emissions Zones in most major cities. Registration required.

⬤ **EU Member** | ⬤ **Schengen Area**

Tourism website france.fr/en

⬤⬤⬤○○ **Accessible Travel Score**

Efforts to improve accessibility are being made but the Paris metro is unusable for wheelchair users.

Driving in France There is a comprehensive road system of Autoroutes, N roads, D roads and local C roads. Vehicles made before 2011 are banned in Paris as part of the LEZ. If you plan to drive in or through major cities, you will need a Crit'Air sticker. Drink-driving, using your mobile or earphones whilst driving or sat navs that warn of speed cameras are illegal.

 Dashcams are legal

 Speed camera detectors are **illegal**

France

View all campsites in France
alanrogers.com/france

See campsite map pages 476–478

Climate Warmer in the south, wetter in the north and west, snow in the mountains.

Emergency services Call 112 for the police, ambulance and fire and rescue.

Units France uses the metric system. To convert km to miles, multiply by 0.6.

From the hot sunny climate of the Mediterranean to the more northerly and cooler regions of Normandy and Brittany, with the Châteaux of the Loire and the lush valleys of the Dordogne, and the mountain ranges of the Alps, France offers holidaymakers a huge choice of destinations to suit all tastes.

France boasts every type of landscape, from the wooded valleys of the Dordogne to the volcanic uplands of the Massif Central, the rocky coast of Brittany to the lavender-covered hills of Provence and snow-capped peaks of the Alps. The diversity of these regions is reflected in the local customs, cuisine, architecture and dialect.

France has a rich cultural heritage with a wealth of festivals, churches, châteaux, museums and historical monuments to visit. Many rural villages hold festivals to celebrate the local saints. You can also find museums devoted to the rural arts and crafts of the regions. The varied landscape and climate ensure many opportunities for outdoor pursuits from hiking and cycling, wind- and sand-surfing on the coast and rock climbing and skiing in the mountains. And no trip to France is complete without sampling the fantastic local food and wine.

Scan QR code to browse more campsites on our website

Camping de Bordeneo

Alan Rogers Code: FR56550
97 accommodations
104 pitches
GPS: 47.35460, -3.16853
Post Code: F-56360

Morbihan, Brittany

www.alanrogers.com/fr56550
reservation@groupecamping.fr
Tel: +33 5 79 87 02 59
www.bordeneo.com

Open (Touring Pitches):
Start May - End September.

Camping de Bordeneo is ideally located in Belle Ile en Mer, in a beautiful wooded park just 600 metres from the beach. The campsite has various services, an aquatic area and entertainment in summer, but also throughout the season, an indoor heated swimming pool with massage jets, a gym, a multisport field and a large playground. 104 touring pitches are offered in various locations on the site. They also have 97 attractive, fully equipped mobile homes to hire.

You can also take advantage of a bicycle and scooter rental service within the campsite to explore the surrounding areas. Appreciated for its heritage, gastronomy and culture, Camping de Bordeneo is the perfect hub to explore the surrounding areas, such as the Citadelle Vauban Hôtel-musée, where you can learn more about the city and its culture.

Clean, modern style, fully equipped sanitary facilities, Children's Facilities, Washing machine/dryer. Motorhome services, Evening entertainment (high season), children's club, grocery store (high season), bar, snack bar, takeaway. Play area. Kids Club, Indoor and Outdoor Swimming pool, Multisport Pitch, Accommodation to rent, WiFi, Bicycle Hire. Canoeing on site.

Key Features

 Book Online

 Pets Accepted

 Disabled Facilities

 Beach Access

 Swimming Pool

 Play Area

 Bar/Restaurant

 Bike Hire

Scan me for more information.

Alan Rogers Code: FR56130
180 accommodations
197 pitches
GPS: 47.61419, -2.92596
Post Code: F-56870

Morbihan, Brittany

Camping Mané Guernehué

www.alanrogers.com/fr56130
info@yellohvillage-mane-guernehue.com
Tel: +33 2 97 57 02 06
yellohvillage-mane-guernehue.com

Open (Touring Pitches):
Early April - Early November.

Located close to the Morbihan gulf, Yelloh! Village Mané Guernehué is a smart, modern site with excellent amenities, including an equestrian centre and a variety of pitches. Some are terraced beneath pine trees, others in a former orchard with delightful views of the surrounding countryside.

The 377 pitches are generally large, with 180 occupied by mobile homes and chalets. Many are level but a few, particularly in the centre of the site, slope to varying degrees. Most pitches have 10A electricity, and a few also have water and drainage. An impressive indoor pool complex has been added to the existing complex of outdoor pools, and there is an equally impressive spa and wellness facility.

Three modern toilet blocks include washbasins in cabins. Facilities for disabled visitors. Washing machines and dryers. Small shop, bar and takeaway (seasonal). Heated outdoor pool with slides (seasonal). Modern aqua splash water park. Heated indoor pool (all season), water slide. Spa complex. Fishing. Minigolf. An equestrian centre and pony trekking. Fitness room. Teenagers' room with games and TV. Play area. Tree top adventure area. Varied entertainment programme in high season, based around a sizeable purpose-built hall. Mobile homes to rent. WiFi (charged).

Key Features

 Book Online

 Pets Accepted

 Disabled Facilities

 Beach Access

 Swimming Pool

 Play Area

 Bar/Restaurant

 Bike Hire

Scan me for more information.

Alan Rogers Code: FR29430
369 accommodations
50 pitches
GPS: 47.86289, -4.09578
Post Code: F-29950

Finistère, Brittany

Camping Escale Saint-Gilles

www.alanrogers.com/fr29430
vacances@sandaya.fr
Tel: +33 2 98 57 05 37
www.sandaya.co.uk/our-campsites/
escale-saint-gilles

Open (Touring Pitches):
Early April - Late September.

Camping Sandaya Escale Saint-Gilles is a large, busy holiday-style campsite with 419 pitches but only around 50 for touring units. Facing the Glénan Islands, it is 50 metres from the beach, close to the River Odet and offers various types of accommodation. Families with young children, rather than teenagers, could find that the wide range of activities and entertainment offered, as well as a large sports and fitness complex (100 m. away off-site), make l'Escale St-Gilles a good choice.

The touring pitches are small to medium in size and nicely hedged. Adults will enjoy unwinding in the spa, with sauna and Turkish baths. The whole family will enjoy the indoor and outdoor pools with flumes, slides and moving rivers.

Two toilet blocks with showers and washing facilities in cubicles. Baby room. Facilities for disabled visitors. Laundry room with washing machines and dryers. Large shop. Restaurant (from end of May until end of August). Takeaway (all season). Bar. Indoor heated swimming pool complex and fun pool with water slides, paddling pool and moving river. Spa and massage. Fitness room. Games room. Programme of entertainment. Multisports court. Bicycle hire. WiFi (charged). Dogs are only accepted on touring pitches (except for July/Aug).

Key Features

 Book Online

 Pets Accepted

 Disabled Facilities

 Beach Access

 Swimming Pool

 Play Area

 Bar/Restaurant

 Bike Hire

Scan me for
more information.

Alan Rogers Code: FR29000
406 accommodations
68 pitches
GPS: 48.65807, -3.92833
Post Code: F-29660

Finistère, Brittany

Camping Les Mouettes

www.alanrogers.com/fr29000
contact@les-mouettes.com
Tel: +33 2 98 67 02 46
www.yellohvillage.co.uk/camping/
les_mouettes

Open (Touring Pitches):
Early April - Early September.

Yelloh! Village Camping Les Mouettes is a sheltered site on the edge of an attractive bay, with access to the sea at the front of the site. In a wooded setting with many attractive trees and shrubs, the 474 pitches include 68 for touring units, all with electricity, water and drainage. The remainder are taken by tour operators and by 406 mobile homes and chalets to rent.

At the centre of the 'village' are shops, a bar, a restaurant, an entertainment stage, sports facilities and an impressive heated pool complex with swimming, paddling and water slide pools, plus a 'Tropical river', jacuzzi and sauna. There is also an excellent indoor swimming pool.

A clean sanitary block with controllable showers and washbasins in cabins. There are showers with washbasins and delightful rooms for children and babies. Facilities for disabled visitors. Laundry. Shop (limited hours outside the main season). Takeaway. Bar with TV. Restaurant/pizzeria/grill. Heated pool complex indoor (all season) and outdoor. Beauty salon. Games rooms (a special one for under 5s). Play area. Multisports ground. Minigolf. Bicycle hire. Entertainment all season. Large units should phone first. Free WiFi throughout.

Key Features

 Book Online

 Pets Accepted

 Disabled Facilities

 Beach Access

 Swimming Pool

 Play Area

 Bar/Restaurant

 Bike Hire

Scan me for more information.

Alan Rogers Code: FR22080
401 accommodations
96 pitches
GPS: 48.82798, -3.47623
Post Code: F-22700

Côtes d`Armor, Brittany

www.alanrogers.com/fr22080
ranolien@sandaya.fr
Tel: +33 2 96 91 65 65
www.sandaya.co.uk/our-campsites/
le-ranolien

Open (Touring Pitches):
Early April - Late September.

Camping le Ranolien

Camping Sandaya le Ranolien has been attractively developed around a former Breton farm – everything here is either made from or placed on or around the pink rocks, some of them massive. Of around 500 pitches, approximately 100 are for touring, mostly large and flat, but some quite small, all with 10A electricity, water and drainage.

The rest of the site comprises mobile homes and chalets to rent and pitches used by two tour operators. The site is on the coast, with beaches and coves within walking distance and spectacular views from some pitches.

The main toilet block is heated in cool weather and has washbasins in cabins, mostly British style WCs and good showers, some spacious and with washbasins. Facilities for disabled visitors. Laundry. Motorhome services. Supermarket and gift shop. Restaurant, crêperie and bar. Indoor (all season) and outdoor (from the end of May) swimming pool complex. Wellness centre. Disco in high season. Minigolf. Games room. Play area. Cinema. Gym and steam room. Mobile homes for hire, including Romany-style caravans and luxury chalets. Internet and WiFi (on payment).

Key Features

 Book Online

 Pets Accepted

 Disabled Facilities

 Beach Access

 Swimming Pool

 Play Area

 Bar/Restaurant

Scan me for more information.

Alan Rogers Code: FR22000
41 accommodations
85 pitches
GPS: 48.50042, -2.75921
Post Code: F-22000

Côtes d`Armor, Brittany

Camping des Vallées

www.alanrogers.com/fr22000
contact@camping-desvallees.com
Tel: +33 296 94 05 05
www.camping-desvallees.com

Open (Touring Pitches):
Early April - End September.

A well-managed town centre campsite, within easy reach of the popular ferry port and the walled heritage town of St Malo. St Brieuc's shops, restaurants and local amenities are within easy walking distance. At the same time, the old quarter of the town and the excellent street markets on Wednesday and Saturday mornings are worth a visit. Wonderful north Brittany beaches are close by, such as the Rosaires beach in Plérin (15 minutes) and Erquy on the famous Pink Granite Coast.

Flower Camping des Vallées has 85 good-sized pitches, 35 with electricity (10A), water and drainage, set mainly on flat terraced grass and separated by shrubs and bushes, with 12 hardstandings for large motorhomes. Mature trees are plentiful, providing shade if required, and a small stream winds through the middle of the site creating a quiet, peaceful atmosphere.

The two main toilet blocks include some washbasins in cabins, facilities for disabled visitors and a baby room. Laundry facilities. Motorhome services. Two further smaller blocks are at the bottom of the site. Shop with basic provisions and a compact bar with snacks and takeaway (high season). Play area. Arcade games. Bicycle hire. Entertainment is organised in peak season, also weekly pony days for children. Mobile homes and equipped tents for hire. Water park nearby (150 metres). WiFi (charged). BMX track, Riding nearby.

Key Features

 Book Online

 Pets Accepted

 Disabled Facilities

 Beach Access

 Swimming Pool

 Play Area

 Bar/Restaurant

 Bike Hire

Scan me for more information.

Alan Rogers Code: FR35020
560 accommodations
136 pitches
GPS: 48.49030, -1.72780
Post Code: F-35120

Ille-et-Vilaine, Brittany

www.alanrogers.com/fr35020
info@lesormes.com
Tel: +33 2 99 73 53 00
www.lesormes.com

Open (Touring Pitches):
Early April - Early November.

Domaine des Ormes

This impressive site in the grounds of the Château des Ormes is in the northeast part of Brittany, in an estate of wooded parkland and lakes. With many facilities and a wide range of accommodations such as treehouses, floating cabins, wooden chalets, etc. Of the 696 pitches, 136 are for tourers (most with 6A electricity, some with 16A and their own water and wastewater). They are of varying sizes (80-150 sq.m), and there is a choice of terrain – flat or gently sloping, wooded, walled or open. The rest are occupied by tour operators (560) and mobile homes (120 to rent).

There is a soundproof nightclub on site. Fresh bread is available on-site. Bikes on rent. Great site for teenagers with a climbing tower, tree top adventure park, zip wire, cricket field and cable waterski. A large dome covers the aquatic parc and wave swimming pool.

The heated sanitary blocks are of a good standard, with family cubicles (shower and washbasin) and facilities for babies, children and disabled visitors. Motorhome services. Supermarket, bar, restaurant, pizzeria and takeaway. Games room, bar and disco. Indoor and outdoor pools, an impressive aqua park and a wave pool. Indoor Adventure play area. Golf (charged). Bicycle hire. Fishing. Equestrian centre (charged). Minigolf. Tennis. Sports ground. Paintball. Archery. Zip wire. Climbing wall. Cricket club. Charcoal and gas barbecues are permitted. WiFi in the bar area is free (elsewhere charged).

Key Features

 Book Online

 Pets Accepted

 Disabled Facilities

 Beach Access

 Swimming Pool

 Play Area

 Bar/Restaurant

 Bike Hire

Scan me for more information.

Alan Rogers Code: FR50030
60 accommodations
134 pitches
GPS: 48.79778, -1.52498
Post Code: F-50380

Manche, Normandy

www.alanrogers.com/fr50030
bonjour@lez-eaux.com
Tel: +33 2 33 51 66 09
www.lez-eaux.com

Open (Touring Pitches):
Start April - Mid September.

Château de Lez Eaux

Set in the grounds of a château, Castel Camping le Château de Lez Eaux lies in a rural situation just off the main route south, under two hours from Cherbourg. Of the 134 touring pitches, all with electricity (10A, Europlug) and 90 with water and drainage. Most of the pitches are of a very good size, partly separated by trees and shrubs on flat or slightly sloping, grassy ground overlooking Normandy farmland and a small fishing lake.

The campsite offers several kinds of camping accommodation and pitches depending on your desires and needs - from treehouses to mobile-home with Jacuzzi and chalets to camping pitches for tents, caravans and mobile homes. Activities include an indoor tropical-themed water park complete with water slides and a children's aqua splash fun area. Paddling pool, swimming pools, games area, bouncy castles, fishing lake, tennis court and bike rental.

Three sanitary blocks (1 heated) are equipped with showers, private washing cubicles and baby facilities. Washing machines and dryers. Shop. Bar. Takeaway. Fresh bakery in the morning. Covered water park (pool, slides, paddling pool) 1 outdoor pool. Games areas and bouncy castles. Fishing lake. Football. Volleyball grounds. TV room and games room. Bicycle hire. Tennis court hire. Kids club during the summer. Summer activities: 2 concerts per week, local market, daily aqua aerobics in the indoor pool.

Key Features

 Book Online

 Pets Accepted

 Disabled Facilities

 Beach Access

 Swimming Pool

 Play Area

 Bar/Restaurant

 Bike Hire

Scan me for
more information.

Alan Rogers Code: FR50420
19 accommodations
16 pitches
GPS: 49.69150, -1.43794
Post Code: F-50840

Manche, Normandy

www.alanrogers.com/fr50420
campingdelaplage.fermanville@
wanadoo.fr
Tel: +33 2 33 54 38 84
www.campingdelaplage-fermanville.
com

Open (Touring Pitches):
Start April - Mid October.

Key Features

 Book Online

 Pets Accepted

 Disabled Facilities

 Beach Access

 Play Area

 Bar/Restaurant

Camping de la Plage

Camping de la Plage is located near the north coast of Cotentin in Normandy. You'll soon feel at home with pitches among flowers and a few luxury glamping tents. A few minutes walk, and you're on the sandy beach of the jagged coastline of the English Channel.

The 16 touring pitches have been carefully laid out between the flowers on beautiful lawns, with 40 places reserved for regular guests, mainly French. They are all friendly holidaymakers looking for peace and small-scale conviviality. The touring campers come from all over Europe to enjoy the calm life on the coast of the English Channel. You'll find a small cave with a sandy beach just four hundred metres from the campsite. There you can sunbathe or take a dip in the sea.You'll find playgrounds, a mini-golf course, and a court to play jeu de boules on the campsite. The recreation room has a friendly bar with tables and chairs. The modern sanitary facilities are immaculate, and the showers are free of charge.

Disabled sanitary facilities, Fresh bread available at the campsite, Groceries: limited selection, Shop, restaurant, Snack bar, Takeaway meals, Bar, Communal barbecue area, Children's playground: large Entertainment programme (at least 2x a week), Games room, Trampoline, Bouncy castle, Crazy golf, Table tennis table, Jeu de boules alley, Pets allowed, WiFi.

Scan me for
more information.

Alan Rogers Code: FR14230
510 accommodations
30 pitches
GPS: 49.15720, -0.92273
Post Code: F-14490

Calvados, Normandy

www.alanrogers.com/fr14230
mo.reception@siblu.fr
Tel: +33 20 34 81 91 93
www.siblu.co.uk

Open (Touring Pitches):
Start May - Start September.

Domaine de Litteau

Siblu Camping Domaine de Litteau consists of two vast areas with Mobile Homes to rent or own. The touring site is separated from the main site, where 30 spacious, well-maintained touring/tent pitches are separated by low hedging. There is a modern sanitary block. All other facilities are on the main site.

The touring site has separate access via a coded gate and is very secure. This entrance is perfect for all sizes of units. The site is ideal as a stopover for the ferry ports, or with all the facilities the site offers and local attractions; you could easily make this a base for your holiday. Check-in was effortless and efficient, and we were allocated a pitch that met our requirements.

There are two new sanitary blocks with disabled facilities that are cleaned several times a day. Restaurant, Bar, and modern laundry facilities. WiFi is free at the bar area but chargeable throughout the rest of the site. Supermarket, takeaway food, Children's Playground, Outdoor swimming pool, Evening Entertainment, Bicycle hire on site.

Key Features

 Book Online

 Pets Accepted

 Disabled Facilities

 Swimming Pool

 Play Area

 Bar/Restaurant

 Bike Hire

 Fishing

Scan me for more information.

Alan Rogers Code: FR61030
18 accommodations
228 pitches
GPS: 48.54778, -0.41983
Post Code: F-61140

Orne, Normandy

www.alanrogers.com/fr61030
camping@bagnolesdelorne.com
Tel: +33 2 33 37 87 45
www.campingbagnolesdelorne.com

Open (Touring Pitches):
Early March - Mid November.

Camping de la Vée

Camping de la Vée is a pleasant municipal site in the town of Bagnoles de l'Orne, and is open for a long season (March to November). The 246 pitches (228 for touring) are large and grassy and are grouped around the two well-maintained toilet blocks. All have 10A electricity. Some 51 hardstandings are available for motorhome users. On-site amenities include a snack bar with special meal offers in peak season, a play area and free WiFi. Several fully equipped mobile homes are available to rent.

Bagnoles is an important thermal spa centre and can be reached on the shuttle bus. The town's Belle Epoque quarter is deservedly famous, lined with fine villas with extravagant polychrome façades influenced by the Art Deco style.

Sanitary facilities especially for children. Snack bar. Play area. Mobile homes to rent. Shuttle bus to the spa. Bar. WiFi throughout (free). Only electric barbecues are permitted.

Key Features

 Pets Accepted

 Disabled Facilities

 Play Area

 Bar/Restaurant

Scan me for more information.

Drone

Alan Rogers Code: FR14220
25 accommodations
130 pitches
GPS: 49.28290, -0.19070
Post Code: F-14810

Calvados, Normandy

www.alanrogers.com/fr14220
loisirs-ariane@netcourrier.com
Tel: +33 2 31 24 52 52
www.camping-ariane.com

Open (Touring Pitches):
Early April - Early November.

Camping Loisirs Ariane

You will get a warm welcome in English at Loisirs Ariane Camping Village, just 300 metres from the long sweep of sandy beach. It's well laid out, with around 160 good-sized grassy pitches (90 for touring), all with 10A electricity, water and waste points close by. Shade is limited, and pitches are well-demarcated by neat hedges and small trees. Everything is well maintained, with easy access for larger units and gate-controlled entry.

There are numerous beaches nearby, and possible days out include the moving D-Day Beaches, Pegasus Bridge, Bayeux with its excellent Saturday market and famous tapestry, fashionable Deauville and picturesque Honfleur. The iconic Mont St Michel is under 2 hours away, and the lush Calvados heartland, dotted with orchards and grazing cattle, is on the doorstep. The site is conveniently located for the ferry ports of Caen (Ouistreham 12 km) and Le Havre (65 km).

Heated sanitary building, including showers and washbasins in cubicles. Shower and toilets for children. Baby bath. Facilities for disabled visitors. Washing machines and dryers. Motorhome service. Fresh bread at reception (on demand). Covered outdoor swimming pool. Sauna. Games room. Play area. Volleyball and basketball. Boules. Animation (High season). Inflatable play castle (high season). Mini golf nearby. WiFi (90% of the site).

Key Features

 Book Online

 Disabled Facilities

 Beach Access

 Swimming Pool

 Play Area

Scan me for more information.

Alan Rogers Code: FR14200
80 accommodations
150 pitches
GPS: 49.32864, 0.08634
Post Code: F-14800

Calvados, Normandy

www.alanrogers.com/fr14200
contact@camping-deauville.com
Tel: +33 2 31 88 58 17
www.camping-deauville.com/en

Open (Touring Pitches):
Start April - End October.

La Vallée de Deauville

This large, modern site is close to the traditional seaside resorts of Deauville and Trouville. With a total of 450 pitches, there are many mobile homes, both to rent and privately owned, and 150 for touring units (including a 70-pitch tent field). The main pitches are level, of a reasonable size and mostly hedged, 80 have 10A electricity.

A recent swimming pool complex with flumes, lazy river, jacuzzi and fun pool makes an attractive focal point near the entrance and a large fishing lake. The bar and restaurant are large and comfortable, and a shop is on-site.

Two heated toilet blocks with showers and washbasins in cubicles. Good facilities for babies and disabled visitors. Laundry facilities. Small shop. Bar and restaurant. Takeaway. Outdoor heated swimming pool complex (high season). Modern spa. Good play area and games room. New multisports court. Bicycle hire. Entertainment in high season. WiFi (charged).

Key Features

 Pets Accepted

 Disabled Facilities

 Beach Access

 Swimming Pool

 Play Area

 Bar/Restaurant

 Bike Hire

 Fishing

Scan me for more information.

Alan Rogers Code: FR76135
34 accommodations
40 pitches
GPS: 49.41252, 0.81198
Post Code: F-76480

Seine-Maritime, Normandy

www.alanrogers.com/fr76135
campingdelaseine@gmail.com
Tel: +33 6 65 69 34 50
www.campingdelaseine.com

Open (Touring Pitches):
Mid March - Late November.

Camping de la Seine

Views of France's most famous river and the wooded hills opposite can be seen from Camping de la Seine, a small riverside campsite tucked away not far from Le Havre. This rural setting has 40 touring pitches, grassy and dotted with fruit trees. The campsite offers spa services, bike hire and a large grassy expanse where youngsters can run around and let off steam. The staff here are keen to ensure a warm welcome and can arrange trips to local attractions and activities. Local farmers occasionally bring fresh local produce to the site.

Camping de la Seine is a five-minute drive to the old town of Jumièges, with its beautiful 7th-century ruined abbey, shops, restaurants and amenities. Also close by is an outdoor activities park alongside a large swimming lake, making it a popular day out with options for all ages. Excellent and easy-going cycle routes and walking trails are all around, running through this largely flat landscape. This could be a useful stopover en route to/from the northern Channel ports.

Heated sanitary facilities with facilities for the disabled. Shop (small). Daily bread delivery. Children's play area. Grassy games area. Mini golf. Bicycle hire. Wellness area. Laundry. Pets allowed. Barbecues allowed. WiFi. Fishing, zip wire, climbing, archery, riding, canoeing and golf are nearby.

Key Features

 Book Online

 Open All Year

 Pets Accepted

 Disabled Facilities

 Play Area

 Bar/Restaurant

 Bike Hire

 Fishing

Scan me for more information.

Alan Rogers Code: FR27050
7 accommodations
53 pitches
GPS: 49.40308, 1.47822
Post Code: F-27480

Eure, Normandy

Camping Saint Paul

www.alanrogers.com/fr27050
camping-saint-paul@orange.fr
Tel: +33 2 32 49 42 02
www.camping-saint-paul.fr

Open (Touring Pitches):
Start April - End October.

The village of Lyons-la-Forêt, with its Mediaeval covered market and magnificently preserved half-timbered buildings, is classified as one of 'les Plus Beaux Villages de France.' Within walking distance of the village, next to the playing field and public pool, this quiet municipal campsite is a delightful and peaceful spot. The site has one hundred level grass and numbered pitches, separated by hedges with various mature trees providing shade.

There are 53 are for touring units, each with 6A electricity, water and drainage; hardstandings are available. Seven chalets to rent occupy some of the pitches overlooking the clear shallow stream that runs the site's length.

Central toilet block includes controllable showers and washbasins in cubicles; facilities for disabled visitors are on the ladies' side and are a basic shower room and separate washbasin and WC; they are a bit cramped. Washing machine and dryer. A second block near reception opens in the high season. Motorhome services. The reception sells some basic food and drinks. TV/games room also used by campers: table and chairs plus free use of fridge, freezer and microwave. Small play areas. Pétanque. A field for games. Bicycle hire. Seven chalets to rent. Wifi throughout (charged).

Key Features

 Book Online

 Pets Accepted

 Disabled Facilities

 Swimming Pool

 Play Area

 Bike Hire

 Scan me for more information.

Alan Rogers Code: FR76290
27 accommodations
73 pitches
GPS: 50.02557, 1.30846
Post Code: F-76910

Seine-Maritime, Normandy

www.alanrogers.com/fr76290
camping.criel@wanadoo.fr
Tel: +33 2 35 50 81 19
www.camping-lemontjolibois.com

Open (Touring Pitches):
Early March - Late September.

Camping le Mont Joli Bois

This is a well-maintained mature site, open for a long season and located 500 metres from the beach, south of the pretty resort of Le Tréport. The 96 pitches (73 for touring) are neat, grassy, and of a good size, most with electrical connections, some with attractive sea views. Around six fully equipped mobile homes are available to rent. In high season a van selling takeaway food visits the site, and several good restaurants and various shops are available in Criel-Sur-Mer, a short walk from the site. On-site leisure facilities include a children's playground and bouncy castle.

Criel-Sur-Mer is a pleasant resort with a long history dating back to the 11th century. It is surrounded by towering cliffs, rising to over 100 metres and offers some invigorating cliff-top walks. Criel became a popular resort after the Great War as one of the closest seaside resorts to Paris. The town is now home to cider production activity (guided tours and tastings are available) and is close to the majestic landscape of the vast Baie de Somme, whose nature reserve teems with wildfowl.

Key Features

 Book Online

 Pets Accepted

 Disabled Facilities

 Beach Access

 Play Area

 Bike Hire

Basic sanitary block with hot showers and facilities for disabled visitors and children. Small shop. Takeaway food (High season). Children's playground. Bouncy castle. Table tennis. WiFi throughout (charged). Mobile homes to rent.

Scan me for more information.

Alan Rogers Code: FR80220
28 accommodations
79 pitches
GPS: 50.07726, 1.41447
Post Code: F-80350

Somme, Picardy

Camping le Rompval

www.alanrogers.com/fr80220
lerompval@baiedesommepleinair.com
Tel: +33 2 35 84 43 21
www.camping-lerompval.com

Open (Touring Pitches):
Start April - Start November.

Le Rompval is a former municipal site located in the pleasant seaside resort of Mers-les-Bain, around 25 km. West of Abbéville, at the mouth of the Bresle river. There are 132 pitches (79 for touring), which are grassy and good-sized. All are equipped with 8A electricity, and 30 have water and wastewater connections. 53 pitches are occupied by chalets (28 available to rent).

The site boasts some interesting architecture and several amenities, including a small shop, takeaway food service, and a heated, covered pool and paddling pool. The nearest beach is 2.5 km. distant. This is a great sweep of sand, ideal for sand yachting and windsurfing. Mers is an attractive resort with all normal services, including a supermarket. It is closely linked with its neighbours, Eu and Le Tréport. The older part of the town was developed in the later 19th century as the popularity of seaside holidays grew.

Key Features

 Book Online

 Pets Accepted

 Beach Access

 Swimming Pool

 Play Area

 Bar/Restaurant

 Bike Hire

Facilities for disabled visitors. Motorhome services. Shop. Bar and takeaway (high season). Heated, indoor pool (all season). Play area. Activity programme (high season). Chalets to rent. Bicycle hire. WiFi over part of site (free).

Scan me for more information.

Camping les 3 Sablières

Alan Rogers Code: FR80330
20 accommodations
30 pitches
GPS: 50.24826, 1.59858
Post Code: F-80550

Somme, Picardy

www.alanrogers.com/fr80330
contact@camping-les-trois-sablieres.com
Tel: +33 3 22 27 01 33
www.camping-les-trois-sablieres.com

Open (Touring Pitches):
Start April - Early November.

This peaceful family-run site is only 300 m. from kilometres of sandy beach and dunes on the edge of the Baie de Somme. There are 97 grass pitches of about 100 sq.m, 30 of which are for touring units scattered amongst the other pitches. The pitches are flat, equipped with 6/10A electricity and water, and are separated by neatly trimmed hedges (the grass is very worn in places).

Large units might have difficulty entering the site and negotiating some of the site's roads. A separate meadow with water and electricity but no marked pitches is for tent campers. The site attracts horse owners as there are paddocks to rent. This quiet coastal site is well suited to couples and country-loving families for exploring the miles of beach and mudflats (with care) or for walking sections of the Sentier Littoral coastal path.

One well insulated, unisex sanitary block in the centre of the site has washbasins in cubicles. Baby room. Hairdryers. Washing machine and dryer. Motorhome service point. More toilets near bar. Bread delivery. Bar and snack bar (July/Aug and w/ends). Heated swimming pool. Sauna (charged). Small play area (3-12 yrs). WiFi near reception (charged).

Key Features

 Book Online

 Pets Accepted

 Disabled Facilities

 Beach Access

 Swimming Pool

 Play Area

 Bar/Restaurant

Scan me for more information.

Camping Parc des Cygnes

Alan Rogers Code: FR80100
9 accommodations
136 pitches
GPS: 49.92077, 2.25962
Post Code: F-80080

Somme, Picardy

www.alanrogers.com/fr80100
contact@amiens-campingdescygnes.com
Tel: +33 3 22 43 29 28
amiens-campingdescygnes.com

Open (Touring Pitches):
Start April - Mid October.

Parc des Cygnes is just a few minutes from the N1, the A16 Paris-Calais motorway and the A29/A26 route to Rouen and the south, so it is useful as a stopover, being about 50 km. from the ports. It enjoys a riverside position with good access to Amiens. The 3.2 hectares have been completely levelled and attractively landscaped. Bushes and shrubs divide the site into areas, and trees around the perimeter provide some shade.

Of the 145 pitches, 136 are for touring, with nine mobile homes to rent. All pitches are grassed, with plenty of space on the tarmac roads in front of them for motorhomes to park in wet conditions. There are 81 pitches with electricity (10A), of which 37 also have water and drainage; further water points can be accessed throughout the rest of the site.

Two toilet blocks (both open when the site is busy) with separate toilet facilities but unisex shower and washbasin area. Baby bath. Facilities for disabled visitors. Reception building also has toilets, showers and washbasins (heated when necessary). Laundry facilities. Shop (open on request all season), bar and takeaway (seasonal; weekends only in low season). TV/games room. Bicycle hire. Fishing. WiFi over part of the site (charged).

Key Features

 Book Online

 Pets Accepted

 Disabled Facilities

 Play Area

 Bar/Restaurant

 Bike Hire

 Fishing

 Scan me for more information.

Alan Rogers Code: FR62010
60 accommodations
146 pitches
GPS: 50.86632, 1.85698
Post Code: F-62340

Pas-de-Calais, Nord/Pas-de-Calais

Camping la Bien-Assise

www.alanrogers.com/fr62010
castels@bien-assise.com
Tel: +33 3 21 35 20 77
www.camping-la-bien-assise.com

Open (Touring Pitches):
Mid April - Mid September.

Le Castel Camping de La Bien-Assise is a mature and well-developed campsite in the grounds of a country house dating back to the 1500s. There are around 200 grassy pitches here, including 4 with hardstanding, mainly set among mature trees with others on a newer field. They're connected by surfaced, and gravel roads and are of a good size (up to 300 sq.m), with well-maintained shrubs and hedging dividing most of the pitches. The old outbuildings have been sensitively restored and converted over the years to create wonderful modern facilities, notably a superb restaurant.

Being close to Calais, the Channel Tunnel exit, and Boulogne makes this a good stopping point en route, but La Bien-Assise is well worth a longer stay to explore the beautiful Opal Coast. It is a very popular site which is also used by tour operators but is well managed, and there are no adverse effects.

Three well-equipped toilet blocks provide many washbasins in cubicles, showers and baby rooms. Laundry facilities. The main block is in four sections, two unisex. Two motorhome service points. Shop. Restaurant. Bar/grill and takeaway (all from mid-April). TV room. Pool complex (mid April - mid Sept) with toboggan, covered paddling pool and outdoor pool. Play areas. Minigolf. Tennis. Bicycle hire. WiFi (charged, but free with a drink in the bar).

Key Features

 Book Online

 Pets Accepted

 Disabled Facilities

 Beach Access

 Swimming Pool

 Play Area

 Bar/Restaurant

Scan me for
more information.

Alan Rogers Code: FR62030
38 accommodations
110 pitches
GPS: 50.81924, 2.17753
Post Code: F-62910

Pas-de-Calais, Nord/Pas-de-Calais

www.alanrogers.com/fr62030
contact@chateau-gandspette.com
Tel: +33 3 21 93 43 93
www.chateau-gandspette.com

Open (Touring Pitches):
Start April - End September.

Château du Gandspette

This excellent and spacious, family-run site is set on the grounds of a 19th-century château. It is a great campsite when you're travelling via Calais as it is quite close to the Channel ports and tunnel, providing overnight accommodation and a range of facilities for more extended stays.

There are 110 touring pitches, with 10A electricity hook-ups and 31 hardstanding. These are interspersed with 20 privately owned mobile homes and caravans, with a further 18 for hire. Trees and hedging delineate most pitches. Mature trees form the site's perimeter, through which there is access to woodland walks. Even when the site is busy, there is still a sense of space with large green areas free of caravans and tents.

Two sanitary blocks with good showers and some washbasins in cubicles. Good facilities for babies and disabled visitors. Laundry facilities. Motorhome services. Bar, grill restaurant (booking highly recommended) and takeaway (start May - mid Sept). Swimming pools (start may Mid - Sept). Playground with a bouncy castle. Multisports court. Tennis. Table tennis tables. Pétanque. Outdoor fitness equipment. Room for children. Charcoal and Gas barbecues are accepted. WiFi over site (charged).

Key Features

 Book Online

 Pets Accepted

 Disabled Facilities

 Beach Access

 Swimming Pool

 Play Area

 Bar/Restaurant

Scan me for more information.

Huttopia Versailles

Huttopia sites are rather different; when the French owners visited Canada and experienced 'back to nature' camping, they were so impressed that they decided to introduce the idea to France.

This is a bit like camping as it used to be, but with some big differences. Gone are the formal pitches with neatly trimmed hedges, and instead, 125 of varying sizes are arranged informally amongst the trees, 93 with electricity (10A). The terrain is as nature intended, with very little grass and much of it steep and rugged. Long electricity leads are required and be prepared to use blocks, and corner steadies on many pitches.

Three well-designed toilet blocks (wood cabin style – one is closed in low season) are evenly situated around the site and provide basic facilities, including those for children and disabled visitors. Laundry. Motorhome services. Special bivouacs are set up for cooking and washing up. Restaurant with takeaway (July/August and weekends). Bar (all season). No shop but a supermarket nearby, and essentials can be purchased from reception. Games room. Heated outdoor swimming and paddling pools (seasonal). Playground. Bicycle hire. Boules. No charcoal barbecues.

Alan Rogers Code: FR78060
55 accommodations
125 pitches
GPS: 48.79396, 2.16075
Post Code: F-78000

Yvelines, Paris/Ile de France

www.alanrogers.com/fr78060
versailles@huttopia.com
Tel: +33 1 39 51 23 61
europe.huttopia.com/en/site/camping-versailles

Open (Touring Pitches):
Late March - Early November.

Key Features

 Book Online

 Pets Accepted

 Disabled Facilities

 Swimming Pool

 Play Area

 Bar/Restaurant

 Bike Hire

Scan me for more information.

Alan Rogers Code: FR77030
15 accommodations
139 pitches
GPS: 48.91378, 2.73451
Post Code: F-77450

Seine-et-Marne, Paris/Ile de France

www.alanrogers.com/fr77030
welcome@camping-jablines.com
Tel: +33 1 60 26 09 37
www.camping-jablines.com

Open (Touring Pitches):
Late March - End October.

International de Jablines

International de Jablines is a modern site in a prime location for active families. The leisure facilities of the adjacent Espace Loisirs are a big draw, with large lakes offering many water sports and activities like tree climbing, riding, children's playground, sports fields and more. The 400 metres of fine sandy beaches are open every day in July and August and on the weekends in May and June - the Grand Lac is said to have the largest beach in the Ile-de-France. But for some, the close proximity to Disneyland Paris (6 km, and there's even a shuttle at certain times) and Paris (30 km) seals the deal.

The site itself has 154 pitches, of which 139 are for touring units. Most are of a good size (100-120 sq.m), often slightly sloping, with gravel hardstanding and grass, accessed by tarmac roads and marked by young trees. All have 10A electrical connections; 60 are fully serviced. There are about a dozen wooden chalets to rent.

Two toilet blocks, heated in cool weather, include pushbutton showers, and some washbasins in cubicles. Facilities for disabled visitors. Laundry facilities. Motorhome services (charged). Shop (all season). Sailing, waterskiing, windsurfing, kayaking, pedalos. Mini golf. Tennis. Table tennis. Football. Play area. Boules. WiFi throughout (free). Ticket sales for Disneyland and Parc Astérix. Mobile homes to rent.

Key Features

🐾 Pets Accepted

♿ Disabled Facilities

🛝 Play Area

Scan me for more information.

L' international
de Jablines ★★★
☎ +33 (0)1 60 26 09 37

9 km from Disneyland Paris, very quiet, a 450 ha site in the nature with the longest beach of Ile de France. Restaurant, tennis, mini golf, playground, fishing, sailing, mountain bike rental, horse riding, water ski lift and all the comforts of a quality campsite.

Sale of tickets for Disneyland Paris

www.camping-jablines.com

Alan Rogers Code: FR51020
10 accommodations
138 pitches
GPS: 48.93590, 4.38320
Post Code: F-51000

Marne, Champagne-Ardenne

www.alanrogers.com/fr51020
camping.chalons@aquadis-loisirs.com
Tel: +33 3 26 68 38 00
www.aquadis-loisirs.com

Open (Touring Pitches):
Early March - Early November.

Châlons en Champagne

The location of Châlons, south of Reims and near the A4 and A26 autoroutes, about 300 km. from Calais and Boulogne, makes this an ideal stopover. This site on the southern edge of town now belongs to the Aquadis-Loisirs group. The wide entrance, with its neatly mown grass and flowerbeds, leads to tidy rows of large pitches separated by hedges, many with taps and drains adjacent.

Of the 138 pitches, 89 are on gravel, the rest on grass, and 96 have electricity (10A). Some overlook a small lake. Trees abound, although there is no shade in some parts. The site is ideally situated for exploring this famous region in the plain of the River Marne and its historical connections.

Three toilet blocks, one open only in high season, and the other two, one that can be heated, are functional and clean. These include washbasins in cabins, baby room and hairdressing stations. A large Unit for disabled visitors (key entry). Laundry facilities. Shop. Bread to order. Open-air bar, snack bar and takeaway (Seasonal). Games (pool and Table football) and TV rooms. Fishing lake. Playground. Minigolf. Tennis. Volleyball. Boules. Mini-football. Motorhome services. Free WiFi near reception. Ten mobile homes to rent.

Key Features

 Book Online

 Pets Accepted

 Disabled Facilities

 Play Area

 Bar/Restaurant

 Bike Hire

 Fishing

Scan me for more information.

Alan Rogers Code: FR08040
15 accommodations
98 pitches
GPS: 49.42640, 4.94010
Post Code: F-08240

Ardennes, Champagne-Ardenne

www.alanrogers.com/fr08040
contact@camping-lasamaritaine.fr
Tel: +33 3 24 30 08 88
www.camping-lasamaritaine.fr

Open (Touring Pitches):
Mid April - Mid September.

Camping la Samaritaine

This delightful site, a member of the Flower group, is situated in the heart of the Ardennes between Reims and Luxembourg. It is peacefully located just outside the village beside a stream, and the rolling countryside is delightful, perfect for family bike rides and for exploring on foot. A feature is a large lake, popular with anglers but with a designated beach area for swimming and splashing about. Not far from the lake is a playground and a boules pitch, while at the lake is some play equipment (adult supervision only). Lake swimming is supervised only at certain times (2 m. deep, with a paddling area up to 1.2 m).

This is a charming, well-run site with an attractively floral entrance and plenty of bushes and small trees separating the pitches. The 98 numbered touring pitches all have electricity (10A) and are on level grass off hard access roads. They vary in size up to 130 sq.m. and 55 have water and drainage.

Sanitary blocks provide private cabins, family room and facilities for disabled visitors. Laundry facilities. Motorhome services. Bread is delivered daily. Essentials are kept in reception. Snack bar/takeaway (seasonal). Large recreation room with TV, games and books. Play area. Boules. Accompanied walks and entertainment programme (high season). Bicycle hire. WiFi throughout (free).

Key Features

 Book Online

 Pets Accepted

 Disabled Facilities

 Play Area

 Bike Hire

Scan me for more information.

Alan Rogers Code: FR67140
33 accommodations
129 pitches
GPS: 48.73109, 7.35529
Post Code: F-67700

Bas-Rhin, Alsace

www.alanrogers.com/fr67140
camping@vacances-seasonova.com
Tel: +33 3 88 91 35 65
www.vacances-seasonova.com

Open (Touring Pitches):
Start April - Start November.

Les Portes d'Alsace

This charming site on the southern edge of the town of Saverne has a relaxed and quiet feel thanks to its grassy open spaces and mature trees, which shade the large pitches. There are 145 pitches in total, 129 being touring pitches with electric hook-up points. The site is adjacent to a riding school, with some pitches overlooking the outdoor schooling area. The facilities are very clean and include a pool, play area and bicycle hire - there are some excellent cycling routes. A takeaway van visits three times a week, and activities are organised for children in high season.

This is a lovely setting at the foot of the Vosges mountains, with superb access to the heart of nature and Alsace's picturesque scenery, yet with handy access to local facilities. Saverne is a lovely town just a short walk away, and the magnificent 18th century Rohan Castle with its museum and arts centre, is a must-see, just a couple of kilometres away. Families will enjoy Océanide, the town's water park, and those looking to venture further afield can easily reach elegant Strasbourg by train.

Key Features

 Book Online

 Pets Accepted

 Disabled Facilities

 Swimming Pool

 Play Area

 Bar/Restaurant

 Bike Hire

 Horse Riding

Bar. Barbecues allowed (charcoal, gas, electric). Café. Disabled facilities. Late arrivals area without electric hook-up. Motorhome service point. Shop. Swimming pool. Children's playground. Entertainment (high season). Takeaway. TV room. WiFi charge.

Scan me for more information.

Alan Rogers Code: FR52030
26 accommodations
180 pitches
GPS: 47.87317, 5.38069
Post Code: F-52200

Haute-Marne, Champagne-Ardenne

www.alanrogers.com/fr52030
contact@camping-liez.fr
Tel: +33 3 25 90 27 79
www.campingliez.com

Open (Touring Pitches):
Start April - Start October.

Camping de la Liez

This excellent lakeside site is near the city of Langres. Only twenty minutes from the A5/A31 junction, Camping de la Liez provides an ideal spot for an overnight stop en route to the south of France. However, there is also a lot on offer for a longer stay.

The site provides 180 fully serviced pitches, including 16 with private sanitary units. Attractive terracing on the site's lower part means that some have views of the 250-hectare lake with its sandy beach and small harbour where boats and pedaloes may be hired. Perfect for watersports, access to the lake is down steps and across quite a fast road.

Two older heated toilet blocks (one closed in low season) have all facilities, including washbasins in cabins, controllable showers and facilities for babies and disabled campers. A more recent block has eight en-suite units along with 16 pitches with private sanitary facilities. Laundry facilities. Motorhome services. Shop (from mid-April). Bar and restaurant with takeaway (from mid-April). Indoor pool with spa and sauna. Heated outdoor pool with slide. Games room. Playground. Extensive games area. Tennis (free in low season). Bicycle hire. WiFi throughout (charged). Chalets and Gipsy Wagons for rent.

Key Features

 Book Online

 Pets Accepted

 Disabled Facilities

 Swimming Pool

 Play Area

 Bar/Restaurant

 Bike Hire

 Horse Riding

Scan me for more information.

Alan Rogers Code: FR88040
34 accommodations
100 pitches
GPS: 48.16692, 6.35990
Post Code: F-88390

Vosges, Lorraine

Camping Club Lac de Bouzey

www.alanrogers.com/fr88040
lacdebouzey@orange.fr
Tel: +33 3 29 82 49 41
www.lacdebouzey.com

Open (Touring Pitches):
All year.

Open all year, Camping Lac de Bouzey is 8 km. west of Épinal, at the start of the Vosges Massif. The 134 reasonably level grass pitches are separated by tall trees and neat hedging giving varying amounts of shade. There are 100 for touring, all with access to 6/10A electricity and water. They are on a gently sloping hillside above the lake with its sandy beaches.

In the high season, an extensive timetable of activities is arranged for all ages, especially teenagers, and the site will be very lively. Golf can be arranged at a local course with discounted rates. English is spoken.

The toilet block includes a baby room and one for disabled visitors (there are some gradients). A small, heated section in the main building with toilets, washbasins and showers is used in winter. Family shower room and facilities for children. Laundry facilities. Motorhome services. Shop. Bar (seasonal). Restaurant and takeaway (seasonal). Heated pool (high season). Fishing. Riding. Games room. Archery. Bicycle hire. Soundproofed room for cinema shows and discos (high season). Lake beach, bathing and boating. WiFi throughout.

Key Features

 Book Online

 Open All Year

 Pets Accepted

 Disabled Facilities

 Swimming Pool

 Play Area

 Bar/Restaurant

 Skiing

Scan me for
more information.

Alan Rogers Code: FR88110
43 accommodations
125 pitches
GPS: 48.12088, 6.82914
Post Code: F-88640

Vosges, Lorraine

www.alanrogers.com/fr88110
steniole@wanadoo.fr
Tel: +33 3 29 51 43 75
www.steniole.com

Open (Touring Pitches):
Start April - Mid October.

Camping la Sténiole

Set in a peaceful, rural area in the heart of the magnificent Vosges forest, this attractive site is run by a dedicated and friendly couple, Rudi and Natacha. The 125 pitches (4/10A electricity) open from 1 April to 15 October are either separated by hedges or beside the water and are well-shaded. They also have accommodation for rental from April to November.

The site has an indoor heated pool, a water slide, and small ponds, one for fishing and one for boating, where the kids can splash about. The final approach to the site is on a steep single-track road, a 250-metre climb in two kilometres. This is an 'outdoorsy' spot - campfires are permitted, and the area is very popular for hiking, mountain biking and fishing. The large ski resort of Gérardmer is only 10 km. away.

Five sanitary blocks and additional facilities in the main building include facilities for children and visitors with disabilities. Washing machines and tumble dryers. Bar and restaurant (high season). Take away pizza (high season). Indoor heated swimming pool from April to November (with slide open in high season). Fishing. Games room with TV and library. Playground. Football pitch. Volleyball court. Pétanque. Trampoline. Table tennis. Mini Club for children. WiFi in certain areas (free). Electric car charging points.

Key Features

 Book Online

 Pets Accepted

 Disabled Facilities

 Swimming Pool

 Play Area

 Bar/Restaurant

 Fishing

 Horse Riding

Scan me for more information.

Alan Rogers Code: FR88120
25 accommodations
64 pitches
GPS: 48.16826, 6.89025
Post Code: F-88430

Vosges, Lorraine

www.alanrogers.com/fr88120
info@camping-closdelachaume.com
Tel: +33 3 29 50 76 76
www.camping-closdelachaume.co.uk

Open (Touring Pitches):
Mid April - Mid September.

Au Clos de la Chaume

Sites et Paysages Camping Au Clos de la Chaume is a pleasant site within walking distance of the town, on level ground with a small stream. The friendly family owners, who are British and French, live on-site and do their best to ensure campers have an enjoyable, relaxing stay. The grassy pitches are level, of varying sizes and with varying amounts of sun and shade. All touring pitches have electricity hook-ups (6/10A), and some are divided by shrubs and trees.

The site carries the LPO (League for Bird Protection) label with over 30 species present. There is an attractive, well-fenced, modern swimming pool and an excellent small adventure-style playground. Wine-tasting evenings are held in July and August.

Two modern sanitary blocks provide all the necessary facilities for families and disabled visitors. Children's sanitary facilities. Laundry with washing machines and dryers. Motorhome services. Reception keeps basic supplies (June-Aug). Modern covered swimming pool (seasonal). Play area. Games room with pool table, table football and library. Boules. Volleyball. Ping-pong tables. WiFi throughout (charged) and also a limited free WiFi zone.

Key Features

 Book Online

 Pets Accepted

 Disabled Facilities

 Swimming Pool

 Play Area

Scan me for more information.

Alan Rogers Code: FR44150
155 accommodations
105 pitches
GPS: 47.14111, -2.15229
Post Code: 44770

Loire Atlantique, Pays de la Loire

www.alanrogers.com/fr44150
camping@lesvallonsdelocean.com
Tel: +33 2 40 21 58 83
camping-lesvallonsdelocean.com

Open (Touring Pitches):
Early April - Mid September.

Les Vallons de l'océan

Owned and managed by the Barré family, this campsite is pleasant, peaceful and immaculate. It will suit those who want to enjoy the local coast and towns but return to an oasis of relaxation. However, it still provides activities and fun for those with energy remaining.

Perfectly positioned on the coast for a fun and adventurous family holiday, you'll be spoilt with 6 acres of open countryside where every morning starts with the blissful sound of birdsong. From here, you can visit a wide selection of places such as Pornic, Saint Nazaire, La Baule, Guérande, Nantes, The Island Of Normoutier, St. Jean de Montes, and more, all within 30 miles.

Two toilet blocks are equipped with showers and baby facilities. Washing machines and dryers near the pool require coins from the grocery store. Bar, a grocery store with bread (May to September) Take away (July and August). Indoor heated swimming pool with four water slides. Multisports ground, 18-hole crazy-golf course, mini-tennis, table tennis, pétanque grounds, games room, free outdoor fitness, children's playground. Inflatable castles and children's club (July to August). Bike rental. Fishing. WiFi throughout the campsite.

Key Features

 Book Online

 Pets Accepted

 Beach Access

 Swimming Pool

 Play Area

 Bar/Restaurant

 Bike Hire

Scan me for more information.

Alan Rogers Code: FR44190
266 accommodations
99 pitches
GPS: 47.23486, -2.16757
Post Code: F-44250

Loire-Atlantique, Pays de la Loire

Le Fief

www.alanrogers.com/fr44190
camping@lefief.com
Tel: +33 2 40 27 23 86
www.camping-le-fief.com

Open (Touring Pitches):
Early April - Late September.

Sunêlia Le Fief is in a wonderful setting just 900 metres from a vast sandy beach and the gently shelving waters of southern Brittany's Jade Coast, yet close to handy local amenities. The beautiful seaside resort of Saint-Brevin-Les-Pins is on the doorstep, making this a great choice for a family beach holiday with young children or lively teenagers. Le Fief is a well-established site, long a favourite for its magnificent aquapark with outdoor and covered swimming pools, paddling pools, slides, river rapids, fountains, jets and more. There's plenty of space for sun lounging, and the bar/restaurant terrace overlooks the whole complex. It's all very well thought through and run.

The site has 99 pitches for touring units, all of a good size (around 100 m sq) with 8A electricity and partly shaded and with lush, well-established vegetation. There are also 227 mobile homes and chalets to rent and 39 privately owned units. An impressive Taos mobile home village includes a well-organised Sunny Club for children.

Key Features

 Book Online

 Pets Accepted

 Disabled Facilities

 Beach Access

 Swimming Pool

 Play Area

 Bar/Restaurant

 Bike Hire

Bar, restaurant, takeaway. Shop. Pool complex with slides and various pools (usually May-September). Covered pool (open all season). Wellness centre/spa. Play area. Padel tennis. Pétanque. Archery. Games room. Organised entertainment & children's activities (April/June weekends, high season daily). Bike hire. WiFi (payable).

Scan me for
more information.

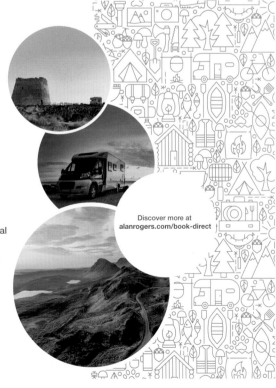

Alan Rogers Code: FR44340
89 accommodations
63 pitches
GPS: 47.35383, -2.51733
Post Code: F-44420

Loire-Atlantique, Pays de la Loire

www.alanrogers.com/fr44340
info@camping-de-la-falaise.com
Tel: +33 2 40 23 32 53
www.camping-de-la-falaise.com

Open (Touring Pitches):
Start April - End October.

Camping la Falaise

La Falaise is a simple site enjoying direct access to a wide sandy beach with enticing rock pools at low tide and benefitting from the mild climate of southern Brittany. There are 150 pitches, of which 63 are for touring units with water and electricity (Europlugs). Other pitches are occupied by mobile homes and chalets (some to rent). The pitches are reasonably sized and marked by low hedges but are not shaded. This is a popular family campsite, becoming busy in high season, as is the norm, but well positioned to take advantage of the wonderful beaches and attractions of the area.

Just 500 metres down the road is La Turballe, a bustling fishing port with a good selection of shops and eateries. You can catch a boat trip out to the pretty islands of Morbihan from here. Nearby, Guérande, on the edge of the Grande Brière natural park, merits a visit with its excellent market and fascinating salt marshes. Further south around the Guérande peninsula lies La Baule, with its famous crescent of sandy beach, just the highlight of many in the area.

Key Features

 Pets Accepted

 Disabled Facilities

 Beach Access

 Swimming Pool

 Play Area

 Bar/Restaurant

 Bike Hire

 Fishing

Heated sanitary block. Bar, snack bar and takeaway (April-October). Heated covered pool (all season). Play area (unfenced). Bicycle hire. Car rental. Mobile homes and chalets to rent. Direct access to the beach. Watersports, riding, and boat trips nearby. WiFi throughout (free).

Scan me for more information.

Camping l'Hermitage

Alan Rogers Code: FR44130
46 accommodations
55 pitches
GPS: 47.62595, -1.81810
Post Code: F-44290

Loire-Atlantique, Pays de la Loire

www.alanrogers.com/fr44130
camping.hermitage@wanadoo.fr
Tel: +33 2 40 79 23 48
www.campinglhermitage.com

Open (Touring Pitches):
End March - End October.

L'Hermitage is a pretty, wooded site set in the Vallée du Don and would be useful for en-route stops or for longer stays. The enthusiastic staff, even though their English is a little limited, provide a warm welcome and maintain this reasonably priced site to a good standard.

There are 101 pitches, of which 55 are a good size for touring and camping. Some are formally arranged on open, level grass pitches, whereas others are informal amongst light woodland. Electricity (6A) is available to all (a long lead may be useful). A further 29 pitches are taken by mobile homes, most of which are available to rent.

Both Nantes and Rennes are 30 minutes away, La Baule, with its beaches, is 40 minutes away. The attractive small town of Guémené-Penfao set on the Rover Don is typical with its cafés, bars and restaurants and is a pleasant ten minutes away.

Clean and well-serviced toilet block includes some washbasins in cabins with warm water. Laundry and dishwashing sinks under cover (cold water, but a hot tap is provided). Smallish pool, paddling pool and slide. Small play area. Pétanque. WiFi (free).

Key Features

 Book Online

 Pets Accepted

 Disabled Facilities

 Swimming Pool

 Play Area

 Bar/Restaurant

 Horse Riding

Scan me for more information.

Alan Rogers Code: FR49210
14 accommodations
130 pitches
GPS: 47.39206, -0.87031
Post Code: F-49570

Maine-et-Loire, Pays de la Loire

www.alanrogers.com/fr49210
contact@campinglapromenade.com
Tel: +33 2 41 39 02 68
www.campinglapromenade.com

Open (Touring Pitches):
Early April - Early September.

Camping la Promenade

Flower Camping la Promenade is traditionally laid out and has 130 touring pitches (electricity 10A, 83 also with water and wastewater), ten mobile homes, three furnished tents and a roulette for hire.

Shaded by various trees, it stands on the left bank of the Loire between Angers and Nantes, close to the little town of Montjean-Sur-Loire, where a few bars, restaurants, and shops exist. The nearby town of Chalonnes-Sur-Loire provides alternatives, whilst historic Angers and its château are within easy reach. In the heart of the Pays de Mauges, this site could be an ideal base from which to explore its villages, châteaux and vineyards.

Sanitary block includes facilities for babies, children and disabled visitors. Laundry room with washing machine and dryer. Motorhome service point. Snack bar and small grocery. Swimming and paddling pools (high season). Playground. Organised entertainment and activities for children and families (July-Aug). Pétanque, table tennis and volleyball. Bicycle, barbecue and TV rentals. WiFi throughout (free). Mobile homes and tents for hire.

Key Features

 Book Online

 Pets Accepted

 Disabled Facilities

 Swimming Pool

 Play Area

 Bar/Restaurant

 Bike Hire

Scan me for
more information.

Alan Rogers Code: FR49000
75 accommodations
143 pitches
GPS: 47.45434, -0.59619
Post Code: F-49000

Maine-et-Loire, Pays de la Loire

www.alanrogers.com/fr49000
camping@lacdemaine.fr
Tel: +33 2 41 73 05 03
www.campingangers.com

Open (Touring Pitches):
Early April - Early January.

Camping du Lac de Maine

Camping d'Angers Lac de Maine lies in the heart of the Anjou region, just on the outskirts of Angers and downstream from glorious Saumur. It offers direct access to the large lake, and there's plenty to see in the surrounding countryside, with medieval castles, vineyards and quaint historic towns to explore, perhaps following one of the bike trails. Stroll into Angers in an exceptional setting in the heart of the Loire Valley with its castle, cathedral, gardens, quays and markets.

Most of the 143 level touring pitches are a mix of grass and gravel hardstanding. They are well laid out and demarcated by hedging and small trees, and all have water, drainage and 10A electricity. Some pitches are not suitable for awnings. The main entrance has a height restriction of 3.2 m, although there is an alternative gate for higher vehicles. This family site offers a relaxed, rural feel while being close to useful amenities.

Two sanitary blocks, one which can be heated and includes some washbasins in cubicles. British style WCs. Facilities for babies and disabled visitors. Laundry facilities. Motorhome services. Restaurant, takeaway and bar (May-September). Heated swimming pool (high season). Watersports, riding nearby. Spa. Pétanque. Bicycle hire. Play area. Internet point and WiFi (free). Barrier card (deposit payable).

Key Features

 Book Online

 Pets Accepted

 Disabled Facilities

 Bar/Restaurant

 Bike Hire

Scan me for more information.

Alan Rogers Code: FR53010
18 accommodations
59 pitches
GPS: 48.39191, -0.61709
Post Code: F-53300

Mayenne, Pays de la Loire

www.alanrogers.com/fr53010
parcdevaux@camp-in-ouest.com
Tel: +33 2 43 04 90 25
www.parcdevaux.com

Open (Touring Pitches):
Mid April - Late October.

Camping Parc de Vaux

Parc de Vaux is an ex-municipal site which was acquired in 2010 by the owners of FR72080. This 3.5-hectare site has 90 pitches, 18 occupied by mobile homes, chalets and bungalow tents available to rent. The 59 touring pitches are generally grassy and well-sized (mostly with 10A electricity and water). The site is located close to the pretty village of Ambrières-Les-Vallées, and there is direct access to the village from the site by a footbridge over the river.

The village is around 12 km. north of Mayenne and may prove a convenient en-route stop. There is a swimming pool adjacent (with a water slide), and the site has access to a lake and a good range of amenities.

Three small toilet blocks, one with facilities for disabled visitors. No facilities for children. Laundry. Motorhome services. Bar and snack bar/takeaway in high season. Heated outdoor swimming pool (high season). Sports field. Fishing. Football. Basketball. Minigolf. Boules. Canoes. Pedalos. Bicycle hire. Archery and tennis adjacent. Games room with TV and library. Play area. Mobile homes/chalets/bungalow tents to rent. Free WiFi on part of the site.

Key Features

 Book Online

 Pets Accepted

 Disabled Facilities

 Swimming Pool

 Play Area

 Bar/Restaurant

 Bike Hire

Scan me for more information.

Alan Rogers Code: FR72040
37 accommodations
129 pitches
GPS: 48.20422, -0.12858
Post Code: F-72140

Sarthe, Pays de la Loire

www.alanrogers.com/fr72040
lac-sille@huttopia.com
Tel: +33 2 43 20 16 12
europe.huttopia.com/en/site/lac-de-sille

Open (Touring Pitches):
Late April - Late September.

Huttopia Lac de Sillé

Huttopia Lac de Sillé (formerly Indigo Les Molières) is an attractive recent addition to the Huttopia group. It is a good choice for families looking for an active holiday in a verdant setting. It can be found close to Sillé-le-Guillaume, around 30 km. north of Le Mans. There are 166 large shady pitches here, with 129 for touring units. Most are equipped with 10A electricity connections. A large lake of 32 hectares is ideal for sailing and windsurfing, and the forested surrounds of the Parc Naturel Régional provide an excellent environment for cycling or walking.

Swimming is also popular from the large sandy beach. The Maison du Lac et de la Forêt is an interesting centre with a wealth of information about the area. In high season a little tourist train trundles around the lake.

Sanitary facilities include those for disabled visitors. Washing machine and dryer (token). Motorhome services. Small shop for essentials and regional produce. Bread and pastries to order. Weekly market. Snack bar/takeaway (July/Aug). Heated outdoor pool (from mid-April). Covered social area with barbecue. Direct access to the lake. Sailing. Fishing. Bicycle hire. Play area. Children's entertainment (5-11 yrs, high season. Themed dinners and an open-air cinema. Max. 1 dog. Only electric barbecues are permitted. WiFi by snack bar (free).

Key Features

 Book Online

 Pets Accepted

 Disabled Facilities

 Swimming Pool

 Play Area

 Bar/Restaurant

 Bike Hire

 Fishing

Scan me for more information.

Alan Rogers Code: FR28140
36 accommodations
84 pitches
GPS: 48.55330, 1.04146
Post Code: F-28250

Eure-et-Loir, Val de Loire

www.alanrogers.com/fr28140
senonches@huttopia.com
Tel: +33 2 37 37 81 40
europe.huttopia.com/en/site/village-senonches

Open (Touring Pitches):
Mid May - Mid October.

Huttopia Senonches

Huttopia Senonches is a ten-hectare site hidden away in the huge Forêt Dominiale de Senonches; In keeping with other Huttopia sites, it combines a high standard of comfort with a real sense of backwoods camping.

There are 84 touring pitches here, some with 10A electricity. The large pitches range from 100 sq.m. to no less than 300 sq.m. There are also 36 Canadian-style log cabins and tents available to rent. A good range of on-site amenities includes a shop and a bar/restaurant. The chlorine-free natural pool, with a terrace, overlooks an unfenced lake and is open from early July until September.

The modern sanitary blocks are heated in the low season and have special facilities for disabled visitors. Shop (all season). Bread to order. Breakfast service. Bar, snack bar and takeaway (weekends in low season). Swimming pool (June-Sept). Living area with library, TV, games and coffee machine. Fishing. Play area. Bicycle hire. Entertainment and activity programme. Kids' club (July/Aug, 5-12 yrs). Wood and canvas tents, Cahuttes and chalets to rent. Gas barbecues only. Max. 1 dog.

Key Features

 Book Online

 Pets Accepted

 Disabled Facilities

 Swimming Pool

 Play Area

 Bar/Restaurant

 Bike Hire

 Fishing

Scan me for more information.

Alan Rogers Code: FR37050
47 accommodations
92 pitches
GPS: 47.12303, 1.00223
Post Code: F-37600

Indre-et-Loire, Val de Loire

www.alanrogers.com/fr37050
reservation@groupecamping.fr
Tel: +33 5 79 87 02 59
www.lacitadelle.com

Open (Touring Pitches):
Mid March - End September.

Camping la Citadelle

A pleasant, well-maintained site, la Citadelle's best feature is probably that it is within walking distance of Loches, noted for its perfect architecture and its glorious history, yet at the same time, the site has a rural atmosphere.

The 92 standard touring pitches are all level, good-sized, and have 10A electricity. Numerous trees offer varying degrees of shade. The 30 larger serviced pitches have 16A electricity but little shade, and six luxury pitches have all facilities, including furniture, fridge and barbecue. Mobile homes (27 for hire) occupy the other 47 pitches. Loches, with its château and dungeons, is a gentle 500 m. walk along the river.

Three sanitary blocks provide mainly British-style WCs, washbasins (mostly in cabins) and controllable showers. Laundry facilities. Motorhome services. Two baby units and provision for disabled visitors. Heated swimming pool (May-Sept). Paddling pool and play area (adult supervision strongly recommended). Small bar and snack bar (July/Aug; bread can be ordered at reception). Boules. Volleyball. Games room. Miniclub (July/Aug). Internet access and TV. WiFi over site (charged).

Key Features

 Book Online

 Pets Accepted

 Disabled Facilities

 Swimming Pool

 Play Area

 Bar/Restaurant

 Fishing

Scan me for more information.

Alan Rogers Code: FR45075
122 pitches
GPS: 47.95886, 2.27966
Post Code: F-45530

Loiret, Val de Loire

Camping Étang de la Vallée

www.alanrogers.com/fr45075
camping@vacaces-seasonova.com
Tel: +33 2 38 55 47 60
vacances-seasonova.com/fr/
camping/etang-de-la-vallee

Open (Touring Pitches):
Start April - End October.

Slow the pace of life with a stay at Camping Étang de la Vallée, a nature-filled site on the banks of a Loiret lake in the Forest of Orléans.

With 122 large shaded pitches, all with electrical connections and views out over the water, this is a place where you and your family can relax, perhaps taking a walk in the woods or using your lakeside location for a bit of fishing, watersports or swimming from the lake beach (supervised in high season). If the lake wasn't enough, there are many activities for the children, including a playground, miniature golf course and games area with table tennis.

A café, food shop and bread delivery service are all on hand to provide you with local produce and barbecues are allowed. A local produce market is open once a week in July and August to give you a taste of the local area's best.

Disabled facilities in the same building as other campers, baby room. Restaurant (limited) bar, Snack Bar, shop, Lake beach on site, Children's playground, Fishing, Table tennis table, Jeu de boules alley(s), Multi-sports field, Animal meadow, Crazy golf, TV, Pets allowed, WiFi.

Key Features

 Book Online

 Pets Accepted

 Disabled Facilities

 Play Area

 Bar/Restaurant

 Fishing

Scan me for more information.

Alan Rogers Code: FR41100
19 accommodations
145 pitches
GPS: 47.48110, 1.45011
Post Code: F-41700

Loir-et-Cher, Val de Loire

www.alanrogers.com/fr41100
contact@camping-cheverny.com
Tel: +33 2 54 79 90 01
www.camping-cheverny.com

Open (Touring Pitches):
Start April - Mid September.

Camping les Saules

Set in the heart of the château region, Sites et Paysages Camping Les Saules has developed into a popular, friendly campsite run by a local family, Laurent and Isabelle, who are dedicated to the environment and nature. They have their own bees, honey and over 50 species of birds present on the site.

The well-renovated, traditional reception buildings in their lakeside setting give a very pleasant welcome. There are 164 good-sized, level pitches, with 145 for touring units. All have shade from the many trees on the site, 10A electricity connections (some will require leads longer than 25 m), and there are ample water taps. A large, grassy field provides room for youngsters to play safely. The area has many designated cycle paths and walking circuits, often linking châteaux through attractive, sleepy countryside.

Two sanitary blocks with toilets, showers, washbasins in cubicles and facilities for disabled visitors (One recently renovated to be an eco-friendly self-sufficient block). Laundry facilities. Motorhome services. Gas supplies. Shop, snack bar and takeaway (seasonal). Restaurant (July/Aug). Bar. Heated swimming and paddling pools (high season). TV/social room with toys, board games, and books. Two play areas. Large grass area for ball games. Minigolf (free). Fishing. Bicycle hire. Internet and WiFi.

Key Features

 Book Online

 Pets Accepted

 Disabled Facilities

 Swimming Pool

 Play Area

 Bar/Restaurant

 Bike Hire

 Fishing

Scan me for
more information.

Alan Rogers Code: FR18000
16 accommodations
152 pitches
GPS: 47.04000, 2.24000
Post Code: F-18000

Cher, Val de Loire

www.alanrogers.com/fr18000
camping.bourges@aquadis-loisirs.com
Tel: +33 2 48 20 16 85
www.aquadis-loisirs.com/en/camping-bourges-robinson

Open (Touring Pitches):
Early March - Early November.

Camping de Bourges

Set up for a stay at Camping Municipal de Bourges, and you'll be within easy reach (whether walking or cycling) of many attractions and useful amenities. Here you'll camp on the edge of the historic centre of Bourges, which has been identified by UNESCO for its world heritage cathedral. This campsite is ideal for a stopover for a city visit.

From this green tree-filled spot in suburban Bourges, it's a gentle 20-minute stroll to the historic city centre or the leisure facilities around the Val d'Auron lake (tennis, golf, horse riding, sailing and fishing among them). Restaurants, cafés, shops, markets and a supermarket are within distance too. You can take advantage of the site's delivery service that provides fresh bread and pastries in the mornings, and other snacks and drinks can be acquired at the small on-site grocery store.

Two sanitary blocks (one heated), including one with laundry and one with children's facilities. Disabled Facilities. Children's playground. Volleyball and basketball. Fresh bread and pastries are available daily. Little grocery at the reception. Pétanque. Free WiFi at the reception. Pets allowed.

Key Features

 Book Online

 Pets Accepted

 Disabled Facilities

 Play Area

 Bike Hire

Scan me for more information.

Alan Rogers Code: FR85720
100 accommodations
386 pitches
GPS: 46.99690, -2.22010
Post Code: F-85330

Noirmoutier-en-l'Ile, Vendée

www.alanrogers.com/fr85720
noirmoutier@huttopia.com
Tel: +33 2 51 39 06 24
europe.huttopia.com/en/site/
noirmoutier

Open (Touring Pitches):
Early April - Early October.

Huttopia Noirmoutier

Located in woodland and on dunes along a two-kilometre stretch of sandy beach, just east of the attractive little town of Noirmoutier on the island of the same name, this could be a paradise for those who enjoy a simple campsite in a natural setting. On land belonging to France's forestry commission, this site is operated by Huttopia, whose aim is to adapt to the environment rather than take it over.

The touring pitches, all with electricity (10A), are situated among the pine trees and accessed along tracks. Those on the sand dunes have fantastic views across the Baie de Bourgneuf. They cost a few euros extra – if you are lucky enough to get one. Some pitches may experience noise from a nearby bar.

Five unheated sanitary blocks provide preset showers and washbasins in cubicles. The central one is larger and more modern. Facilities for children and disabled visitors. Laundry. Motorhome services. Freezer Service. Bread to order. Snack bar and takeaway (July/Aug). Picnic tables. New play area. Boules. Volleyball. Bicycle and canoe hire. Only electric barbecues are allowed. Free WiFi over part of the site.

Key Features

 Book Online

 Pets Accepted

 Disabled Facilities

 Beach Access

 Play Area

 Bar/Restaurant

 Bike Hire

 Fishing

Scan me for more information.

Alan Rogers Code: FR85545
30 accommodations
80 pitches
GPS: 46.95697, -1.24540
Post Code: F-85600

La Guyonnière, Vendée

www.alanrogers.com/fr85545
camping@chausseliere.fr
Tel: +33 2 51 41 98 40
www.chausseliere.com

Open (Touring Pitches):
Star April - Start September.

Lac de la Chausselière

Situated On a large lake in the Vendée, five kilometres from Montaigu and half an hour's drive from Puy du Fou, you'll find Flower Camping du Lac de la Chausselière. The campsite is suitable for families with children and those looking for peace and quiet, where you can enjoy peaceful fishing on the lake. The campsite is situated in a quiet area directly on the water. Well-paved paths lead to the 80 spacious touring pitches with grassy ground and the thirty rental accommodations. Green hedges delimit both the touring pitches and the accommodations, so you will always find an area with privacy.

You will find an outdoor covered swimming pool directly behind the restaurant on the campsite. Also on-site, there is a snack bar, a grocery store, a games room (billiards, table football, molkky, shuffleboard, board games, books), multi-sports ground, a petanque ground, ping-pong tables, a mini-farm (sheep, alpaca and chickens) and a brand new playground for the younger children that has two trampolines.

Sanitary block with children's facilities and baby room and disabled access. Restaurant, Snack Bar, Bar, shop (small), Covered outdoor swimming pool, Entertainment (high season), Children's playground, Bicycle hire, Table tennis table, Multi-sports field, Jeu de boules alley(s), WiFi, Pets allowed.

Key Features

 Book Online

 Pets Accepted

 Swimming Pool

 Play Area

 Bar/Restaurant

 Bike Hire

 Fishing

 Sailing

Scan me for more information.

Camping l'Evasion

Camping l'Evasion is located close to the Lac de Jaunay, well known for its water-based activities. This modern, well-equipped site boasts a natural swimming pool bordered by white sand. There is also a traditional outdoor swimming pool with slides, plus a large, covered pool with a Jacuzzi.

There are just 12 good-sized touring pitches here, all equipped with electrical connections and the special feature of each one having its own private chalet with a shower room, separate toilet and a room with a fridge and sink. There are also numerous mobile homes available for rent. Other amenities at l'Evasion include a bar/restaurant (with takeaway food service).

Shop. Bar/restaurant. Takeaway. Outdoor swimming pool and paddling pool with jacuzzi and water slides. Covered heated pool, paddling pool and jacuzzi. Aqua gym. Multisports pitch. Bicycle hire. Play area. Activity and entertainment programme. Mobile homes for rent. WiFi throughout (charged). Max. one dog.

France

Alan Rogers Code: FR85885
139 accommodations
12 pitches
GPS: 46.63500, -1.79747
Post Code: F-85220

Landevieille, Vendée

www.alanrogers.com/fr85885
contact@camping-levasion.fr
Tel: +33 5 82 06 01 30
www.camping-levasion.fr

Open (Touring Pitches):
Start April - Early October.

Key Features

 Book Online

 Pets Accepted

 Disabled Facilities

 Beach Access

 Swimming Pool

 Play Area

 Bar/Restaurant

 Bike Hire

Scan me for more information.

Alan Rogers Code: FR17610
129 accommodations
31 pitches
GPS: 46.17740, -1.38651
Post Code: F-17580

Charente-Maritime, Poitou-Charentes

www.alanrogers.com/fr17610
vacances@sandaya.fr
Tel: +33 5 46 09 24 01
www.sandaya.co.uk/our-campsites/amis-de-la-plage

Open (Touring Pitches):
Early April - Late September.

Les Amis de la Plage

Camping Sandaya Les Amis de la Plage, a former municipal site, is located on the southern side of the Ile de Ré at Le Bois-Plage-en-Ré. The site has direct gated access across the sand dunes to a superb sandy beach.

There are 160 pitches, some of which are occupied by mobile homes, chalets and fully equipped tents. The 31 touring pitches are sandy with varying shade; some are a little small, and others can be on undulating land. Just over half have electrical connections (10A). The island's largest market is held daily, just 500 m. from the site.

Four toilet blocks (two closed low season) provide some washbasins in cubicles and facilities for disabled visitors and children. Laundry. Motorhome services. No shop, but bread to order daily. Play area with a bouncy castle. Boules. Activity and entertainment programme (high season). Direct access to the beach. Communal barbecue area. No charcoal barbecues on the pitch. Mobile homes, chalets and tents to rent. WiFi (charged in high season). Bicycle hire.

Key Features

 Book Online

 Pets Accepted

 Disabled Facilities

 Beach Access

 Play Area

 Bike Hire

Scan me for more information.

Alan Rogers Code: FR17010
316 accommodations
251 pitches
GPS: 45.58358, -0.98653
Post Code: F-17110

Charente-Maritime, Poitou-Charentes

www.alanrogers.com/fr17010
info@bois-soleil.com
Tel: +33 5 46 05 05 94
www.bois-soleil.com

Open (Touring Pitches):
Early April - Early October.

Camping Bois Soleil

Located in the popular seaside resort of Saint-Georges-de-Didonne, near sunny Royan, Bois Soleil is surrounded by woods and overlooks the sea. It is a large site in three parts, with serviced pitches for touring units and a few for tents. All the touring pitches are hedged and have electricity (10A), with water and drainage between two pitches. The main part, Les Pins, is attractive, with trees and shrubs providing shade. Opposite is La Mer, with direct access to the beach, some areas with less shade and an area for tents. The third part, La Forêt, is for caravan holiday homes.

The magnificent sandy beach is the big draw, but best to book early as the site can be full from mid-June to late August. Excellent private sanitary facilities are available to rent, either on your pitch or at a block (subject to availability).

Each area has one large and one small toilet block. Heated block near reception. Facilities for disabled visitors and babies. Launderette. Supermarket, bakery, beach shop (all seasonal). Restaurant, bar and takeaway (all seasonal). Swimming pool (heated seasonally). Steam room. Fitness room. Tennis. Play area. Entertainment & kids' clubs (high season). TV room and library. Internet terminal (free). WiFi throughout (charged). Charcoal and electric barbecues are not permitted. Dogs are not accepted in high season.

Key Features

 Book Online

 Pets Accepted

 Disabled Facilities

 Beach Access

 Swimming Pool

 Play Area

 Bar/Restaurant

 Bike Hire

Scan me for more information.

Alan Rogers Code: FR16140
32 accommodations
52 pitches
GPS: 46.01480, 0.21416
Post Code: F-16700

Charente, Poitou-Charentes

www.alanrogers.com/fr16140
camping@lerejallant.fr
Tel: +33 6 58 12 88 18
www.camping-du-rejallant.com

Open (Touring Pitches):
All year.

Camping le Rejallant

In the heart of Poitou-Charentes, Le Réjallant is a family-friendly campsite in a rural setting beside the River Charente. Of its 84 grassy pitches, some are shaded, others in the open; they include several very large pitches, and 10A electricity connections are available throughout. The recently installed pool is very popular and has a paddling pool alongside.

The owners have now added a fully-equipped gym. Snacks are available in the bar between April and September, and a large, covered, outdoor eating area doubles up as a TV room when major sporting events are televised. This lively site offers something for everyone: an active holiday or a quiet stroll by the beautiful River Charente.

Heated sanitary block includes facilities for disabled visitors, washing machines, dryers, and dishwashing sinks. Motorhome services. Heated swimming and paddling pools (seasonal). Playground with a bouncy castle. Small shop with regional produce and bread to order. Bar. Snack bar with terrace (July/Aug). WiFi throughout (free). Communal barbecue.

Key Features

 Book Online

 Open All Year

 Pets Accepted

 Disabled Facilities

 Swimming Pool

 Play Area

 Bar/Restaurant

Scan me for more information.

Alan Rogers Code: FR89200
2 accommodations
60 pitches
GPS: 47.56268, 3.64651
Post Code: F-89660

Yonne, Burgundy

www.alanrogers.com/fr89200
campingmerrysuryonne@yahoo.com
Tel: +33 7 54 52 28 54
www.campingmerrysuryonne.com

Open (Touring Pitches):
All year.

Camping Merry-sur-Yonne

Tucked away in central France, this rural campsite lies west of the gorgeous rolling hills of the Burgundy wine region. The idyllic River Yonne gently flows just metres away, as does the Nivernais Canal. The campsite is an oasis of tranquillity, surrounded by vineyards, castles and attractive villages, all demanding to be investigated.

The grassy pitches are spacious and well laid out, most with some shade. All have electrical hook-ups, and some on the perimeter provide magnificent views. There are also ten pitches with hard standing. There is plenty to do in the immediate vicinity: canoeing, fishing, walking and cycling - take a bike and cycle along the beautiful 'voies vertes', following the canal or a disused railway. Hire a canal boat or try climbing at the Rochers du Saussois (just outside the gates). The highly regarded restaurant is excellent, with a tempting menu and a pleasant candle-lit atmosphere.

Luxury sanitary facilities include baths as well as showers. Wet room with full access for wheelchairs. Washing machines and dryers. Bar. Café. Restaurant. Takeaway. Shop. Sports field. Motorhome services. Campers' kitchen. Free Wifi and internet access point. Two tennis courts. Games room with arcade games. Pool. Table-football. Air-hockey. Play area. Giant chess. Bicycle hire. Riding, boat hire nearby.

Key Features

 Book Online

 Open All Year

 Pets Accepted

 Bike Hire

Scan me for more information.

Alan Rogers Code: FR58020
47 pitches
GPS: 47.18861, 3.93917
Post Code: F-58230

Nièvre, Burgundy

www.alanrogers.com/fr58020
camping.ouroux@orange.fr
Tel: +33 3 86 78 22 88
www.camping-genets-morvan.com

Open (Touring Pitches):
Mid May - Mid September.

Les Genêts du Morvan

Les Genêts du Morvan is a small, comfortable site with just 50 pitches under the same ownership as Camping l'Etang de la Fougeraie. It can be found between the region's two largest lakes: Lac de Pannecière and Lac des Settons. The pitches are large and have 10A electricity. There are also some fully equipped mobile homes for rent. On-site amenities include a small swimming pool with a sunbathing terrace, a convivial snack bar and a small but well-stocked shop. There are many excellent footpaths in the vicinity, and the site's friendly owners will be pleased to recommend routes.

The nearby village of Ouroux en Morvan is a lively centre with a good selection of shops, cafés and restaurants, and even a cinema. It is also a focal point for the many activities for which the Morvan is renowned, such as mountain biking, riding, canoeing and rafting. The town of Château Chinon is 25 km. away and is widely considered to be the capital of the Morvan, with several interesting museums.

Two sanitary blocks have facilities for babies and disabled visitors. Washing machine and dryer. Motorhome services. Shop (high season, bread to order). Bar. Snack bar (July/Aug, closed Tues). Small outdoor swimming pool (July/Aug). Play area. Mobile homes for rent. Free WiFi over part of the site.

Key Features

 Pets Accepted

 Disabled Facilities

 Swimming Pool

 Play Area

 Bar/Restaurant

Scan me for more information.

Alan Rogers Code: FR58170
6 accommodations
100 pitches
GPS: 47.18168, 4.05273
Post Code: F-58230

Nièvre, Burgundy

www.alanrogers.com/fr58170
campinglesmesanges@orange.fr
Tel: +33 3 86 84 55 77
www.campinglesmesanges.fr

Open (Touring Pitches):
Late May - Late September.

Camping les Mésanges

This rural haven is located in the heart of the beautiful Morvan national park. It's just 100 metres from the tranquil Lac des Settons, with its own beach and water-based activities, as well as walking and cycling. This attractive and carefully landscaped site has its own well-stocked fish pond with a few pitches along its bank. There are 100 spacious pitches (100-200 sq.m.), all for touring, set among leafy trees and neatly trimmed hedges that provide shade. One side of the site has an open area, ideal for small groups of campers. All have 10-16A electricity and access to water.

Les Mésanges is close to the borders of Burgundy's four départements: Nièvre, Côte d'Or, Saône-et-Loire and Yonne. Extensive forests, several lakes, rivers and canals characterise the area. The land rises to about 900 m. in Morvan, and the natural surroundings are ideal walking terrain. Within reach are the Burgundian vineyards, with Auxerre and the Chablis area to the north and Beaune to the east.

Three toilet blocks have individual washbasins and facilities for disabled visitors. Baby bath. Laundry facilities. Shop with essentials and fresh bread daily. Takeaway (high season). Play area. Swings. Large multisports court. Volleyball. Basketball. Pétanque. Games room. Free WiFi over part of the site.

Key Features

 Pets Accepted

 Disabled Facilities

 Play Area

Scan me for more information.

Alan Rogers Code: FR71240
20 accommodations
145 pitches
GPS: 46.45738, 4.10486
Post Code: F-71600

Saône-et-Loire, Burgundy

www.alanrogers.com/fr71240
camping.plm@gmail.com
Tel: +33 3 85 88 89 20
www.campingaubonendroit.fr

Open (Touring Pitches):
Start May - End September.

Camping Au Bon Endroit

Paray-Le-Monial is one of Burgundy's well-established pilgrimage destinations and is well-located for exploring southern Burgundy. Previously known as 'Le Mambré' Camping Au Bon Endroit can be found close to the west of the town centre and is a well-equipped family site. There are 82 pitches reserved for caravans and motorhomes and a further 63 smaller pitches reserved for tents. Please note that twin-axle caravans and large motorhomes are not accepted. Pitches are grassy and well-shaded. Several mobile homes and chalets are available to rent. On-site amenities include a swimming pool, paddling pool, and a small snack bar in reception.

Paray-le-Monial is located on the Voie Verte, a 100 km. cycle circuit, which has been established on disused railway lines. The route passes through some delightful countryside, including some of Burgundy's world-class vineyards. This is also great walking country, and the site's friendly owners will be pleased to recommend routes. A little further afield, the great châteaux at Digoin, Demigny and Saint Aubin all merit a visit.

Key Features

 Pets Accepted

 Disabled Facilities

 Swimming Pool

 Play Area

 Bar/Restaurant

 Bike Hire

Sanitary blocks with hot showers and facilities for disabled visitors. Laundry facilities. Café/snack bar. Shop (July/Aug). Swimming pool. Paddling pool. Playground. Picnic areas. Games room. Bicycle hire. Mobile homes and chalets to rent.

Scan me for more information.

Alan Rogers Code: FR71010
256 pitches
GPS: 46.33027, 4.84366
Post Code: F-71000

Saône-et-Loire, Burgundy

www.alanrogers.com/fr71010
camping@ville-macon.fr
Tel: +33 3 85 38 16 22
www.macon.fr/vivre-et-bouger-a-
macon/camping

Open (Touring Pitches):
Mid March - End October.

Camping Municipal Mâcon

A well cared for site worth considering as a stopover or for longer stays, as it is close to the main route south. The 256 good-sized, level, grassy pitches, 190 with 6A electricity and 60 with fresh and waste water points, are easily accessed by tarmac roads.

This is a pleasant site, remarkably quiet considering its location, and with a generally bright and cheerful ambience. Extra charge for outfits over 3,5 tonnes and with twin axles. Only gas and electric barbecues. Reservations are not accepted, so in July and August, arrive by late afternoon to avoid disappointment. Some road and rail noise.

Four modern, well-maintained toilet blocks. All necessary facilities, including those for campers with disabilities. Washing machine and dryer. Motorhome services (with Fiamma sewage couplings). Shop, bar, takeaway and restaurant (le Tipi) open midday and evenings all season. Heated swimming and paddling pools (campers only, high season). TV lounge. Playground. WiFi throughout (free).

Key Features

 Pets Accepted

 Disabled Facilities

 Swimming Pool

 Play Area

 Bar/Restaurant

Scan me for more information.

129

Alan Rogers Code: FR21060
46 pitches
GPS: 47.02458, 4.88712
Post Code: F-21200

Côte d`Or, Burgundy

www.alanrogers.com/fr21060
camping-les-bouleaux@hotmail.fr
Tel: +33 3 80 22 26 88
www.campinglesbouleaux.wixsite.
com

Open (Touring Pitches):
All year.

Camping les Bouleaux

Family-run since 1974, Camping Les Bouleaux is an excellent little campsite located at Vignoles, 4 km from the centre of historic Beaune. There are just 46 pitches, all with an electrical connection (3-6A, long leads may be required on some pitches). The large, flat and grassy pitches are attractively laid out, and most are separated by hedges and trees, giving some shade. It's a rural, sleepy area, backing onto fields, with plenty of scope for easy-going walks and is popular with those (mainly couples) who enjoy gastronomy, wine and culture. It is a handy stopover site.

The wine-related attractions on the doorstep need little introduction. The vineyards of Meursault, Pouligny-Montrachet and Pommard are just the start, and the world-famous 'Hospices des Beaune' are a must-see. Don't miss the chance of a wine tasting - maybe take a bike and follow one of the cycle routes or the 'voie vert', which leads through charming, picturesque scenery and rolling vineyards.

An older unisex building provides Turkish-style WCs, while the adjacent modern block houses British-style WCs (no paper). Washbasins in cabins or communal. Controllable showers and excellent facilities for visitors with disabilities. No shop, but wine and basic groceries can be bought at the reception. Supermarket 3 km. Children's playground. Gas exchange. WiFi.

Key Features

 Book Online

 Open All Year

 Pets Accepted

 Disabled Facilities

 Play Area

Scan me for more information.

Alan Rogers Code: FR25160
10 accommodations
99 pitches
GPS: 47.26588, 6.07151
Post Code: F-25220

Doubs, Franche-Comté

www.alanrogers.com/fr25160
contact@campingdebesancon.com
Tel: +33 3 81 88 04 26
www.campingdebesancon.com

Open (Touring Pitches):
Mid March - End October.

Camping de Besançon

You'll find no noisy entertainment at Camping de Besançon La Plage, so the site is perfect for those looking for peace. That said, children enjoy the sprawling lawns, spacious sports field, large swimming pool and playground, while the adults appreciate the handy location on the outskirts of Besançon and right beside the River Doubs, overlooked by the wooded hills opposite.

The pitches are of a good size, and all have electricity (16A), water and drainage. Most have some degree of shade, and most are grassy. There are also bungalows and tents for rental. Within a short walk from the site is a large supermarket, and nearby is a tram stop from where you can be whisked to the elegant town centre. Visit the imposing citadel, the museums and 600 metres of ancient ramparts. There's plenty of scope for cycling and walking through this stunning landscape, with various designated trails according to fitness and arduousness. The site is only an hour from the Swiss border, with plenty of epic scenery to enjoy on the way.

Clean sanitary facilities with unisex private sinks and showers. Baby room. Washing machines. Dryers. Washing up sinks. Snack bar. Restaurant. Fresh bread daily. Large swimming pool with diving boards. Playground. Crazy golf. Multi-sports field. Table tennis. Bike hire (e-bikes available). Boules. WiFi.

Key Features

 Pets Accepted

 Swimming Pool

 Play Area

Scan me for more information.

Alan Rogers Code: FR25070
30 accommodations
65 pitches
GPS: 47.10055, 6.12795
Post Code: F-25290

Doubs, Franche-Comté

www.alanrogers.com/fr25070
campinglechanet@gmail.com
Tel: +33 3 81 62 23 44
www.lechanet.com

Open (Touring Pitches):
Start April - Mid October.

Domaine le Chanet

Located in the heart of the Jura in the Loue valley on the edge of historic Ornans, this traditional site is on a fairly steep slope with terraced pitches. The area has plenty of outdoor activities, including canoeing and kayaking, mountain biking, caving and fishing. With 95 pitches (65 for touring), there are around 50 with electricity hook-ups (3-16A), including nine with multi-services. There are also 25 mobile homes, caravans or tents to rent on the site and three gîtes. Larger units will find access difficult.

A café and bar with an outside terrace are beside the freshwater eco pool and a paddling pool. A small shop, which is open all season, stocks basic needs, toys, postcards etc. Entertainment and a children's club are arranged in the main season, and guided visits, caving and climbing and canoeing trips are also available. A path for cycling and walking leads along the old railway track from the town into the mountains for 10 km.

Two toilet blocks, one at the rear of the reception building, include a baby room and facilities for children and disabled visitors. Small laundry area. Shop (all season). Café, bar and takeaway (seasonal). Heated outdoor eco-pool and paddling pool (seasonal). Sauna and gym (charged). Washing facility for caving suits and equipment. Games room. Play area. Boules. Bicycle hire. Safety deposit boxes. Entertainment and a children's club in high season. WiFi on the part of the site (free).

Key Features

 Book Online

 Pets Accepted

 Swimming Pool

 Play Area

 Bar/Restaurant

 Bike Hire

Scan me for more information.

Alan Rogers Code: FR25130
33 accommodations
41 pitches
GPS: 46.77408, 6.36751
Post Code: F-25370

Doubs, Franche-Comté

Camping le Miroir

www.alanrogers.com/fr25130
accueil@camping-lemiroir.com
Tel: +33 3 81 49 10 64
www.camping-lemiroir.com

Open (Touring Pitches):
Mid December - Early October.

Camping Le Miroir is a quiet site in the village of Les Hôpitaux-Neufs in the Alps, at an altitude of 1000 metres and close to the Switzerland/France border. The village is in a valley of fields and fir forests overlooked by the Mont d'Or massif. There is plenty to do in the surrounding area, whatever the season. In summer, you will have easy access to hiking and cycle paths and other outdoor activities such as horse riding, archery and water sports, including windsurfing, kayaking and paddleboarding.

In winter, there is downhill skiing from Métabief ski station, a kilometre away, and cross-country skiing, snowshoeing and other activities. The village of Hôpitaux-Neufs is the commercial centre of the resort of Métabief. Located between the Mont d'Or massif and the Herba massif, the territory is covered with meadows, pastures and forests. Amenities at the site include free WiFi, a laundry, a dishwashing area and a toilet/shower block with accessible facilities. The site has 41 touring pitches. There are also 33 mobile homes and chalets, of which nine are available to hire.

Key Features

 Pets Accepted

 Disabled Facilities

 Bar/Restaurant

The heated toilet block has showers, washbasins and WCs. Facility for guests who are disabled. Chemical toilet point. Laundry. Dishwashing area. Children's play area. Table tennis. Multi-sports pitch. WiFi zone. Restaurant. Bar. Bakery, supermarket, butcher, post office, newsagent and electric car charging points nearby. Dogs allowed.

Scan me for more information.

Alan Rogers Code: FR39080
70 accommodations
130 pitches
GPS: 46.65252, 5.72106
Post Code: F-39130

Jura, Franche-Comté

www.alanrogers.com/fr39080
info@domaine-epinette.com
Tel: +33 3 84 25 71 44
www.domaine-epinette.com

Open (Touring Pitches):
Mid May - Mid September.

Domaine de l'Epinette

This site is set in the heart of the Jura, just 5 km from the serene Lac de Chalain. It's charming countryside, with the wooded slopes rising up from the slow-moving River Ain and the Swiss border not far away. The photogenic waterfalls, Cascades du Hérisson, are 15 km away and stretch for 3 km, and there are countless cycling and hiking trails to follow through the sublime scenery. The winding country lanes link picturesque villages like Baume-Les-Messieurs, one of France's 'most beautiful villages' with its famous caves. The town of Lons-le-Saunier is just 20 minutes away.

This family-friendly site has mostly grassy pitches, some slightly sloping, with around 130 for touring units. These are arranged on terraces and separated by hedges, bushes and trees, about half being shaded. Nearly all have electricity hook-ups, although some long leads are needed. Ten pitches have hard standing.

Two modern toilet blocks. Unit for disabled visitors. Baby bath. Washing machine and dryer. Small shop for basics. Snack bar and takeaway (evenings, high season). New reception, bar, TV room and shop. Takeaway (high season). Swimming pool with slide and paddling pool. Playground. Children's activities (high season). Boules. Direct access to the river for fishing, swimming and canoeing. WiFi (free). Gas and charcoal barbecues are permitted.

Key Features

 Book Online

 Pets Accepted

 Disabled Facilities

 Swimming Pool

 Play Area

 Bar/Restaurant

 Fishing

Scan me for more information.

Alan Rogers Code: FR39120
49 accommodations
192 pitches
GPS: 46.59976, 5.68824
Post Code: F-39130

Jura, Franche-Comté

www.alanrogers.com/fr39120
reception@juracampingbeauregard.com
Tel: +33 3 84 48 32 51
www.juracampingbeauregard.com

Open (Touring Pitches):
Early April - Early October.

Camping Beauregard Jura

Well under 2 hours drive north of Geneva, Sites et Paysages Beauregard is a charming, well-kept site nestled in the immaculately beautiful countryside of the Jura. Surrounded by fields and overlooked by wooded hills, it's a natural setting that is popular with families who value the activities on offer and the safe environment, as well as those who enjoy cycling and hiking amidst stunning scenery. Aside from the beautiful lakes (Clairvaux, Chalain, Vouglans and Ilay), there are magical waterfalls, vast caves and ancient abbeys to explore.

Run by the Péan family since 1976, Beauregard has 192 level grass pitches, all well delimited with neat hedging, small trees and colourful shrubs. There are 143 for touring units, all with 6A electricity (long leads may be necessary). There is a relaxed, friendly ambience here - it's a well-equipped site where the owners allow the surrounding scenery to speak for itself.

Key Features

 Book Online

 Disabled Facilities

 Swimming Pool

 Play Area

 Bar/Restaurant

 Fishing

Three clean toilet blocks (one is high season only). Baby room and facilities for disabled visitors. Motorhome services. Shop (high season). Bar, restaurant and takeaway (May-September). Indoor (all season) and outdoor pools (high season) with toilet and shower facilities. Sauna. Play areas. Outdoor fitness equipment. Minigolf. Sports field. Tennis. Football. Volleyball. Children's activities (high season). WiFi throughout (charged).

Scan me for more information.

Alan Rogers Code: FR87170
15 accommodations
36 pitches
GPS: 46.13177, 1.27057
Post Code: F-87290

Haute-Vienne, Limousin

www.alanrogers.com/fr87170
camping-chateauponsac@orange.fr
Tel: +33 5 55 76 55 33
www.campingdelagartempe.fr

Open (Touring Pitches):
Start April - End October.

Camping de la Gartempe

In the heart of Limousin in the Haute-Vienne department, Camping de la Gartempe is situated in a protected area next to the River Gartempe and also is close to the small village of Châteauponsac. This wooded, terraced site has 36 grassy pitches with electricity (10/16A, Europlug) and water. Some pitches have shade, and others have a more open aspect. There are also 15 mobile homes, cottages and chalets to rent. The bar and terrace overlook the river and valley. The area is well known for its rural and water activities, culture, and history.

It is only 13 km. from the Saint-Pardoux area, a major tourist attraction covering 330 hectares, with a lake in the heart of the forest. It is perfect for outdoor activities with three beaches with lifeguards (July and August), three hiking circuits, walking, fishing, horse riding and mountain biking facilities, and a tree climbing course.

Heated sanitary facilities with provision for children and visitors with disabilities. Baby room. Laundry. Motorhome services. Bread to order. Bar with terrace (July/Aug). Playground. Boules. Volleyball. Basketball. Children's club (July/Aug). TV/Games room. Table tennis. Marked walking trails. River fishing. Communal barbecue and barbecue rental. Bicycle and mountain bike hire. WiFi (free by reception).

Key Features

 Book Online

 Pets Accepted

 Disabled Facilities

 Swimming Pool

 Play Area

 Bar/Restaurant

 Bike Hire

 Fishing

Scan me for more information.

Alan Rogers Code: FR87185
23 accommodations
83 pitches
GPS: 45.94366, 1.51484
Post Code: F87240

Haute-Vienne, Limousin

www.alanrogers.com/fr87185
contact@aupontdudognon.fr
Tel: +33 6 75 73 25 30
www.aupontdudognon.fr

Open (Touring Pitches):
Mid April - Start October.

Camping Au Pont du Dognon

Camping -Au Pont du Dognon is a small and quiet site situated on the banks of the Taurion river, between Ambazac and Saint Léonard de Noblat and 30 kilometres from Limoges. The campsite offers 83 camping and hard-standing pitches so everyone can find their ideal camping spot. There are also 63 touring pitches with 10a electrical hookups available. This campsite is perfect if you love the outdoors, with fishing, kayaking and hiking on your doorstep. Camping Au Pont Du Dognon also has extensive facilities for its size: an outdoor swimming pool, entertainment during high season miniature golf, a bar, a pizzeria and a creperie.

The pilgrimage route of Santiago de Compostela crosses the Taurion at the site's nearby town of Saint-Laurent-Les-Églises. You can find a bar and restaurant half a kilometre from the campsite, but most amenities will be located 10 kilometres away in Ambazac. There are mountain bike trails and kilometres' worth of hiking trails that stretch through the Ambazac mountains and the Taurion valley areas, around 30 kilometres away.

Heated Sanitary facilities with baby change and disabled facilities, Bar, Snack Bar (high season), Shop (small), Children's playground, Entertainment, Outdoor swimming pool, Tennis court, Game room, Bouncy castle, Mini golf, Pets allowed, WiFi.

Key Features

 Book Online

 Pets Accepted

 Disabled Facilities

 Swimming Pool

 Play Area

 Bar/Restaurant

 Fishing

Scan me for more information.

Alan Rogers Code: FR19090
2 accommodations
118 pitches
GPS: 45.04640, 1.88210
Post Code: F-19400

Corrèze, Limousin

Camping le Vaurette

www.alanrogers.com/fr19090
info@vaurette.com
Tel: +33 5 55 28 09 67
www.vaurette.com

Open (Touring Pitches):
Mid May - Late September.

You are assured of a warm welcome at this immaculate site, beautifully situated beside the shallow River Dordogne and just a few kilometres from Argentat. There are 120 large, gently sloping grass pitches, 118 for touring. Separated by a large variety of beautiful trees and shrubs offering varying amounts of shade, all have 6A electricity, and many have good views over the River Dordogne as the pitches nearest the river are slightly terraced.

The owners run an active campsite for all the family while maintaining tranquillity (no radios). Excellent English and Dutch are spoken. The ancient barn at the far end of the site houses the bar and a large TV room (large screen), and the terrace overlooks the good-sized and attractive heated swimming and paddling pools.

Two very clean traditional toilet blocks offer all the expected facilities, including facilities for disabled visitors. Further facilities are near the bar and heated outdoor pool. Motorhome services. Shop. Two bars with terrace and takeaway. Football. Gym. Badminton. Boules. Tennis. Fishing. River bathing. Accompanied canoe trips, walks and mountain bike rides. Organised activities for all the family (July/Aug) but no late-night discos. WiFi (charged).

Key Features

 Book Online

 Pets Accepted

 Disabled Facilities

 Swimming Pool

 Play Area

 Bar/Restaurant

 Bike Hire

 Fishing

Scan me for
more information.

Alan Rogers Code: FR63280
65 accommodations
145 pitches
GPS: 45.66800, 2.99030
Post Code: F-63970

Puy-de-Dôme, Auvergne

www.alanrogers.com/fr63280
info@camping-lac-aydat.com
Tel: +33 4 73 79 38 09
www.camping-lac-aydat.com

Open (Touring Pitches):
Start May- End September.

Camping du Lac d'Aydat

The site consists of two areas, a very large area with Mobile Homes and Chalets to rent, which you pass through to get to a much smaller area where the 80 touring pitches are. These vary in size from 80 m2 to 100 m2, 73 have 10 amp hookups, and you can select sun or shade; if you are fortunate, there are nine lakeside pitches, all pitches are close to the lake, and you do have direct access to swim or picnic.

Walking or cycling around the lake is very popular and as you would expect there are many activities on the lake. There is a new modern sanitary block within the touring area with baby change and laundry rooms. There is a small swimming pool, mini golf, and children's play area on-site, all by the restaurant/bar with outside seating.

Heated Sanitary block with specific facilities only open for the disabled. Children's sanitary facilities, Restaurant, Bar, Snack Bar, Pizzeria, Take away meals, Communal BBQ area, Outdoor swimming pool, Windsurfing permitted, Windsurfing course, Kayaking course, Sailing permitted, Sailing lessons, Children's playground, Entertainment (high season) Kids Club (high season) Table tennis table, Multi-sports field.

Key Features

 Book Online

 Pets Accepted

 Disabled Facilities

 Swimming Pool

 Play Area

 Bar/Restaurant

 Fishing

 Sailing

Scan me for more information.

Alan Rogers Code: FR63450
43 accommodations
100 pitches
GPS: 45.90309, 3.59900
Post Code: F-63550

Puy-de-Dôme, Auvergne

www.alanrogers.com/fr63450
contact@revea-vacances.com
Tel: +33 4 73 94 31 71
www.camping-leschanterelles.com

Open (Touring Pitches):
Mid April - Late September.

Camping les Chanterelles

Lying in the heart of the Auvergne between Clermont-Ferrand and Lyon, Camping Paradis les Chanterelles is in an enviable location. Surrounded by rolling wooded hills and rural countryside, the site drops down to a large lake with its own sandy beach and a grassy expanse for lounging and playing. Guests have access (a few minutes walk) to this and rental of canoes, paddle boards and pedalos (open high season).

There are around 140 pitches, mostly grassy and with decent shade from mature trees. Some are terraced, some on slightly rolling ground. This is a region rich in culture, gastronomy and epic natural scenery. You'll find enticing trails for cycling and hiking leading in all directions and leading you through some gorgeous scenery. This is a great choice for families seeking a good range of outdoor activities and couples who enjoy relaxing with good food and wine after some gentle exercise.

Heated sanitary block with disabled access. Basic motorhome service point. Laundry. Basic grocery supplies, including bread and pastries (July/Aug). Lake with kayaking, fishing, swimming, and boating. Covered swimming pool. Tennis nearby. Playroom. TV room. Organised entertainment and Kids' Club (high season). Playground. Pétanque. Volleyball. Bicycle hire (not all season). Riding 4 km. Mini golf. Free WiFi at reception.

Key Features

 Pets Accepted

 Disabled Facilities

 Play Area

 Bike Hire

Scan me for more information.

Alan Rogers Code: FR69020
29 accommodations
60 pitches
GPS: 46.18790, 4.69916
Post Code: F-69820

Rhône, Rhône Alpes

www.alanrogers.com/fr69020
info@beaujolais-camping.com
Tel: +33 4 74 69 80 07
www.beaujolais-camping.com

Open (Touring Pitches):
Mid April - Early October.

La Grappe Fleurie

With easy access from both the A6 autoroute and the N6, this attractive and welcoming site is perfect for overnight stops. But stay awhile and get to know this delightful region with its wine heritage, historical monuments and magical rolling landscape. This is a neat, well-ordered campsite situated in the heart of Beaujolais. In fact, it's surrounded by vineyards and just walking distance (within 1 km) of the pretty village of Fleurie (one of the premier Beaujolais crus). Here you'll find all the shops and amenities you'll need. The winding lanes meander through the charming vineyards, with familiar names from the wine list all around - a great way to explore is by bike or on foot.

This popular site has 60 generous, grassy and fairly level touring pitches delimited by substantial hedging and shady trees and with individual access to water, drainage and electricity connections (10A). The English-speaking owners arrange interesting wine tastings on-site twice weekly in the high season.

Key Features

 Book Online

 Pets Accepted

 Disabled Facilities

 Swimming Pool

 Play Area

Two modern sanitary blocks. Facilities for disabled visitors. Washing machine and dryer. Fridge. Bread to order. Snack bar with homemade pizza (May-Sept). Covered and heated swimming pool (15x7m). Playground. Tennis court. Large TV/games room. Pétanque. Regular wine tastings (no charge). Sauna. Gas barbecues only. Free WiFi.

Scan me for more information.

Alan Rogers Code: FR38010
14 accommodations
178 pitches
GPS: 45.54115, 5.60778
Post Code: F-38490

Isère, Rhône Alpes

www.alanrogers.com/fr38010
contact@coin-tranquille.com
Tel: +33 4 76 32 13 48
www.coin-tranquille.com

Open (Touring Pitches):
Start April - Start November.

Camping le Coin Tranquille

Le Coin Tranquille is well placed for visits to the Savoie regions and the Alps. It is an attractive, well-maintained site of 192 grass pitches (178 for touring units), all with 10A electricity. Neat hedges of hydrangea separate them, flowering shrubs and a range of trees make a lovely environment doubly enhanced by the rural aspect and marvellous views across to the mountains.

This popular, family-run site with friendly staff makes it a wonderful base for exploring the area. Set in the Dauphiny countryside north of Grenoble, le Coin Tranquille is a quiet corner, especially outside school holidays. However, it is still popular with families in high season.

The central well-appointed sanitary block is well-kept and heated in low season. Facilities for disabled visitors. Two smaller blocks provide facilities in high season. Busy shop. Excellent restaurant. Indoor swimming pool (seasonal). Outdoor heated swimming pool (high season). Bermuda-style shorts are not permitted. Play area. TV and games in the bar. Quiet reading room. Weekly entertainment for children and adults (July/Aug), including live music (not discos). Bicycle hire (limited). WiFi near reception (free).

Key Features

 Book Online

 Pets Accepted

 Disabled Facilities

 Swimming Pool

 Play Area

 Bar/Restaurant

 Bike Hire

Scan me for more information.

Alan Rogers Code: FR42040
20 accommodations
72 pitches
GPS: 45.59272, 4.33542
Post Code: F-42330

Loire, Rhône Alpes

Camping Le Val de Coise

www.alanrogers.com/fr42040
val-de-coise@campeole.com
Tel: +33 4 77 54 14 82
www.campeole.co.uk/camping/post/
le-val-de-coise-st-galmier

Open (Touring Pitches):
Late March - Late September.

Val de Coise is a member of the Campéole group and is situated in the undulating landscape of the Massif Central, north of Saint Etienne. It is an attractive site located between the River Coise and a dense forest. Of the 72 grassy pitches, 30 are for tourers (28 with 16A electricity); a further 20 house mobile homes, chalets and fully equipped tents to rent.

There is plenty of activity here in high season, with a children's club and regular discos and karaoke evenings. This is rugged, dramatic country – ideal for walking and mountain biking. The nearby spa town of Saint Galmier is home to the Badoit water plant, a casino, restaurants and some art galleries.

The single toilet block is central. It is kept clean and neatly tiled and painted. Small baby room. Facilities for disabled visitors. Good motorhome services. Fridge hire. Small shop in reception. No bar or snacks. Heated outdoor swimming pool (seasonal). Multisports terrain. TV room. Play area. Minigolf. Boules. Bouncy castle. Fishing. Activities and entertainment programme. WiFi (charged). Mobile homes, chalets and equipped tents to rent.

Key Features

 Book Online

 Pets Accepted

 Disabled Facilities

 Swimming Pool

 Play Area

 Fishing

Scan me for
more information.

Alan Rogers Code: FR26360
29 accommodations
126 pitches
GPS: 45.25280, 5.02672
Post Code: F-26390

Drôme, Rhône Alpes

Camping le Château

www.alanrogers.com/fr26360
contact@camping-hauterives.com
Tel: +33 4 75 68 80 19
www.camping-hauterives.com/en

Open (Touring Pitches):
Start April - End September.

Flower Camping le Château, as you would expect, the site is set on the grounds of an old Chateau and is a very short walk into the lovely French village of Hauterives. Access to the site is easy, and sat nav can be relied upon; opposite the site is a new supermarket, pharmacy, petrol station with car wash, laundry pod and bottled gas. Arrival and check-in is easy and efficient, and you are invited to view the site to select your pitch (English is spoken at reception). The site comprises 126 pitches which are well-spaced and large; some offer a good deal of privacy and shade.

Facilities are excellent and cleaned regularly throughout the day, and a laundry room is also on-site. The best thing about this site has to be the Pool Complex with an adjoining Bar/Restaurant located in the courtyard of the old Chateau, access is free, and there is a full-time lifeguard on duty (please note shorts are not allowed. Swimming trunks only, these are sold in reception if you don't own a pair). This site makes a good overnight stop, but with the excellent facilities, you will likely want to stay longer.

Key Features

 Book Online

 Pets Accepted

 Disabled Facilities

 Swimming Pool

 Play Area

 Bar/Restaurant

 Bike Hire

 Fishing

Sanitary buildings include controllable showers. Facilities for disabled visitors. Bar/snack bar (May-Sept). Heated and supervised outdoor pools and a children's pool. TV room. Playground. Library. Boules. Bicycle hire. Accommodation to rent. WiFi throughout (free at reception, elsewhere charged).

Scan me for more information.

Alan Rogers Code: FR07630
264 accommodations
70 pitches
GPS: 44.44470, 4.36630
Post Code: F-07120

Ardèche, Rhône Alpes

Aluna Vacances

www.alanrogers.com/fr07630
contact@alunavacances.fr
Tel: +33 4 75 93 93 15
www.alunavacances.fr

Open (Touring Pitches):
Early April - Late September.

Situated on the doorstep of the Ardèche Gorges, Sunêlia Aluna Vacances is well-placed for all kinds of outdoor activities. The famous Pont d'Arc itself is only 15 km away, popular for canoeing excursions amidst spectacular scenery. The surrounding wooded hills offer wonderful cycling and hiking trails through the wild herbs of the garrigue landscape.

This leafy site is well laid out around an impressive pool complex, forming a natural focal point. Some pitches are grassier than others, but all are set among the trees, all with 10A electricity and decent shade to most, and they're at least 100m sq. Extra large pitches are also available, as well as some hardstandings. Nearby medieval Ruoms is attractive and handy for its shops and amenities. There are plenty of local natural attractions: Cocalière cave and chestnut museum are charming in various ways.

Key Features

 Book Online

 Pets Accepted

 Disabled Facilities

 Swimming Pool

 Play Area

 Bar/Restaurant

Four sanitary blocks with showers, private washing cubicles and facilities for babies and disabled guests. Washing machines and dryers. Well-stocked shop. Bar with TV. Restaurant and takeaway. Waterpark with heated outdoor pools, indoor pool and slides. Aquagym. Spa. Sports and kid's club (seasonal). Tennis. Volleyball. Table tennis. Boules. Multisports field. Playground. Entertainment programme. Cycling, rafting, horse riding, and canoeing are nearby. WiFi (extra charge).

Scan me for
more information.

Alan Rogers Code: FR07050
310 accommodations
50 pitches
GPS: 44.41410, 4.27290
Post Code: F-07120

Ardèche, Rhône Alpes

Le Ranc Davaine

www.alanrogers.com/fr07050
contact@rancdavaine.fr
Tel: +33 4 75 39 60 55
www.camping-ranc-davaine.fr

Open (Touring Pitches):
Late April - Late September.

In the heart of the Ardèche and close to the famous gorges, Sunêlia Le Ranc Davaine is a large, busy, family-oriented site with direct access to the River Chassezac with its own pebble beach. There are approximately 500 pitches, with 50 for touring, all with electricity (10/16A), for which very long leads are required (some may cross roads). Most pitches are scattered between static caravan and tour operator pitches on the fairly flat, stony ground under a variety of trees, some of which are quite low, giving much-needed shade.

The site can get very busy for much of the season, with the extensive aqua park acting as a focal point, especially as the sun goes down and the evening's entertainment begins. New features are planned for 2023, including a covered pool area, more slides, a wave machine and an improved two-storey bar with a veranda.

Key Features

 Book Online

 Pets Accepted

 Disabled Facilities

 Swimming Pool

 Play Area

 Bar/Restaurant

Three sanitary blocks with facilities for visitors with reduced mobility. Washing machines and dryers. Large shop. Bar/restaurant, pizzeria, takeaway. Indoor swimming pool (heated), various pools, water slides and water park (all facilities all season, no shorts allowed). River beach. Large playground. Spa. Tennis. Football, volleyball, table tennis. Fishing, riding, golf, quad biking nearby. Extensive entertainment programme (Jul/Aug). Discos. Fitness area. Free WiFi (partial coverage).

Scan me for
more information.

Alan Rogers Code: FR07120
25 accommodations
225 pitches
GPS: 44.39804, 4.39878
Post Code: F-07150

Ardèche, Rhône Alpes

www.alanrogers.com/fr07120
info@ardechois-camping.com
Tel: +33 4 75 88 06 63
www.ardechois-camping.com

Open (Touring Pitches):
Early April - Mid October.

Nature Parc l'Ardéchois

Camping Nature Parc l'Ardéchois is a very high-quality, family-run site within walking distance of the amenities of Vallon-Pont-d'Arc. It borders the River Ardèche, and hugely popular canoe trips are run directly from the site. The campsite is just 4 km from the famous Pont-d'Arc, a huge limestone arch spanning the river, and its river beach. A drive along the gorge is a must, with spectacular viewpoints along the way.

Of the 250 well-maintained pitches, there are 225 for touring units, separated by trees and shrubs. All have electrical connections (6/10A), and, for an additional charge, 125 larger pitches have full services (22 include a fridge, patio furniture, hammock and free WiFi). This is a great choice for active families and anyone interested in good food and wine after some gentle exercise.

Two well-equipped toilet blocks, one superb with everything working automatically. Facilities are of the highest standard, very clean and include good facilities for babies, children and disabled visitors. Laundry facilities. Four private bathrooms to hire. Well-stocked shop. Excellent restaurant, bar and takeaway. Heated swimming pool and paddling pool (no shorts). Wellness area with sauna, hammam, jacuzzi and 4 seasons-shower. Different types of massage and treatments. Yoga. Gym. Tennis. Very good play area. Organised activities and canoe trips. Bicycle hire. Only gas barbecues are permitted. Communal barbecue area. WiFi throughout (charged).

Key Features

 Book Online

 Pets Accepted

 Disabled Facilities

 Swimming Pool

 Play Area

 Bar/Restaurant

 Bike Hire

 Fishing

Scan me for more information.

Alan Rogers Code: FR33110
522 accommodations
618 pitches
GPS: 45.22372, -1.16318
Post Code: F-33990

Gironde, Aquitaine

La Côte d'Argent

www.alanrogers.com/fr33110
info@cca33.com
Tel: +33 5 56 09 10 25
www.camping-cote-dargent.com

Open (Touring Pitches):
Mid May - Mid September.

Camping de la Côte d'Argent is a large, well-equipped site set back a short walk from the sandy beach, part of a long ribbon of golden sand that runs from the Gironde to the Spanish border. The beach is just magnificent, with lots of water sports available too. The huge Landes pine forest encloses the site, so walkers and cyclists can explore over 100 km of trails and cycle paths in the area. Hourtin-Plage itself is a pleasant little resort with a few shops and restaurants.

Aside from its proximity to the beach, the site's big draw is its pool complex, with wooden bridges connecting the pools and islands, sunbathing and play areas, plus an indoor heated pool. The site has 618 touring pitches (all with 10A electricity), not always clearly defined, arranged under shady trees with some on sand.

Key Features

 Pets Accepted

 Disabled Facilities

 Beach Access

 Swimming Pool

 Play Area

 Bar/Restaurant

 Bike Hire

Sanitary blocks include provision for disabled visitors. Washing machines. Motorhome services. Grocery store, restaurant, takeaway, pizzeria and bar. Four outdoor pools with slides and flumes (seasonal). Indoor pool (all season). Fitness room. Massage (Institut de Beauté). Tennis. Multisport area. Beach volleyball. Pétanque. Play areas. Miniclub, fitness and organised entertainment in high season. Bicycle hire (adults only). WiFi partial site (charged). Charcoal barbecues are not permitted (gas barbecue rental on site).

Scan me for more information.

Alan Rogers Code: FR33030
300 pitches
GPS: 44.65139, -1.17417
Post Code: F-33312

Gironde, Aquitaine

www.alanrogers.com/fr33030
info@camping-arcachon.com
Tel: +33 5 56 83 24 15
europe.huttopia.com/site/arcachon

Open (Touring Pitches):
All year (excl. mid-November - mid-December).

Huttopia Arcachon

This campsite enjoys a position well back from the hustle and bustle, where nights are quiet, and facilities are of a high standard. The 300 touring pitches are divided into areas for caravans, motorhomes and tents and are on neatly formed terraces beneath tall pine trees. One-third have electricity (6/10A), water and drainage.

The site is quite hilly, and the narrow roads that wind around it could possibly make it difficult for larger motorhomes to manoeuvre and find suitable pitches. At night, wardens ensure that security and noise levels are controlled. A 1 km. walk takes you to the town of Arcachon, where plenty of shops, bars and restaurants exist.

Three sanitary blocks include facilities for children and disabled visitors. Motorhome services. Washing machine, dryers. Fridge hire. Shop, restaurant, snack bar and takeaway (all April-Oct). Swimming pool (high season). Bicycle hire. Play area. Games room. Children's club and entertainment for all ages (July/Aug). Electric barbecues only, and a communal area is provided. Internet access. Free WiFi throughout.

Key Features

 Book Online

 Pets Accepted

 Disabled Facilities

 Beach Access

 Swimming Pool

 Play Area

 Bar/Restaurant

 Bike Hire

Scan me for more information.

Alan Rogers Code: FR40060
129 accommodations
356 pitches
GPS: 43.95166, -1.35212
Post Code: F-40560

Landes, Aquitaine

Camping Club Eurosol

www.alanrogers.com/fr40060
contact@camping-eurosol.com
Tel: +33 5 58 47 90 14
www.camping-eurosol.com

Open (Touring Pitches):
Mid May - Mid September.

Camping Club International Eurosol is an attractive, friendly and well-maintained site deep in the Landes pine forests of Aquitaine. The fabulous golden sandy beach is just a few minutes walk away (700m), with supervised swimming (high season) and a range of watersports. Several cycle trails lead from the site through the vast forests, and a riding centre is located just 500 metres away. To the south, the Basque country and Biarritz are within easy access.

The site extends over undulating ground, with pitches set amongst shady pine trees. Of the 356 touring pitches, 232 have electricity (10A), and 120 are fully serviced. This is very much a family site with loads of activities, organised events and shows and a landscaped swimming pool complex that boasts three large pools. This is a well thought out campsite, professionally run with plenty of English spoken, with the facilities to cater to all tastes throughout the season.

Four main toilet blocks and two smaller blocks with facilities for babies and disabled visitors. Motorhome services. Fridge rental. Well-stocked shop and bar (all season). Restaurant, takeaway (seasonal). Live shows in July/Aug. Outdoor swimming pool, paddling pool (all season) and heated, covered pool (May-July). Tennis. Multisports court. Bicycle hire. WiFi (charged). Charcoal barbecues are not permitted.

Key Features

 Book Online

 Pets Accepted

 Disabled Facilities

 Beach Access

 Swimming Pool

 Play Area

 Bar/Restaurant

 Bike Hire

Scan me for more information.

Alan Rogers Code: FR40200
380 accommodations
234 pitches
GPS: 43.59570, -1.45638
Post Code: F-40530

Landes, Aquitaine

www.alanrogers.com/fr40200
info@yellohvillage-sylvamar.com
Tel: +33 5 59 45 75 16
www.camping-sylvamar.com

Open (Touring Pitches):
Early April - Late September.

Yelloh! Village le Sylvamar

Yelloh! Village le Sylvamar is just a kilometre from the endless sandy beach, just north of Bayonne on the southern edge of the Landes. There are around 600 pitches, of which 234 are for tourers, all level, numbered and mostly separated by low hedges. Several newer pitches are less shaded. All have electricity (16A), water and drainage; some have private sanitary facilities and premium pitches with pergolas are available.

The extensive pool complex is remarkable, featuring several pools, a wild water river, toboggans, slides and a spectacular 'volcano'. In a sunny setting, all are surrounded by ample sunbathing terraces and overlooked by the excellent bar/restaurant. An 800-seat amphitheatre hosts entertainment. Visit the local resorts of Capbreton and Hossegor, with a marina and fishing port, museums and beaches, plenty of surf culture and amazing seafood.

Four modern toilet blocks have washbasins in cabins. Excellent facilities for babies and disabled visitors. Laundry. Fridge hire. Shop, bar/restaurant and takeaway. Swimming pool complex. Spa treatments. Yoga, aquagym, pilates. Play area. Games room. Cinema, TV and video room. Fitness centre. Wellness amenities. Tennis. Football pitch. Bicycle hire. Library. Extensive entertainment programme for all ages. WiFi over site (charged). No charcoal barbecues.

Key Features

 Pets Accepted

 Disabled Facilities

 Beach Access

 Swimming Pool

 Play Area

 Bar/Restaurant

 Bike Hire

Scan me for more information.

Alan Rogers Code: FR40140
26 accommodations
142 pitches
GPS: 43.52406, -1.41196
Post Code: F-40390

Landes, Aquitaine

www.alanrogers.com/fr40140
contact@louptitpoun.com
Tel: +33 5 59 56 55 79
www.louptitpoun.com

Open (Touring Pitches):
Start May - Late September.

Camping Lou P'tit Poun

Part of the Sites et Paysages group, the manicured grounds surrounding Lou P'tit Poun give it a well-kept appearance, a theme carried throughout this very pleasing site which opened in 1989. It is only after arriving at the car park you feel confident it is not a private estate.

Beyond this point, an abundance of shrubs and trees is revealed. Behind a central sloping flower bed lies the open-plan reception area. The avenues around the site are wide, and the 168 pitches (142 for touring) are spacious. All have 10A electricity, many also have water and drainage, and low hedges separate some. The jovial owners welcome their guests and extend their enthusiasm to organising weekly entertainment (at the café/restaurant) for young and old during high season.

Two unisex sanitary blocks, maintained to a high standard and kept clean, include washbasins in cabins, a baby bath and provision for disabled visitors. Laundry facilities with washing machine and dryer. Motorhome services. Shop, bar and café/restaurant (all seasonal). Outdoor swimming pool (all season). Play area. Games room, TV. Half-court tennis. No charcoal barbecues. WiFi on the part of the site (charged).

Key Features

 Book Online

 Pets Accepted

 Disabled Facilities

 Beach Access

 Swimming Pool

 Play Area

 Bar/Restaurant

Scan me for more information.

Alan Rogers Code: FR64020
15 accommodations
36 pitches
GPS: 43.12140, -0.73232
Post Code: F-64570

Pyrénées-Atlantiques, Aquitaine

www.alanrogers.com/fr64020
atso64@hotmail.com
Tel: +33 5 59 34 12 21
www.camping-pyrenees.com

Open (Touring Pitches):
Start March - Mid October.

Camping Barétous-Pyrénées

Located on the edge of the Pyrenees, this quiet site is well away from the tourist bustle, particularly in the early or late season. Set in a rural location yet close to the town, its excellent position is ideal for exploring the region and offers a peaceful haven for those wishing to stay in quiet surroundings.

The shady grass pitches are attractive and of a good size with hedges. They offer both water and electricity (10A). The welcoming reception (limited English spoken) sells local produce and organic food. The heated swimming and paddling pool area is overlooked by a small sun terrace with a café/bar.

Two sanitary blocks, one old and one modern offer clean facilities with unisex toilets and showers. Facilities for disabled visitors. Laundry facilities. Small shop selling organic food. Café/bar with hot and cold meals. Swimming and paddling pools (heated July/Aug). Sauna and spa pool. Communal room with TV, games, library and drinks. Boules. Small play area with sandpit. WiFi (charged).

Key Features

 Book Online

 Pets Accepted

 Disabled Facilities

 Swimming Pool

 Play Area

 Bar/Restaurant

 Bike Hire

Scan me for more information.

Alan Rogers Code: FR24060
62 accommodations
134 pitches
GPS: 45.00207, 1.07110
Post Code: F-24290

Dordogne, Aquitaine

www.alanrogers.com/fr24060
le-paradis@perigord.com
Tel: +33 5 53 50 72 64
www.le-paradis-campsite.com

Open (Touring Pitches):
Start April - Late October.

Camping le Paradis

Le Paradis is an excellent, well-maintained riverside site, halfway between Les Eyzies and Montignac in the Valley of the Vézère. The site is landscaped with a variety of mature shrubs and trees. The gardens are beautiful, which gives a wonderful sense of tranquillity. It is very easy to relax on this ecologically friendly site. Systems of reed filters enhance the efficient natural drainage.

This is a family-run site, and you are guaranteed a warm and friendly welcome. There are around 200 good-sized pitches with 62 mobile homes to rent. The 134 touring pitches are level and with easy access, all with 10A Europlug, water and drainage.

Two sanitary blocks equipped with showers, private washing cubicles and facilities for babies. Laundrette: Washing machines, dryers and iron. Shop. Bar. Restaurant and Takeaway. Heated outdoor pools. Indoor pool with Spa, Sauna and Hammam. Playground area. Football field. Tennis court. Sports field. River access. Kids club, sports activities and entertainment programmes in July and August. Bicycle hire. Canoe trips. Fishing. WiFi: low-speed free, high-speed charged.

Key Features

 Book Online

 Pets Accepted

 Disabled Facilities

 Swimming Pool

 Play Area

 Bar/Restaurant

 Bike Hire

 Fishing

Scan me for more information.

Alan Rogers Code: FR47180
25 accommodations
55 pitches
GPS: 44.29216, 0.54035
Post Code: F-47360

Lot-et-Garonne, Aquitaine

www.alanrogers.com/fr47180
neguenou@dartybox.com
Tel: +33 5 53 95 00 67
www.lacdeneguenou.fr

Open (Touring Pitches):
Start April - Late October.

Camping du Lac de Néguenou

Lac de Néguenou is a quiet, 3-hectare family park in the Midi-Pyrénées, 18 km. from Agen, in a unique environment close to a lake. There are 55 level, shaded, grassy pitches for touring units, 14 with 6A electricity. Mobile homes occupy a further 25 pitches with wooden terraces.

On-site amenities include two swimming pools (open to the public) located near the snack bar, where visitors can buy drinks, ice cream and takeaway food. A welcome drink is provided, and there are themed dining evenings in high season. This site offers plenty for young and old, and there are regular competitions and evening entertainment in the season.

One small sanitary block with toilets, showers and washbasins. Children's facilities. Laundry. Motorhome services. Shop, bar, restaurant, takeaway (all high season). Swimming and paddling pools (high season; supervised in high season). Play area. Small farm for children. Gym equipment. Fishing. Boules. Trampoline. Bicycles, paddleboats, canoes and kayaks for hire. Barbecue area. Entertainment in high season. No gas or electric barbecues. Free WiFi on part of the site.

Key Features

 Book Online

 Pets Accepted

 Disabled Facilities

 Swimming Pool

 Play Area

 Bar/Restaurant

 Bike Hire

 Fishing

Scan me for more information.

Alan Rogers Code: FR32020
16 accommodations
73 pitches
GPS: 43.53230, 0.16670
Post Code: F-32230

Gers, Midi-Pyrénées

www.alanrogers.com/fr32020
info@camping-marciac.com
Tel: +33 5 62 08 21 19
www.camping-marciac.com

Open (Touring Pitches):
Early March - Early November.

Camping du Lac Marciac

Camping du Lac Marciac is a well-kept little site tucked away in the heart of the gorgeous Gers. Historic Tarbes lies around 60 km south, while the charming village of Marciac, a fortified bastide, is an easy walk for shops, restaurants and, notably, a world-famous annual jazz festival. There's great cycling and hiking, with an endless supply of unspoilt countryside on the doorstep, not to mention some of France's 'most beautiful villages' such as Fourcés and Larressingle. This is a great gastronomic region - don't miss the Madiran wines, Armagnacs, enviable menus and occasional wine and cheese tastings.

The well-shaded site has around 90 pitches, of which 73 are spacious touring pitches, 60 with electrical connections (6/10A, Europlug) and water. There are five with hardstanding for motorhomes, and an attractive natural terrace has 20 pitches without electricity for tents.

Key Features

 Book Online

 Pets Accepted

 Disabled Facilities

 Swimming Pool

 Play Area

 Bar/Restaurant

 Bike Hire

Sanitary block with washbasins in cubicles. Facilities for disabled visitors (two separate bathrooms with shower, WC and washbasin). Washing machine. Motorhome services. Small shop, bar, takeaway (all season). Bread is delivered daily (order at reception). Swimming pool (from mid-April). Table tennis. Pétanque. Swimming, fishing, and kayaking in the nearby lake (5 minutes walk). A small library and communal room. Play area. WiFi throughout (charged).

Scan me for more information.

Alan Rogers Code: FR65060
19 accommodations
47 pitches
GPS: 42.94152, -0.17726
Post Code: F-65400

Hautes-Pyrénées, Midi-Pyrénées

www.alanrogers.com/fr65060
info@camping-pyrenees-natura.com
Tel: +33 5 62 97 45 44
www.camping-pyrenees-natura.com

Open (Touring Pitches):
Mid May - Late September.

Camping Pyrénées Natura

Pyrénées Natura, at an altitude of 1,000 m. on the edge of the national park, is the perfect site for lovers of nature. The 66 pitches (47 for tourers), all with electricity (3-10A), are in a landscaped area with 75 varieties of trees and shrubs – but they do not spoil the fantastic views. A traditional-style building houses the reception, bar and indoor games/reading room.

There is a small, well-stocked shop in the former watermill. Prices are reasonable, and homemade bread can be purchased. There is a small beach on the river belonging to the site for supervised water play. Discover the countryside on foot, bicycle or mountain bike, including Pic du Midi, le cirque de Gavarnie, Pont d'Espagne, and not forgetting the Hautacam, Col de Tourmalet, Soulor, Aubisque.

Two sanitary blocks are equipped with showers, private washing cubicles and facilities for babies. Washing machines and dryers. Well-stocked shop. Bread and pastries are available every day. Snack bar and takeaway. Motorhome services. Bar and small shop (all season). Lounge, library, TV, upstairs games/reading room. Birdwatching is a speciality of the site, and equipment is available. Infrared sauna and jacuzzi. Play area for the very young. A small beach beside the river. Boules. Giant chess. Weekly evening meal in May, June and Sept. Wine tasting and barbecues (July-Aug). Riding and rafting can be booked on-site. Fishing. Internet access and WiFi (charged) or free in the bar.

Key Features

 Book Online

 Pets Accepted

 Disabled Facilities

 Play Area

 Bar/Restaurant

 Fishing

Scan me for more information.

Alan Rogers Code: FR82030
12 accommodations
97 pitches
GPS: 44.09644, 1.08862
Post Code: F-82200

Tarn-et-Garonne, Midi-Pyrénées

www.alanrogers.com/fr82030
camping-bidounet@moissac.fr
Tel: +33 5 63 32 52 52
www.camping-moissac.com

Open (Touring Pitches):
Start April - End September.

Camping du l'ile de Bidounet

Located on an island in the Tarn river, this rustic site has a rather unique location. Reception is at the entrance to an old watermill, and you reach the pitches by passing through a three-metre-high passageway through the building itself, then over a short, curved bridge onto the island.

There are 97 touring pitches, arranged in groups of three and most give views of the river. Others have views of the old buildings of Moissac on the river bank. A small pool complex is situated in the grass area before the pitches, and you can watch people sailing and fishing on the river.

Two toilet blocks in the traditional style are well-placed and should be adequate. Some washbasins in cubicles, modern showers. Facilities for babies and young children. Excellent unit for disabled visitors. Washing machines and dryer. Motorhome service point. Basic provisions from reception, bread delivery. Games room with small bar (high season). Swimming pool (seasonal). Boules. Bright play area. Organised activities for children (high season). No electric barbecues are permitted on pitches or communal areas. Fishing. WiFi room (free).

Key Features

 Book Online

 Pets Accepted

 Disabled Facilities

 Swimming Pool

 Play Area

 Bar/Restaurant

 Fishing

Scan me for more information.

Alan Rogers Code: FR31040
24 accommodations
35 pitches
GPS: 43.35558, 1.64828
Post Code: F-31560

Haute-Garonne, Midi-Pyrénées

www.alanrogers.com/fr31040
camping@thesauque.com
Tel: +33 5 61 81 34 67
www.campingthesauque.com

Open (Touring Pitches):
All year.

Camping du Lac de la Thésauque

Camping du Lac de la Thésauque sits pretty on the banks of a lake of the same name. It's also less than 50 kilometres from Toulouse and the Pyrénées Ariégeoises Natural Regional Park for when you want to sightsee in the city or the countryside.

Back at the campsite, there are many activities to enjoy on the lake. Exploring in a canoe might be the first option, or trying the floating inflatable obstacle course; you can also enjoy swimming, fishing, and pedal boats. When you've enjoyed the lake, you can relax at the campsite restaurant terrace with a drink or enjoy the outdoor pool. The rest of the park has been planned to facilitate family stays, with the brightly coloured playground and the miniature golf course.

Heated sanitary facilities, Beach showers, Disabled sanitary facilities, Restaurant, Bar, Snack Bar, shop (small), Outdoor swimming pool, Direct access to the lake, Kids club (high season), Mini Golf, Table tennis table, Jeu de boules alley(s), Kayaks, Pets allowed, WiFi.

Key Features

 Book Online

 Open All Year

 Pets Accepted

 Swimming Pool

 Play Area

 Bar/Restaurant

 Fishing

Scan me for more information.

Alan Rogers Code: FR81180
20 accommodations
54 pitches
GPS: 43.90889, 1.98278
Post Code: F-81600

Tarn, Midi-Pyrénées

www.alanrogers.com/fr81180
info@camping-lespommiers.com
Tel: +33 5 63 33 02 49
www.camping-lespommiers.com

Open (Touring Pitches):
Start April - End September.

Les Pommiers d'Aiguelèze

This pleasant site is located between Albi and Gaillac at the heart of the Tarn. Of the 74 pitches, 54 are reserved for touring, with the remainder for mobile homes. The pitches are of a good size and are located in a natural setting around the site. All are separated by hedges and have 13A electricity and water points nearby. There is a modern heated swimming pool.

The River Tarn is very close and has a marina where you can fish, canoe, or take boat trips to the nearby city of Albi. Albi is just 17 km. distant and richly merits a visit, with its riverside cafés and lovely gardens, as well as the vast 13th-century Gothic cathedral, the largest brick building in the world. Or you can wander through the warrens of cobbled streets and half-timbered shops, or visit Toulouse-Lautrec's childhood home, now an excellent museum.

Sanitary facilities include provision for disabled visitors. Small shop for basics. Bar. Fresh bread and croissants all season. Heated swimming pool with spa. Paddling pool. Trampolines. Ball games area. Pétanque. Play area. Bicycle hire. No charcoal barbecues. WiFi over site (charged).

Key Features

 Book Online

 Pets Accepted

 Disabled Facilities

 Swimming Pool

 Play Area

 Bar/Restaurant

 Bike Hire

Scan me for more information.

Alan Rogers Code: FR46645
22 accommodations
68 pitches
GPS: 44.65015, 1.43476
Post Code: F-46310

Lot, Midi-Pyrénées

www.alanrogers.com/fr46645
contact@lot-camping.com
Tel: +33 5 65 31 00 71
www.lot-camping.com

Open (Touring Pitches):
Mid April - End September.

Camping Moulin de Bel Air

On the banks of the river Céou, this campsite built around an 18th-century mill is the ideal starting point for discovering the Lot, the Dordogne valley and the many villages listed among the Most Beautiful Villages in France surrounding it.

A small site with 90 lovely grassy pitches, 68 for touring(16A). They are very spacious to keep your intimacy. You can choose shady, half-shady or sunny pitches depending on your preferences. These pitches are flat and grassy. On-site, you'll find two sanitation blocks with showers and WC, An outdoor swimming pool, bicycle hire and a children's playground. There is also a cosy indoor lounge and an outdoor terrace/restaurant where you can taste the owner's home cooking using the area's seasonal produce, which is famous for its gastronomy.

Two sanitation blocks with showers and WC, Water and toilet facilities for those with disabilities, Children's playground, Bar, Restaurant, Snack bar, Takeaway, Entertainment, Children's playground, Outdoor heating swimming pool, Table tennis table, Jeu de boules alley, Fishing on-site, Bicycle hire, Multi-sports field, Tennis court, Animal meadow, Crazy golf, WiFi, Pets allowed.

Key Features

 Book Online

 Pets Accepted

 Disabled Facilities

 Play Area

 Bar/Restaurant

 Bike Hire

 Fishing

Scan me for more information.

Alan Rogers Code: FR12380
2 accommodations
71 pitches
GPS: 44.51376, 2.81847
Post Code: F-12500

Aveyron, Midi-Pyrénées

www.alanrogers.com/fr12380
bellerive12@orange.fr
Tel: +33 5 65 44 05 85
camping-bellerive-aveyron.com

Open (Touring Pitches):
Start April - End September.

Camping Belle Rive

You are assured of a friendly welcome on this small, family-run campsite beside the River Lot, on the edge of a delightful medieval village. The region has many historic towns and villages with châteaux and ancient churches and is close to the Pilgrim route. The local produce, for example, Roquefort cheese, is well worth sampling.

The site is good for those seeking a tranquil spot with little in the way of on-site activities. There are 71 good-sized, grassy pitches delineated by various tall trees giving good shade on most pitches (6-10A electricity). Access to the site is unsuitable for large outfits due to the many small twisting roads. The village of Saint Côme-d'Olt is classified as one of the most beautiful villages in France. It has many 17th-century houses and a 16th-century church with its twisted spire, one of just 34 in France.

Two very clean, old-style toilet blocks with combined shower and washbasin cubicles. Washing machine. Facilities for disabled visitors. Small play area. Some family activities (high season). River bathing and fishing. Torches useful. Some English is spoken.

Key Features

 Book Online

 Pets Accepted

 Disabled Facilities

 Play Area

 Fishing

Scan me for more information.

Alan Rogers Code: FR12020
89 accommodations
225 pitches
GPS: 44.10123, 3.09560
Post Code: F-12100

Aveyron, Midi-Pyrénées

www.alanrogers.com/fr12020
info@yellohvillage-lesrivages.com
Tel: +33 5 65 61 01 07
www.yellohvillage-lesrivages.com

Open (Touring Pitches):
Mid April - Late September.

Caravaning les Rivages

Yelloh! Village Camping Caravaning les Rivages is a large, well established site on the outskirts of the town. It is well situated, being close to the high limestone Causses and the dramatic gorges of the Tarn and Dourbie. Smaller pitches, used for small units, abut a pleasant riverside space suitable for sunbathing, fishing and picnics.

Most of the 314 pitches are large and well-shaded. A choice of site packages is offered, with 'Privilège' being the largest at 130-150 sq.m. All pitches have electricity (10A), and 42 have water and drainage. The site offers a very wide range of sporting activities, close to 30 in all.

Four well-kept, modern toilet blocks have all the necessary facilities. Special block for children. Small shop (high season). Terrace, restaurant and bar overlooking heated swimming pool complex with paddling pool and spa (from the start of May). Play area. Entertainment, largely for children, child-minding, mini club. Impressive sports centre with tennis (indoor and outdoor), squash and badminton. Boules. River activities, walking, birdwatching, fishing. WiFi (free in the bar area).

Key Features

 Book Online

 Pets Accepted

 Disabled Facilities

 Swimming Pool

 Play Area

 Bar/Restaurant

 Fishing

Scan me for more information.

Alan Rogers Code: FR66810
20 accommodations
100 pitches
GPS: 42.61723, 2.50097
Post Code: F-66320

Pyrénées-Orientales,
Languedoc-Roussillon

www.alanrogers.com/fr66810
campinglecanigou@gmail.com
Tel: +33 4 68 05 85 40
www.camping-canigou.com

Open (Touring Pitches):
End April - End September.

Camping le Canigou

Mount Canigou dominates much of the department of Pyrénées Orientales and reaches a height of 2,784m. Canigou Camping can be found in the foothills of this magnificent mountain. Heading southeast from here, you will find Mediterranean landscapes, vines and olive trees on beautiful hillsides. The mountain region, however, is a complete contrast, much more rugged and richly wooded, and where you can find exceptional flora and fauna.

The site is divided by the river La Lentillà. There are 100 touring pitches and a small number of chalets for 4 or 6 people (available to rent). On-site amenities include a bar/restaurant with a large shady terrace, which becomes the focal point for entertainment in high season.

The sanitary facilities are kept clean and include free hot showers and disabled facilities. Laundry facilities. Bar/restaurant. Takeaway. River swimming. Fishing. Volleyball. Adventure park. Table tennis table, Multi-sports field, Play area. Activities and entertainment. Games Room, Chalets to rent. WiFi (free). Pets allowed.

Key Features

 Book Online

 Pets Accepted

 Disabled Facilities

 Play Area

 Bar/Restaurant

 Fishing

Scan me for more information.

Alan Rogers Code: FR66030
270 accommodations
378 pitches
GPS: 42.59939, 3.03761
Post Code: F-66750

Pyrénées-Orientales,
Languedoc-Roussillon

www.alanrogers.com/fr66030
camping.calagogo@wanadoo.fr
Tel: +33 4 68 21 07 12
www.camping-le-calagogo.fr

Open (Touring Pitches):
Late April - End September.

Camping Cala Gogo

This is an excellent, well-organised site in Catalan country with direct access to the sandy beach and warm waters of the Med. In addition, the site has an impressive pool complex, attractively laid out with palm trees and sunbathing areas. The large bar complex overlooking the pool area becomes very busy in the high season, with entertainment on some evenings. This is a vibrant family site, offering sun, sea and sand and a vibrant holiday atmosphere for all ages.

There are around 650 pitches in total, with 378 good sized, level pitches for touring, all with electrical connection (6/10A) and some shade. Twenty fully serviced pitches are available. There's no shortage of things to do on-site but a day trip to Spain is an easy option, and the bustling resort of Argelès-Sur-Mer is close by, as is the historic city of Perpignan.

Fully equipped toilet blocks with some Turkish-style WCs. Motorhome services. Good supermarket and a small shopping mall. Sophisticated restaurant. Self-service restaurant. Takeaway. Bar. Small beach bar. Fridge hire. Disco. TV. Three swimming pools (heated) plus one for children, water jets, jacuzzi, and waterfall. Play area. Tennis. Fishing. Diving club. Bicycle hire. Events, sports and entertainment are organised in season. Boat launching. Torches useful. WiFi throughout (charged). Only gas or electric barbecues are allowed.

Key Features

 Book Online

 Pets Accepted

 Beach Access

 Swimming Pool

 Play Area

 Bar/Restaurant

 Bike Hire

 Fishing

Scan me for more information.

Alan Rogers Code: FR66050
34 accommodations
100 pitches
GPS: 42.57581, 2.96481
Post Code: F-66690

Pyrénées-Orientales,
Languedoc-Roussillon

www.alanrogers.com/fr66050
contact@camping-le-haras.com
Tel: +33 4 68 22 14 50
www.camping-le-haras.com

Open (Touring Pitches):
Start April - End September.

Camping Le Haras

Situated in the mature grounds of an old hunting lodge, later an arboretum, le Haras is a rather special site. Well managed and well kept, with plenty of lush vegetation, it is tucked away in this corner of Languedoc-Roussillon, barely 10 km from the coastal resorts of Saint-Cyprien and Argelès-Sur-Mer and offers wonderful views of the snow-capped Pyrenees. The village centre is just a few minutes walk and is famed for traditional glass making, featured on the site. It's a comfortable site popular with British visitors wishing to explore the beautiful Catalan coast and highlights like Banyuls and Collioure, perhaps hopping over the border to Spain (20 km away).

Around 130 pitches are in bays of four arranged amidst a wide variety of trees and shrubs that provide colour and shade for 100 touring units and some 34 mobile homes (16 to rent). All the touring pitches have 10A electricity, and 29 are fully serviced. Some of the access roads are narrow. Rail noise is possible, although large trees screen the line.

Key Features

 Book Online

 Pets Accepted

 Disabled Facilities

 Beach Access

 Swimming Pool

 Play Area

 Bar/Restaurant

 Skiing

Toilet blocks with facilities for disabled visitors. Washing machines. Motorhome services. Fridge hire. Bar, restaurant and takeaway. Swimming and paddling pools (high season). Theme evenings (high season). Riding nearby. Play area. No charcoal barbecues. Max. 1 dog. WiFi throughout (1 hour per day free).

 Scan me for more information.

Alan Rogers Code: FR66070
262 accommodations
699 pitches
GPS: 42.70830, 3.03552
Post Code: F-66141

Pyrénées-Orientales,
Languedoc-Roussillon

www.alanrogers.com/fr66070
info@lebrasilia.fr
Tel: +33 4 68 80 23 82
www.brasilia.fr

Open (Touring Pitches):
Mid April - Early October.

Yelloh! Village Le Brasilia

Situated across the yacht harbour from the resort of Canet-Plage, le Brasilia is an impressive, well-managed family site directly beside the beach. There's much to praise here, from the state-of-the-art reception to the sensational water park, excellent spa and park-like grounds. Although large, it is attractive and well kept with a remarkable range of facilities – with good reason it's always a popular choice.

The 699 touring pitches are neatly hedged, most with electricity (6-10A) and 408 with water and drainage. They vary in size from 80 to 120 sq.m. with some of the longer pitches suitable for two families together. There is decent shade from pines and flowering shrubs, with less on pitches near the beach. A member of Yelloh! Village and the prestigious Leading Campings group.

Nine modern sanitary blocks with British-style WCs and washbasins in cabins. Good facilities for children and for disabled campers. Laundry room. Motorhome services. Range of shops. Gas supplies. Bars and restaurant. Pool complex (heated). Wellness centre including jacuzzi, massage and beauty rooms. Play areas. Sports field. Tennis. Sporting activities. Library, games and video room. Hairdresser. Internet café and WiFi. Daily entertainment programme. Bicycle hire. Fishing. Post office. Weather forecasts. No charcoal barbecues. Free WiFi in the bar.

Key Features

 Book Online

 Pets Accepted

 Disabled Facilities

 Beach Access

 Swimming Pool

 Play Area

 Bar/Restaurant

 Bike Hire

Scan me for
more information.

169

Alan Rogers Code: FR11060
115 accommodations
102 pitches
GPS: 43.12714, 2.25953
Post Code: F-11250

Aude, Languedoc-Roussillon

www.alanrogers.com/fr11060
info@yellohvillage-domaine-arnauteille.com
Tel: +33 4 68 26 84 53
www.yellohvillage-domaine-arnauteille.com

Open (Touring Pitches):
Mid April - Mid September.

Domaine d'Arnauteille

With beautiful panoramas across the Corbières massif and the Pyrenees beyond, Yelloh! Village Domaine d'Arnauteille is a rural site that is ideal for exploring the ancient Aude département and visiting the stunning walled city of Carcassonne (17 km). This is a great spot for those seeking walking and cycling amidst glorious scenery and a chance to explore the charming hilltop villages. Lovers of gastronomy will not be disappointed.

Some pitches are on gently sloping, lightly wooded ground; others are more open. All are of good size, with water, drainage and electricity (10A), semi-terraced and partly hedged. Some even come with views over Montclar village. In the style of a Roman amphitheatre, the swimming pool complex is set in a hollow basin surrounded by fine views. Access, although much improved, could be difficult for large, twin-axle caravans.

Three toilet blocks, two with a Roman theme, are fully equipped with some en-suite provision. Laundry facilities for disabled visitors, children and babies. Motorhome services. Small shop (from mid-May). Bar and restaurant in the converted stable block and takeaway (from mid-May). Swimming pool (from mid-May), two toboggans, paddling pool, river with water massage and sunbathing terrace. Multisports court. Boules. Play area. Riding (July/Aug). Day trips. Library, games room, TV. WiFi (charged). Gas barbecues only.

Key Features

 Book Online

 Pets Accepted

 Disabled Facilities

 Swimming Pool

 Play Area

 Bar/Restaurant

 Horse Riding

Scan me for more information.

Alan Rogers Code: FR34070
650 accommodations
1026 pitches
GPS: 43.26340, 3.32000
Post Code: F-34410

Hérault, Languedoc-Roussillon

www.alanrogers.com/fr34070
info@leserignanplage.com
Tel: +33 4 67 32 35 33
www.leserignanplage.com

Open (Touring Pitches):
Late April - Early October.

Le Sérignan-Plage

Yelloh! Village le Sérignan-Plage is a lively and vibrant Mediterranean site with direct access to a superb 600-metre sandy beach (including a naturist section). There's an impressive aqua park, a huge spa centre with lavish balnéotherapy pools, and all kinds of activities designed with youngsters in mind. This is a family-friendly site, and the bustling resort of Valras-Plage is close by.

There are over 1,000 pitches for touring units, all fairly level, on sandy soil and with 10A electricity. Most are well delimited by hedging and have moderate shade. Take bikes, explore the country lanes and local vineyards, visit historic Béziers or, further afield, head to the Camargue for a fascinating day out.

Seven modern sanitary blocks with facilities for guests with reduced mobility. Baby bathroom. Laundry. Motorhome services. Supermarket, bakery and newsagent. Other shops (high season). ATM. Restaurants, bars and takeaway. Hairdresser. Balnéo spa (afternoons). Gym. Indoor heated pool. Outdoor pools, water playground and waterslides (all season). Tennis. Yoga. Multisport courts. Playgrounds. Trampolines. Children's clubs. Evening entertainment. Sporting activities. Bike rental. Bus to Sérignan village (Jul/Aug). Beach (lifeguards high season). Canoeing, water sports, adventure park nearby. WiFi (charged). Gas barbecues only.

Key Features

 Pets Accepted

 Disabled Facilities

 Beach Access

 Swimming Pool

 Play Area

 Bar/Restaurant

 Bike Hire

Scan me for more information.

Alan Rogers Code: FR34440
132 accommodations
115 pitches
GPS: 43.44970, 3.80603
Post Code: F-34110

Hérault, Languedoc-Roussillon

www.alanrogers.com/fr34440
tamaris@sandaya.fr
Tel: +33 4 67 43 44 77
www.sandaya.co.uk/our-campsites/
les-tamaris

Open (Touring Pitches):
Early April - Late September.

Camping Les Tamaris

Camping Sandaya Les Tamaris is a super site that is unusually situated on a strip of land that separates the sea from the étang, or inland lake and therefore Frontignan-Ville from Frontignan-Plage. We were lucky enough to see flamingos when we visited.

The design of the site is unusual, which adds to its attractiveness. The pitches are laid out in hexagons divided by tall hedging and colourful shrubs. In total, there are about 250 pitches, with 132 taken by mobile homes, which are let by the site. All are 'grand confort' with 10A electricity, water, wastewater, and on level sandy grass. Direct access to the sandy beach is possible via three gates.

Three modern and colourful toilet blocks with some en-suite showers and washbasins. Excellent facilities for children. Unit for disabled visitors. Motorhome services. Shop, bar, restaurant, takeaway, swimming pool (all season). Hairdresser. Gym. Play area. Miniclub. Archery. Bicycle hire. Fishing. Internet access in reception and WiFi throughout (free). Entertainment for all ages. Charcoal barbecues only.

Key Features

 Book Online

 Pets Accepted

 Disabled Facilities

 Beach Access

 Swimming Pool

 Play Area

 Bar/Restaurant

 Bike Hire

Scan me for more information.

Alan Rogers Code: FR30290
82 accommodations
120 pitches
GPS: 43.76579, 4.09743
Post Code: F-30250

Gard, Languedoc-Roussillon

www.alanrogers.com/fr30290
camping@massereau.com
Tel: +33 4 66 53 11 20
www.massereau.com

Open (Touring Pitches):
Mid April - Early October.

Domaine de Massereau

Two brothers, a wine producer and a hotelier opened Domaine de Massereau in August 2006. It is set within a 50-hectare vineyard dating back to 1804, and the idea was to promote their wine, so tours are arranged, and they now produce their own olive oil as well.

There are 202 pitches, 120 available for touring units, all with electricity (86 with 16A electricity, water and drainage). Pitch sizes range from 90-300 sq.m., and some are equipped with a premium option, including a fridge, a plancha, a wooden storage box, deckchairs, a picnic table and unlimited wifi access. The area is lightly wooded, and most pitches are hedged with flowering shrubs. The other pitches are used for chalets, cottages, cabins and mobile homes to rent.

Two modern toilet block incorporates excellent facilities for children and disabled visitors. Laundry area. Motorhome services. Grocery. Restaurant, bar, snacks and pizzeria. Aquatic Park with heated swimming pool with removable dome and slide. Balneotherapy Pool, Aquatic Playground, Solarium, Jacuzzi, Sauna, Steam Bath and massage. Play area with trampoline, mini golf, tennis court, Multisport field, and pétanque. Bicycle hire. Gas barbecue and fridge hire. Free WiFi (partial site)

Key Features

 Book Online

 Pets Accepted

 Disabled Facilities

 Beach Access

 Swimming Pool

 Play Area

 Bar/Restaurant

 Bike Hire

Scan me for more information.

Alan Rogers Code: FR84230
37 accommodations
73 pitches
GPS: 43.86623, 5.41317
Post Code: F-84400

Vaucluse, Provence

www.alanrogers.com/fr84230
contact@campingleluberon.com
Tel: +33 4 90 04 85 40
www.campingleluberon.com

Open (Touring Pitches):
End March - End September.

Camping le Luberon

Camping le Luberon is a friendly, family-run site on a hillside overlooking the historical city of Apt. The well-shaded pitches are laid out in natural clearings in woodland with various mature trees and flowering shrubs. There are 110 pitches, with 73 for touring and 65 with 6A electricity. They vary in size (70-120 sq.m), most are on hard ground with some grass, and rock pegs are advised.

The site is ideal for exploring picturesque Provence with its many attractive villages. Access could be difficult for large outfits, and twin-axle caravans are not accepted. Amenities include three small swimming pools, one for children.

One heated toilet block at one side of the touring area has four showers, a baby room and facilities for disabled visitors. A second block accessed by steps has WCs and showers in cabins. No shop, but baker calls daily. Bar with TV. Snack bar (July/Aug). Swimming pools (one heated, main season). Play area for young children. Activity and entertainment programme (July/Aug). WiFi over part of the site (charged).

Key Features

 Book Online

 Pets Accepted

 Disabled Facilities

 Swimming Pool

 Play Area

 Bar/Restaurant

Scan me for
more information.

Alan Rogers Code: FR05480
28 accommodations
42 pitches
GPS: 44.39540, 5.46103
Post Code: F-05150

Hautes-Alpes, Provence

www.alanrogers.com/fr05480
contact@camping-hautsderosans.com
Tel: +49 2 66 61 55
www.camping-hautsderosans.com

Open (Touring Pitches):
Mid April - Early October.

Camping les Hauts de Rosans

Camping Les Hauts de Rosans is located on the border between the Southern Alps and the Drôme Provençale. Ideally located in the middle of the mountains, at an altitude of 700 metres, the campsite offers a panoramic view of the surrounding countryside. If you can drag yourself away from the views from the campsite swimming pool, camping at Les Hauts de Rosans does have other facilities available for guests. A sports field and playground for kids to let off steam, and there's a games room/library where you can find a pool table and table football. An entertainment programme is held during high season, offering archery, pétanque tournaments and crafts workshops.

In the evenings, themed nights are organised; join a moonlight swim or have a dance to live entertainment. A small shop on site sells various bits of local produce, including sausages and honey, you can pick up other foodie needs in the village of Rosans, a five-minute drive or 20-minute walk away.

Two heated toilet blocks at opposite ends of the site with children's facilities, Bar, Snack bar, Takeaway Pizza (high season) Shop (small), Outdoor swimming pool, Children's playground, Games room, Bicycle hire, Table tennis, Table football, Pétanque, Archery, multisport pitch, Entertainment (high season), WiFi, Pets allowed.

Key Features

- Book Online
- Pets Accepted
- Swimming Pool
- Play Area
- Bar/Restaurant
- Bike Hire

Scan me for more information.

175

Alan Rogers Code: FR05440
40 accommodations
134 pitches
GPS: 44.84415, 6.49008
Post Code: F-05290

Hautes-Alpes, Provence

www.alanrogers.com/fr05440
vallouise@huttopia.com
Tel: +33 4 92 23 30 26
europe.huttopia.com/en/site/vallouise

Open (Touring Pitches):
Mid May - Early November.

Huttopia Vallouise

This former municipal site is a recent addition to the Huttopia group of campsites and is located close to the pretty village of Vallouise, deep in the Hautes-Alpes. The site extends over 6.5 hectares and enjoys some magnificent views of the surrounding mountain scenery. There are 134 touring pitches here, bordered by two glacier streams. Most have 10A electricity. Several fully equipped safari-style tents and chalets are available to rent.

The site lies at the foot of the vast Ecrins National Park and is an ideal base for many adventure sports, including paragliding, rock climbing and mountain biking. The GR54 long-distance footpath passes through Vallouise, and there are many other excellent paths close at hand, including routes to the hamlet of Puy Aillaud or to Le Monetier, passing the Lac de l'Eychauda.

Two excellent sanitary blocks (one heated) are well maintained and include facilities for babies and disabled visitors. Shop. Snack bar (July/Aug). Heated outdoor swimming pool. Play area. Boules. Tennis. Volleyball. TV room. Activity programme (July/Aug). Fully equipped tents and chalets to rent. WiFi over part of site (free).

Key Features

 Book Online

 Pets Accepted

 Disabled Facilities

 Swimming Pool

 Play Area

Bar/Restaurant

Scan me for more information.

Alan Rogers Code: FR83050
275 accommodations
188 pitches
GPS: 43.40905, 6.70893
Post Code: F-83370

Var, Côte d'Azur

www.alanrogers.com/fr83050
rivieradazur@sandaya.fr
Tel: +33 4 94 81 01 59
www.sandaya.co.uk/our-campsites/
riviera-d-azur

Open (Touring Pitches):
Early April - Early November.

Camping Rivièra d'Azur

Camping Sandaya Rivièra d'Azur is an excellent site near the Côte d'Azur that will take you away from the Mediterranean coast's bustle. Spread out over ten hectares, this is a well-equipped holiday destination with pitches arranged along avenues. The 188 touring pitches average 100 sq.m. in size, and all have electricity connections and, unusually, private sanitary facilities (although washbasins double as dishwashing sinks). There are 340 accommodation units for rent, most of which were installed after ongoing investment by the owners. There is a free shuttle to the beach at Saint Aygulf.

A shady terrace surrounds the bar/restaurant, whilst friendly staff provide excellent service. A pleasant pool complex is available for those wishing to stay on-site instead of swimming from the Mediterranean beaches. Saint Aygulf is 2.5 km. away, the nearest beach is 4 km. Activities are organised daily on the site during the summer season.

Private toilet blocks include a washbasin, shower and WC. Laundry area with washing machines. Very well-stocked supermarket. Bar/restaurant with evening entertainment. Takeaway (all open all season). Large swimming pool complex with four water slides (all season). Two tennis courts. Sports area. Minigolf. Boules. Fishing. Bicycle hire. Kindergarten and Kid's Club. Play area. Nightclub (July/Aug). WiFi over site (charged). Only gas or electric barbecues are permitted.

Key Features

 Book Online

 Pets Accepted

 Disabled Facilities

 Beach Access

 Swimming Pool

 Play Area

 Bar/Restaurant

 Bike Hire

Scan me for more information.

Alan Rogers Code: FR20260
35 accommodations
70 pitches
GPS: 42.16250, 8.59792
Post Code: F-20130

Corse-du-Sud, Corsica

www.alanrogers.com/fr20260
contact@camping-torraccia.com
Tel: +33 4 95 26 42 39
www.camping-torraccia.com

Open (Touring Pitches):
Mid April - End September.

Camping Torraccia

On Corsica's west coast, Torraccia is a small, peaceful site set back from the sea but within easy reach of two sandy beaches (5 minutes drive). There are wonderful panoramic views down to Chiuni beach and the neighbouring valley, as well as the soaring mountain peaks of the interior. This is a pleasantly relaxed place to retreat after a day at the beach or an excursion up the hills. The site caters for around 70 touring pitches, most on grass and with decent shade, and also offers accommodation to rent in the form of bungalows and camping pods.

This is excellent walking country, and there are any number of wonderful trails to follow, perhaps through the Aïtone forest or around the lakes of Creno (43 km) or Nino (63 km). The site owners can suggest suitable routes for your needs. The nearest town, Cargese, is well worth visiting and is typical of Corsica's dramatic west coast. Porto (26 km) is a UNESCO site of special interest, while the ancient city of Ajaccio lies around an hour's drive away.

The toilet block provides the usual facilities, including an area for babies. Washing machine. Snack bar/bar. Takeaway. Small shop. Swimming pool with water slide. Play area. Table tennis. Organised entertainment and children's club activities (high season). Accommodation to rent. WiFi (chargeable). Boat trips nearby.

Key Features

 Book Online

 Pets Accepted

 Beach Access

 Swimming Pool

 Play Area

 Bar/Restaurant

Scan me for more information.

Alan Rogers Code: FR20162
260 accommodations
GPS: 42.48497, 9.45425
Post Code: F-20215

Haute-Corse, Corsica

www.alanrogers.com/fr20162
vacances@sandaya.fr
Tel: +33 4 11 32 90 00
www.sandaya.fr/nos-campings/
cap-sud

Open (Touring Pitches):
Early May - Late September.

Camping Cap Sud

Camping Sandaya Cap Sud is located by the sea and surrounded by eucalyptus and juniper trees in the 100% pedestrianised Cap Sud holiday village.

With over 260 rental Accommodation units to rent, you can enjoy many activities whilst holidaying here. Free children's clubs, a restaurant with a roof terrace overlooking the Mediterranean sea, and an aquatic spa area for deep relaxation: everything is done to make your vacation unforgettable. Touring vehicles are not accepted at this mobile home only site.

Sanitary blocks provide good quality facilities, including Children's facilities and facilites for disabled visitors. Motorhome services. Shop, restaurant and bar, Pool complex with large pools (one heated), paddling pool with games. Bicycle hire. Children's Play area. Games room, WiFi throughout (charged). Entertainment (high season).

Key Features

 Book Online

 Pets Accepted

 Disabled Facilities

 Beach Access

 Swimming Pool

 Play Area

 Bar/Restaurant

 Bike Hire

Scan me for more information.

Capital Berlin
Currency Euro (€)
Language German
Time Zone CET (GMT+1)
Telephone Code +49

Shops 9.30am to 8pm weekdays and Sat. All stores including supermarkets close on Sun.

Money ATMs are widespread in towns and cities and usually accessible 24 hours a day. Some have multilingual instructions. Germany is still largely cash-based, don't expect everywhere to accept cards. Amex less widely accepted.

Travelling with Children Very children-friendly with a variety of attractions. Public transport is usually half price for children. Most attractions will let under 18s in for free. Many restaurants offer a kids menu, but children are also expected to behave.

Public Holidays 1 Jan New Year's Day; Mar/Apr Good Friday; Mar/Apr Easter Monday; 1 May Labour Day; May Ascension; May/Jun Whit Monday; 3 Oct Day of German Unity; 25 Dec Christmas Day; 26 Dec Boxing Day.

LEZ Low Emissions Zones in most major cities. Registration required.

● **EU Member** | ● **Schengen Area**

Tourism website germany.travel

●●●●● **Accessible Travel Score**

One of the best-equipped countries in Europe. Access and assistance for wheelchair users and those who are less able is widespread, largely standardised and of good quality.

Driving in Germany The country's network of toll-free and well-maintained autobahns is among the best in the world. Drink-driving, using your mobile whilst driving and sat navs that warn you of speed cameras are illegal. You should overtake trams on the right unless there is not sufficient space. Camper vans and cars with caravans are not allowed to exceed 18.75 metres in length, 4 metres in height and 2.55 metres in width.

 Dashcams are legal

 Speed camera detectors are **illegal**

Germany

View all campsites in Germany
alanrogers.com/germany

See campsite map page 479

Climate Winters are colder and summers a little warmer than in the UK.

Emergency services Call 112 for the police, ambulance and fire and rescue.

Units Germany uses the metric system. To convert km to miles, multiply by 0.6.

With its wealth of scenic, historical and cultural interests, Germany is a land of contrasts. From the flatlands of the north to the wooded mountains in the south, with forests in the east and west, regional characteristics are a strong feature of German life and present a rich variety of folklore and customs.

Each region has its own unique identity. Home of lederhosen, beer and sausages is Bavaria in the south, with small towns, medieval castles and Baroque churches. It is also home to the fairytale 19th-century Romanesque Revival castle of Neuschwanstein. In the southwest, Baden Württemberg is famous for its ancient Black Forest and its spas and boasts the most hours of sunshine. Further west is the stunningly beautiful Rhine Valley, where the river winds through steep hills dotted with castles, ruins and vineyards.

Eastern Germany is studded with lakes and rivers and undulating lowlands that give way to mountains. The north has busy cities such as Bremen and Hamburg as well as traditional North Sea family resorts. The capital city of Berlin, situated in the northeast of the country and once divided by the Berlin Wall, is an increasingly popular tourist destination, with its blend of old and modern architecture, zoos and aquariums, museums, art galleries, green spaces and lively nightlife.

Scan QR code to browse more campsites on our website

Alan Rogers Code: DE29620
380 accommodations
850 pitches
GPS: 53.69598, 7.69055
Post Code: D-26427

Neuharlingersiel, Lower Saxony

www.alanrogers.com/de29620
camping@neuharlingersiel.de
Tel: +49 49 74 18 89 00
www.neuharlingersiel.de/nordsee-
camping

Open (Touring Pitches):
All year.

Campingplatz Neuharlingersiel

Camping Neuherlingersiel is a very large campsite in Lower Saxony on the outskirts of Neuharlingersiel, a fishing village which lies on the shores of the UNESCO World Heritage Wadden Sea. Of the 1,200 small to medium size, level, grassy, undelineated pitches, 850 are for touring. Most of the touring pitches are laid out in rows amongst the statics but a few are set aside for motorhomes and tents. Metered electricity is available and some pitches are fully serviced. There are very few trees or shrubs to give shade and privacy and pitches may be a long way from the beach and site amenities.

The site is separated from the unseen sea by a tall dike which gives the site some protection in inclement weather and, from the top of the dyke, there are magnificent views over the North and Wadden Seas. Neuharlingersiel is a real fishermen's village where not much has changed over the last few hundred years. You can enjoy its many restaurants, bars and cafés, all within walking distance of the site. There are overnight pitches for motorhomes just outside the barrier.

Key Features

 Open All Year

 Disabled Facilities

 Beach Access

Sanitary facilities with hot showers. Baby changing room. Wellness & beauty treatments. Indoor pool. Paddling pool. Beach adjacent. Play area. Sauna. Shop. Snack bar, takeaway. Laundry. WiFi (chargeable). Children's activities (High season). Bar nearby. Riding, bike hire nearby.

Scan me for more information.

Alan Rogers Code: DE25040
115 accommodations
60 pitches
GPS: 54.41145, 10.18433
Post Code: D-24159

Kiel Friedrichsort, Schleswig-Holstein

www.alanrogers.com/de25040
campingplatzkiel@gmail.com
Tel: +49 43 13 92 078
www.campingkiel.de

Open (Touring Pitches):
Start April - End October.

Camping Kiel-Falckenstein

Camping Kiel Falckenstein is located in the middle of a protected landscape. From the terrace you have a wonderful view of the Kiel Fjord where you can watch the boats heading up and down the fjord between Oslo and Gothenburg, including the majestic tall ships in full sail. On one area of the site is a meadow set aside for tents and divided by hedges. In another area there are pitches for caravans and motorhomes. The site has a total of 175 pitches, 60 for touring units.

There are shops and eateries in Kiel-Friedrichsort, about 4 km away, or in Kiel-Schilksee noted for its sandy beaches and sailing heritage. You can reach the city centre either by bus (walk about 15 minutes to the stop) or by boat (walk to the next pier about 15 minutes, but don't forget to bring a bicycle as there are excellent bike trails).

There are two toilet blocks with showers, washbasins and WCs. Facility for visitors who are disabled. Baby room. Laundry with washing machine and dryer. Chemical toilet point. Dishwashing area. Children's play area. Games room. TV room. Communal barbecue area and fire pit. Security barrier. Restaurant (High season). Microwave. Freezer for ice packs. Takeaway. Twin axle caravans allowed. Earliest arrival time 15.00.

Key Features

 Pets Accepted

 Disabled Facilities

 Play Area

Scan me for more information.

Alan Rogers Code: DE38230
110 pitches
GPS: 54.28166, 12.31259
Post Code: D-18347

Ostseebad Dierhagen -
Neuhaus, Mecklenburg-West
Pomerania

www.alanrogers.com/de38230
rezeption@camping-neuhaus.de
Tel: +49 38 22 65 39 930
www.camping-neuhaus.de

Open (Touring Pitches):
Early April - Early October.

Camping in Neuhaus

This small, family campsite is located at the gateway to the Fischland-Darß-Zingst peninsula, directly behind the sheltering dunes of the Baltic Sea. Set back from the shore, and surrounded on all sides by woodland, it's just a stone's throw from the long strip of sandy beach that makes it such a desirable location. It's so easy for youngsters to spend a day here, happily playing in the sand and splashing in the clean waters before strolling back to base.

This is a simple, well maintained campsite in a charming landscape, with plenty of birdlife finding refuge amongst the rolling dunes and tranquil marshes of the hinterland. Take time to explore the unspoilt scenery and the quiet country lanes for cycling and walking. It's a pleasantly rural atmosphere, with flat, grassy pitches dotted with trees and hedging that add interest and shade. There are 110 touring pitches and 50 permanent ones are available all with electric hook ups.

The facilities of the campsite include modern, clean sanitary block with baby changing room, along with a snack bar offering simple meals, ice creams and drinks. Restaurants available in the nearby villages (1-3 km). Children's playground. Laundry. Dogs allowed. WiFi.

Key Features

 Pets Accepted

 Beach Access

 Play Area

 Bar/Restaurant

Scan me for more information.

Alan Rogers Code: DE37690
5 accommodations
150 pitches
GPS: 54.04663, 14.01106
Post Code: D-17459

Koserow, Mecklenburg-West Pomerania

www.alanrogers.com/de37690
camping@amsandfeld.de
Tel: +49 38 37 52 07 59
www.amsandfeld.de

Open (Touring Pitches):
Mid April - End September.

Camping Am Sandfeld

This small, friendly family-run campsite is tucked away among sheltering woodland, just 700 metres from the Baltic Sea (15 minutes walk). Here the long white sand beach extends for 400 km and is the obvious main appeal of this delightful location. Camping Am Sandfeld is located on the outskirts of Koserow, close to the island's highest point. The town centre is only a 15-minute walk away and has useful shops and amenities, while the pier here is attractive and a popular spot for watching the wonderful sunsets.

The Achterwasser lagoon, with its little harbour, is about 1.4km, or a 15-minute walk, and there are many opportunities for hiking, swimming or cycling. The site has 150 grass touring pitches (some seasonal) with a 16 amp hook-up point. All are flat and grassy, some open and sunny, others having shade from the various trees dotted around the site.

There are two toilet blocks one of which is heated. Family bathrooms with shower and toilet. Disabled facilities. Laundry. Dish washing area. TV room. Shop. Games room. Children's play area. Book rental and exchange. Board games. Bread to order. Pizzeria. Security barrier. Dogs allowed. BBQ's allowed. Twin axle caravans allowed. WiFi. Bike hire including electric bikes. Table tennis. Earliest arrival time 13.00.

Key Features

 Pets Accepted

 Disabled Facilities

 Beach Access

 Play Area

 Bike Hire

Scan me for more information.

Alan Rogers Code: DE29400
50 accommodations
600 pitches
GPS: 52.51394, 6.86164
Post Code: D-49849

Wilsum, Lower Saxony

www.alanrogers.com/de29400
info@wilsumerberge.de
Tel: +49 59 45 99 55 80
www.wilsumerberge.nl

Open (Touring Pitches):
Early April - End October.

Camping Wilsumer Berge

This is a very large site close to the Dutch border and based around a lake, with a sandy beach area where youngsters like to swim and splash in the shallows. The campsite is set within a nature reserve, surrounded by forest and open heathland, providing a haven for wildlife.

The site has 1,000 good-sized pitches (120 sq.m), of which over half are for touring in a separate area. They are large, level and arranged in various ways, with some in secluded areas, some with hedge separation, others in open areas and in places shaded, on sandy grass with electricity (6/16A Europlug). Some 150 have fresh and waste water connections, and a designated area for groups of tents is located away from other pitches.

This site has good modern facilities, and the lake, the centrepiece of the site with its 60-metre waterslide and bridge, has separate areas for swimmers and non-swimmers.

Very good sanitary facilities. Washing machines and dryers. Shop. Restaurant, snacks and takeaway. Beach café with open-air terrace. Several playgrounds. Children's theatre. Lake swimming. Fishing pond. Volleyball. Beach volleyball. Multisports court. Basketball. Boules. Bicycle hire. WiFi throughout (charged).

Key Features

 Book Online

 Pets Accepted

 Disabled Facilities

 Swimming Pool

 Play Area

 Bar/Restaurant

 Bike Hire

 Fishing

Scan me for more information.

Alan Rogers Code: DE28815
50 pitches
GPS: 52.52187, 8.36528
Post Code: D-49459

Lembruch, Lower Saxony

www.alanrogers.com/de28815
info@tiemanns-hof.de
Tel: +49 54 47 92 13 39
www.tiemanns-hof.de

Open (Touring Pitches):
All Year.

Campingplatz Tiemanns Hof

This campsite, open all year round, is set on the edge of Lake Dümmer, just 5 minutes from the little town of Lembruch and in a pleasant rural area. There's a sandy beach and various water sports on offer, including fishing, sailing, surfing and canoeing. There is also boat rental on site. In winter, the Dümmer See is transformed into a snowy winter landscape, and locals skate and play ice hockey on the frozen lake.

The campsite welcomes pets and provides a guide to local trails and dog walks, and there are plenty of quiet country lanes to walk and cycle along. DümmerWeserLand is popular with equestrian fans for its 300 km network of bridle paths through the heathland and surrounding countryside.

There are 50 touring pitches for long and short-term camping. The pitches are level, grassy and open but well-demarcated with hedging. Various long paths are suited to guests with mobility issues. You will find everything you need with a snack bar, shop and restaurant.

Modern sanitary facilities with disabled facilities. BBQ. Boules court. Beach volleyball. Boat hire. Approx. 200m to the beach and the Strandlust restaurant. Shops approx. 300m away. Dishwashing. Pets allowed. WiFi.

Key Features

 Open All Year

 Pets Accepted

 Disabled Facilities

 Beach Access

 Play Area

 Bar/Restaurant

 Fishing

 Sailing

Scan me for more information.

Alan Rogers Code: DE29030
3 accommodations
100 pitches
GPS: 52.68896, 9.69707
Post Code: D-29690

Essel, Lower Saxony

www.alanrogers.com/de29030
camping@camping-allerleinetal.de
Tel: +49 50 71 51 15 49
camping-aller-leine-tal.de

Open (Touring Pitches):
Start March - End October.

Camping-Aller-Leine-Tal

This is a simple, family-run campsite on the bank of the River Aller in a wooded location in Lower Saxony. It's a peaceful area with dense woods home to red squirrels and deer, heather-carpeted heathland, slow-moving waterways, windmills and tree-lined country lanes - perfect, unspoilt scenery for cycling and walking along the local trails.

The neighbouring town of Schwarmstedt is handy for shops and various amenities, while Walsrode (20 km) has a large bird park, not to mention grazing animals and an adventure playground. Hanover is a fascinating day out, with an important zoo, and Celle is one of Germany's most interesting historical, half-timbered towns. In stark contrast is the Bergen-Belsen Memorial, with graves and memorials commemorating those who died in the concentration camp - including Anne Frank.

There are 100 touring pitches, mostly level, grassy and well demarcated by trees mature enough to provide shade in summer. Pitches are in the open or under trees, with electricity connections (10A) and water taps nearby and a field for groups and tents. Heated sanitary block with free showers and washbasins in cabins. Baby room. Washing machine and dryer. Bar (all season) and restaurant with terrace (seasonal). Bread supplies. Three mobile homes for hire. Bicycle hire. WiFi (charged).

Key Features

 Pets Accepted

 Play Area

 Bar/Restaurant

 Bike Hire

Scan me for more information.

Alan Rogers Code: DE29210
4 accommodations
100 pitches
GPS: 52.88803, 10.09903
Post Code: D-29328

Müden/Örtze, Lower Saxony

www.alanrogers.com/de29210
info@campingsonnenberg.com
Tel: +49 50 53 98 71 74
www.campingsonnenberg.com

Open (Touring Pitches):
Mid April - Mid October.

Camping Sonnenberg

This is a small, friendly, family campsite tucked away amongst woodland on the edge of the village of Müden/Örtze, also known as the pearl of the southern heath. The village has a range of shops, restaurants and a bakery (fresh bread and rolls can be delivered daily by arrangement at reception). There are trees all around the campsite, but the main area is open and sunny, with views across the neighbouring fields and heath. The name 'Sonnenberg' translates as 'mountain in the sun', and pleasant views can be had from this slightly elevated position. Further afield, Hanover makes a wonderful day trip with plenty of shopping, museums and historical interest.

Lüneburg Heath is perfect for hiking and cycling, its gentle inclines crisscrossed with waymarked trails. A free guide is available at the campsite reception, giving details of local routes, many even starting directly from the campsite. There are 28 circular hiking trails designed to showcase the best of the local flora and fauna. This campsite has around 100 pitches for caravans and motorhomes, all with electric hook-up points.

Key Features

 Book Online

 Pets Accepted

 Play Area

 Bar/Restaurant

 Bike Hire

Private sanitary facilities available. Restaurant (limited). Bar. Snack bar. Children's playground. Occasional music/entertainment (High season). Bicycle hire. Laundry. Games room. Pets allowed. WiFi.

Scan me for more information.

Alan Rogers Code: DE28220
50 accommodations
117 pitches
GPS: 52.30444, 9.85888
Post Code: D-30880

Hannover, Lower Saxony

www.alanrogers.com/de28220
Info@camping-birkensee.de
Tel: +49 511 52 99 62
www.birkensee-hannover.de

Open (Touring Pitches):
All year.

Camping Birkensee

Lying on the southern edge of Hanover and surrounded by fields, Camping Birkensee has 167 grassy touring pitches (half are for seasonal units) for caravans or motorhomes with 16-amp electric hook-up points. The site is idyllic, situated in the middle of the Bockmerholz nature reserve, with the adjacent woods providing a welcome antidote to the bustle of city life. There's a swimming lake and beach, which is a pleasant spot to relax after a day's sightseeing. Hanover is 10 km away, a historic city with museums, shopping and galleries to enjoy.

A hiking and cycling path allows the opportunity to explore the area. The restaurant with a terrace and beer garden offers the perfect setting for convivial evenings, and local shops and restaurants are only a few minutes away by car.

The heated toilet block provides showers, washbasins and WCs. Family room. Disabled facilities. Laundry with washing machines and dryers. Dishwashing area. Chemical toilet point. Restaurant. Beer garden. Snack bar. Takeaway. Bread to order. Children's playground. Gas sales. Beach with football, volleyball and table tennis. Lake swimming. WiFi. TV room. Twin axle caravans are allowed. BBQ's allowed. Dogs allowed. Earliest arrival time is 15.00.

Key Features

 Open All Year

 Pets Accepted

 Disabled Facilities

 Play Area

 Bar/Restaurant

Scan me for more information.

Alan Rogers Code: DE38265
50 accommodations
249 pitches
GPS: 52.65482, 12.42967
Post Code: D-14715

Ferchesar, Brandenburg

Campingpark Buntspecht

www.alanrogers.com/de38265
campingpark-buntspecht@web.de
Tel: +49 33 87 49 00 72
www.campingpark-buntspecht.de

Open (Touring Pitches):
Mid April - Mid October.

Campingpark Buntspecht is a high quality, well-maintained site 85 km west of Berlin, lying alongside the large Ferchesarer lake and surrounded by the Brandenburg Forest and a large nature reserve. The pitches (90-120 sq.m) are laid out on grass in a parkland setting with tall pine trees offering some shade. There are 249 pitches, with 155 average-sized, fully serviced pitches for touring (16A electricity). Sixteen are alongside the lake, and seven are for short stays. The large lake has a sandy beach and is ideal for swimming, boating and fishing, with a range of boats for hire.

This is a great destination for nature lovers and anyone fancying exploring the unspoilt scenery on two wheels or two legs. For a day out, hop on the train from the town of Rathenow, and you'll be in the city of Berlin within the hour.

Two well equipped, modern sanitary blocks with all necessary facilities including those for babies and disabled campers. Dog showers and walking area. Washing machines and dryers. Shop with basics. Bar with terrace. Restaurant. Football. Volleyball. Badminton. Adventure playground with large sand pit. Petting zoo. Bouncy castle. Bicycle and children's go-kart hire. WiFi throughout (charged).

Key Features

 Pets Accepted

 Disabled Facilities

 Play Area

 Bar/Restaurant

 Bike Hire

 Fishing

Scan me for more information.

Alan Rogers Code: DE31385
73 accommodations
130 pitches
GPS: 51.68159, 7.30633
Post Code: D-45711

Datteln, North Rhine-Westphalia

www.alanrogers.com/de31385
info@wehlingsheide.de
Tel: +49 236 33 34 04
www.wehlingsheide.de

Open (Touring Pitches):
All year.

Erholungspark Wehlingsheide

Erholungspark Wehlingsheide is a site in Datteln, North Rhine-Westphalia, some 30 km north of Dortmund. Datteln is about 7 km away and offers the usual range of handy shops, restaurants and amenities. Set amidst rural fields and open countryside, it's a great location for those who enjoy pedalling along country lanes and hiking along the scenic trails, and there's even a sauna and beauty centre on site to help you relax afterwards.

It's a small site with neat pitches, mostly on open grass, many with some degree of shade. The 130 touring pitches, some with their own private toilet facilities, are grouped around a pond with its own small sandy beach. There are also several mobile homes and glamping pods available to rent.

The toilet block provides showers, wash basins and WCs. Disabled facilities. Laundry with washing machine and dryer. Dishwashing area. Motorhome service point. Chemical toilet point. Restaurant. Bar. Takeaway. Bike hire, including electric bikes. Sauna. Children's play area and water play. Multi-sports area. Table tennis. TV room. Fresh bread. WiFi point. Twin-axle vehicles are permitted. BBQ's permitted, charcoal, electricity and gas. Earliest arrival time 15.00. Pets allowed. Dog walks.

Key Features

 Open All Year

 Pets Accepted

 Disabled Facilities

 Bar/Restaurant

 Bike Hire

Scan me for more information.

Alan Rogers Code: DE28780
128 pitches
GPS: 51.88508, 9.44260
Post Code: D-37649

Heinsen, Lower Saxony

Campingplatz Weserbergland

www.alanrogers.com/de28780
info@weserbergland-camping.com
Tel: +49 55 35 87 33
www.weserbergland-camping.com

Open (Touring Pitches):
Mid April - Mid October.

Set amidst glorious rolling countryside, some 80 km south of Hanover, this is an immaculate site on the banks of the Weser river and located between Holzminden and Polle. It is a credit to its Dutch owners Jan and Astrid Reus who have owned it for several years and their passion for making it a great place to stay is evident throughout. The river is the obvious highlight of the site, with plenty of birdlife. It is a quiet site, perfect for a relaxing holiday and ideal for both couples and families with young children.

There are 128 pitches (118 for touring units) which are arranged on two areas. Pitches on the lower area are on grass and alongside the river bank. All are 120 sq.m. and have electrical connections (10A, Europlug). Upon arrival you are shown to your pitch by Jan and he will connect your electric up for you. Reception is in the main building which also houses the bar where you can enjoy a drink either inside or outside on the terrace.

One heated sanitary block. Showers are operated by token (from reception). Facilities for families. Laundry facilities. Motorhome services. Bread available daily (order at reception). Bar with terrace and satellite TV. Swimming pool (open all season). Playground. Games room. Boules pitch. Bicycle hire. WiFi (charged).

Key Features

 Pets Accepted

 Swimming Pool

 Play Area

 Bar/Restaurant

 Fishing

Scan me for more information.

Alan Rogers Code: DE30450
31 accommodations
96 pitches
GPS: 51.58968, 10.62460
Post Code: D-37445

Walkenried, Lower Saxony

www.alanrogers.com/de30450
walkenried@knauscamp.de
Tel: +49 55 25 778
www.knauscamp.de/walkenried

Open (Touring Pitches):
All year.

Campingpark Walkenried

The verdant countryside of the southern Harz area offers much for walkers and anglers, and this site organises many outings ranging from free walks through the woodlands and along the country trails to evenings beside the open fire. This site is also popular in winter for skiing holidays as the closest ski slopes are just 4 km away. It also has the benefit of a heated indoor pool and sauna.

Knaus Campingpark Walkenried has 96 touring pitches, each 80-100 sq.m. and arranged in well-shaded groups on slightly sloping grass and gravel. Most are separated by bushes or trees and have 16A, two-pin electrical connections. There are 13 hardstanding pitches, all fully serviced with electricity, water and drainage. There are some smaller hardstandings for motorhomes. Summer outdoor activities available in the area include tennis, cycling and watersports.

The sanitary facilities are in the main building by the entrance, with washbasins in cabins, child-size washbasins, and a toilet for disabled visitors. Laundry and cooking facilities. Gas supplies. Motorhome services. Shop and restaurant (closed Tuesdays). Order bread at reception. Heated indoor pool. Sauna. Large play areas. Barbecue area. Lake fishing. Large screen TV. Bicycle hire. Extensive entertainment programme in high season.

Key Features

 Open All Year

 Pets Accepted

 Disabled Facilities

 Swimming Pool

 Bike Hire

Scan me for more information.

Alan Rogers Code: DE38680
9 accommodations
100 pitches
GPS: 51.68601, 12.80018
Post Code: D-06905

Bad Schmiedeberg, Saxony

www.alanrogers.com/de38680
camping@lausiger-teiche.de
Tel: +49 34 92 65 74 75
www.lausiger-teiche.de

Open (Touring Pitches):
All year.

Campingpark Lausiger Teiche

In a beautiful setting on the edge of a lake in the Dübener Heide natural park, Lausiger Teiche is close to the spa towns of Bad Schmiedeberg and Bad Duben. Leipzig is around 50 km away, proclaimed as the 'New Berlin' with funky architecture, creative energy, and ancient monuments well worth a visit. This site in a country location has a relaxed atmosphere and is a good choice for anyone looking for an active holiday, with watersports, hiking and cycling routes on the doorstep. The Elberadweg cycle route passes the site and is a great way to get to know the locality - bikes can be hired.

The 100 grassy touring pitches are generous (up to 200 sq.m), separated by hedges and shrubs, with mature trees providing dappled shade to many. An area for motorhomes has pitches right on the edge of the lake, and a further area is reserved for youth groups.

Traditional sanitary block with hot showers (on payment), vanity style washbasins and baby changing. Washing machine. Campers' kitchen. Small shop in reception with breakfast goods and snacks. Snack bar and restaurant. Lake swimming (High season). Games room. Playground. Beach volleyball. Basketball. Giant chess. Bicycle and go-kart hire. WiFi (charged).

Key Features

 Open All Year

 Pets Accepted

 Disabled Facilities

 Play Area

 Bar/Restaurant

 Horse Riding

Scan me for more information.

Alan Rogers Code: DE39280
17 accommodations
130 pitches
GPS: 52.04819, 14.03553
Post Code: D-15913

Gross Leuthen, Brandenburg

www.alanrogers.com/de39280
info@eurocamp-spreewaldtor.com
Tel: +49 35 47 13 03
www.eurocamp-spreewaldtor.com

Open (Touring Pitches):
All year.

Eurocamp Spreewaldtor

Amidst Spreewald's forest and wetland area, only an hour's drive from Berlin and 25 km from Beeskow, you will find EuroCamp Spreewaldtor. This rural campsite is directly located on the shore of the Gross Leuthen lake, with its own jetty, sandy beach and beach for dogs. You can explore the lovely towns in the area, enjoy cycling trips and even take a boat cruise through the extensive Spreewald. A convenient shuttle service whisks you to some of the attractive towns and villages in the area, such as watery Lübbenau.

The site is modern and well laid out, with 130 touring pitches spread over different areas, with landscaped greenery and a sense of calm. There's a small wellness centre with a sauna, a heated outdoor pool with special children's pool and sunbathing lawn. There are a few small shops in Märkische Heide, a village within walking distance of the campsite, and the sociable campsite restaurant serves modest meals.

Wash blocks, including for disabled people. Fresh bread, a small shop. Restaurant (limited choice), takeaway meals. Communal BBQ. Outdoor swimming pool. Lake. Wellness area. Children's playground. Entertainment (high season). Table tennis. Multi-sports field. Beach volleyball. WiFi. Pets allowed.

Key Features

 Book Online

 Open All Year

 Pets Accepted

 Disabled Facilities

 Swimming Pool

 Play Area

 Bar/Restaurant

 Fishing

Scan me for more information.

Alan Rogers Code: DE33300
2 accommodations
60 pitches
GPS: 50.99814, 9.13362
Post Code: D-34632

Jesberg, Hessen

www.alanrogers.com/de33300
gemeindeverwaltung@gemeinde-jesberg.de
Tel: +49 66 95 72 13
www.gemeinde-jesberg.de

Open (Touring Pitches):
All year.

Camping Kellerwald

Camping Kellerwald lies in the wooded and mountainous Hesse region of Germany, surrounded by beautiful countryside and and plenty of trails for easy going walking and cycling. Hike the Kellerwaldsteig, a scenic route that takes you right through the forest, leading up to the Kellerwaldturm, an observation tower offering amazing panoramic views. The campsite is on the fringe of Jesberg village, a peaceful little place which offers basic amenities and shops.

The site has 150 seasonal pitches and 60 grass pitches for touring units situated on neatly mown grass and with 16 amp hook-up. Most are open and sunny with modest shade to some, especially on the perimeter. The unspoilt nature all around creates a natural playground for youngsters with a stream to explore, trees to climb and space for them to run free.

Heated toilet block. Facility for guests who are disabled. Laundry. Dish washing area. Chemical toilet point. Bread to order (High season). Restaurant/Snack bar (High season). Heated outdoor swimming pool and children's pool (High season). Children's play area. Twin-axle caravans allowed. BBQs allowed. Table tennis. Multi-sports field. Boules area. Beach volleyball. Tennis court and horse riding nearby.

Key Features

 Open All Year

 Pets Accepted

 Disabled Facilities

 Swimming Pool

 Bar/Restaurant

Scan me for more information.

Alan Rogers Code: DE32240
180 pitches
GPS: 49.97966, 7.93647
Post Code: D-65385

Rüdesheim am Rhein, Hessen

www.alanrogers.com/de32240
info@campingplatz-ruedesheim.de
Tel: +49 67 22 25 82
www.campingplatz-ruedesheim.de

Open (Touring Pitches):
Late April - Early October.

Campingplatz am Rhein

The campsite was initially opened in 1949, and since 1984, it has been run by the Richter family. It is located directly next to the romantic River Rhine. The colourful seven-acre touring site offers level pitches on grass with shade from trees, and the arrangement is open plan. All pitches have 10A electricity and 40, normally allocated to motorhomes, and also have hardstanding, water and drainage. This is a major tourist area, and the site may become quite busy, although usually quiet and peaceful.

There is a small shop which offers a selection of everyday necessities. In front of the shop is a terrace with seating to relax and enjoy the view of the River Rhine. Next to the camping ground (approx 100 metres) a heated swimming pool, tennis court, mini golf and an adventure playground for children can be found.

Key Features

 Book Online

 Pets Accepted

 Disabled Facilities

 Play Area

 Bar/Restaurant

 Fishing

Two sanitary blocks with washbasins in cabins, one with controllable hot showers. A key is needed for the disabled facilities for which a refundable deposit is required. The facilities are easily accessed, spacious, modern and spotless. Washing machines and dryer. Motorhome services. Shop. Bar and snacks. Play area. Gates closed to vehicles and riverside 22.00-08.00. Pets allowed.

Scan me for
more information.

Alan Rogers Code: DE37240
15 accommodations
200 pitches
GPS: 49.77786, 9.50914
Post Code: D-97877

Wertheim-Bestenheid, Baden-Württemberg

www.alanrogers.com/de37240
wertheim@azur-camping.de
Tel: +49 934 28 31 11
www.azur-camping.com/wertheim

Open (Touring Pitches):
Early April - Late October.

Wertheim am Main

Attractively located along the banks of the River Main, this site is just 2 km north of Wertheim, a picturesque medieval old town centred at the confluence of the Rivers Main and Tauber. The town is packed with timber-framed houses and is overlooked by Germany's largest castle ruin. Rothenburg ob der Tauber dates from the Middle Ages and is steeped in heritage. Wine from the Franken area comes in a Bockbeutel, a uniquely shaped bottle best bought at one of the many vineyards. From the campsite, the River Main provides an ever-changing view as the cruise ships and barges slowly pass.

The site has 200 pitches for touring, and over 50 of its 320 pitches border the river. They are open plan, level, grassed and have 6A electricity. There is tree shade in places, and many pitches enjoy views over the river to the tree-covered hills beyond. With its attractive location in a scenic region and an adjoining swimming pool complex, the site has something to offer all family members.

Two sanitary buildings with washbasins in cabins and facilities for disabled visitors. Washing machines and dryers. Motorhome services. Shop. Comfortable bar/restaurant with beer garden. Snack bar. Play area. Boules. Volleyball. Basketball. Boat slipway. WiFi.

Key Features

  Book Online

  Disabled Facilities

  Play Area

Scan me for more information.

Alan Rogers Code: DE36150
7 accommodations
100 pitches
GPS: 50.16126, 11.51527
Post Code: D-95346

Stadtsteinach, Bavaria (N)

www.alanrogers.com/de36150
info@camping-stadtsteinach.de
Tel: +49 92 25 80 03 94
www.camping-stadtsteinach.de

Open (Touring Pitches):
Mid March - Mid November.

Camping Stadtsteinach

Camping Stadtsteinach is a comfortable base, well placed for exploring this rural region with its interesting towns, forest walks and undulating hills rising to the east. The Fichtel Mountains are nearby, and there are plenty of quiet lanes meandering through the countryside, sometimes following tumbling wooded streams, perfect for hiking and cycling. The campsite lies on the eastern edge of the village of Stadtsteinach, which offers handy shops and amenities.

There are 100 touring pitches laid out on either side of access roads. These are mostly grassy and level with 16A electricity. The site is on a gentle slope, pitches having been terraced where necessary, and there are some hardstandings for motorhomes. High hedges and trees separate pitches or groups of pitches in some areas giving the effect of camping in small clearings, but most pitches are open and sunny.

The sanitary area is part of the administration and restaurant building, heated and of good quality. It has free hot water and some washbasins in cabins. Facilities for visitors with disabilities. Motorhome services. Cooking rings on payment. Laundry facilities. Gas supplies. Restaurant. Bread from reception. Solar heated swimming pool near the entrance is free to campers (high season). Play area. Tennis. TV. Bicycle hire.

Key Features

 Pets Accepted

 Disabled Facilities

 Swimming Pool

 Play Area

 Bar/Restaurant

 Bike Hire

Scan me for more information.

Alan Rogers Code: DE35000
4 accommodations
45 pitches
GPS: 48.78568, 9.98319
Post Code: D-73457

Essingen/Lauterburg, Baden-Württemberg

www.alanrogers.com/de35000
info@hirtenteich.camp
Tel: +49 73 65 296
www.hirtenteich.camp

Open (Touring Pitches):
All year.

Campingplatz Hirtenteich

Campingplatz Hirtenteich lies around 50 km east of Stuttgart, nestling among wooded hills and adjoining fertile fields and just outside the village of Lauterburg. This is the centre of the UNESCO Geopark Swabian Alb, complete with cave systems, castles, rock formations, nature reserves and picturesque old villages and market towns. It's ideal for those who love to get out and about - especially hiking and cycling. There's a wide choice of mountain bike downhill routes through forests and meadows. Visit Charlottenhöhle Cave Adventure World, Steiff Toy Museum in Giengen an der Brenz and the outdoor activities at Skypark epia Kletterwald in Schwäbisch Gmünd. Shopping is available in Aalen, Schwäbisch Gmünd and Heidenheim.

On site simply relax in the campsite's sauna and outdoor swimming pool or have a bite in the site's restaurant. The campsite has 45 touring pitches, well laid out and demarcated with shade from the trees dotted around, some with views of the surrounding hills.

Key Features

 Open All Year

 Pets Accepted

 Disabled Facilities

 Swimming Pool

 Play Area

Two modern sanitary buildings, wheelchair accessible. Supply and disposal station. Shop. Bread service during the season. Restaurant with sun terrace. Outdoor pool and sauna. EasyBe Dishwasher. Play and sports facilities. Children's playground. Barbecue. Dog shower. Gas cylinder exchange service. Tent meadow. WiFi, free.

Scan me for more information.

Alan Rogers Code: DE37100
15 accommodations
200 pitches
GPS: 49.02550, 13.22067
Post Code: D-94227

Zwiesel, Bavaria (S)

Ferienpark Arber

www.alanrogers.com/de37100
info@ferienpark-arber.de
Tel: +49 99 22 80 25 95
www.ferienpark-arber.de

Open (Touring Pitches):
All year.

Ferienpark Arber is a large site on the outskirts of the pleasant town of Zwiesel, right in the heart of the Bavarian Forest and not far from the Czech border. There are views up to the tree-clad hills and a stream runs through the campsite. Not surprisingly, this is fantastic country for hiking and cycling with 320 km of marked trails that take you through some of the finest scenery in Germany. Zwiesel is well known for its skiing and winter sports, as well as its long heritage as a centre of exquisite glass making.

The campsite is on a slight slope with 300 grassy pitches, 200 of which are for tourers, with partial shade. There are various dedicated areas, with an open, grassy section for motorhomes, and another for caravans, all with electricity (some 10A Euro, most 16A German) and water points along the central roadway. Another area is reserved for dog owners and there is an overnight area of hardstanding just outside the entrance. A large pool complex is next door comprising a deep Olympic size pool, a separate pool for children and non-swimmers and a natural pool, open high season.

The two sanitary blocks have some private cabins. Facilities for disabled visitors. Baby room. Laundry facilities. Shop. Pleasant restaurant/bar (closed November). Bicycle hire. Fishing. WiFi (charged).

Key Features

 Open All Year

 Pets Accepted

 Disabled Facilities

 Swimming Pool

 Play Area

 Bar/Restaurant

 Skiing

 Bike Hire

Scan me for more information.

Alan Rogers Code: DE34750
85 pitches
GPS: 47.84796, 7.69821
Post Code: D-79295

Sulzburg, Baden-Württemberg

www.alanrogers.com/de34750
a-z@camping-sulzbachtal.de
Tel: +49 76 34 59 25 68
www.camping-sulzbachtal.de

Open (Touring Pitches):
All year.

Camping Sulzbachtal

This attractive, family-run site nestles between the Rhine and the Black Forest in a quiet rural area close to the French and Swiss borders north of Basel. The campsite is in a peaceful spot among fields on the edge of the village of Sulzburg, which is surrounded by vineyards and an attractive backdrop of tree-covered mountains. It is well situated for walking or cycling, with numerous scenic routes running through the Black Forest. Visitors are entitled to a Konus Card, which gives free bus and train travel throughout the Black Forest. Only a few kilometres to the south is the spa town of Badenweiler, with its modern spa facilities right beside the old Roman baths.

The 85 touring pitches have electricity, water and drainage and are a good size on level gravel. English is spoken, and the Grommek family ensures that the site is well-managed and maintained with enjoyable events like regular barbecue and grill nights.

Sanitary facilities include private cabins, showers and laundry facilities. Facilities for disabled visitors and children. Two family shower rooms. Motorhome services. Snack bar, small shop and bar next to reception. Gas supplies. Natural water pool (May-Sept) and eco garden. Playground. TV/club room. WiFi throughout (charged). Charcoal barbecues are not permitted.

Key Features

 Open All Year

 Pets Accepted

 Disabled Facilities

 Swimming Pool

 Play Area

 Bar/Restaurant

Scan me for more information.

Alan Rogers Code: DE40860
14 accommodations
200 pitches
GPS: 47.63363, 9.64721
Post Code: D-88069

Tettnang, Bavaria (S)

Camping Badhütten

Only ten minutes away from Lake Constance, at Germany's southern edge, in a tranquil rural setting of orchards and hop gardens, Gutshof Badhütten is a well maintained site with good facilities. It's a great area for exploring on foot or two wheels, with lots of trails to follow. There's plenty of interest around the lake: the vast 14th century Montfort Castle, Wolfegg Automobile museum, Burg Meersburg or Meersburg Castle (dating from the 7th century and perhaps the oldest inhabited castle in Germany), are just a few attractions. And of course there's a variety of cruises and boat trips on the beautiful waters as well.

The campsite has around 200 spacious (100 sq.m) touring pitches. All are flat and grassy and have electrical connections while the comfort and premium pitches have water and drainage also. Families with younger children will appreciate the swimming pool, playground and small animal corner. Fully equipped apartments can be rented in the adjacent hotel.

Modern and well maintained sanitary facilities with provision for disabled campers. Laundry facilities. Motorhome services. Bar and restaurant and shop (April-Late September). Outdoor swimming pool. Indoor play area (from mid May). Sand pit and trampoline. Football pitch. Badminton courts. Free WiFi.

www.alanrogers.com/de40860
info@gutshof-camping.de
Tel: +49 754 39 63 30
www.gutshof-camping.de

Open (Touring Pitches):
Start April - End September.

Key Features

 Book Online

 Pets Accepted

 Disabled Facilities

 Swimming Pool

 Play Area

 Scan me for more information.

Alan Rogers Code: DE36080
10 accommodations
70 pitches
GPS: 47.88405, 12.26944
Post Code: D-83093

Bad Endorf, Bavaria (S)

Camping Stein

www.alanrogers.com/de36080
rezeption@camping-stein.de
Tel: +49 80 53 93 49
www.camping-stein.de

Open (Touring Pitches):
Start April - Mid October.

Camping Stein is a family-run 4-star site located on Lake Simssee, between lush meadows, dense forests and shimmering lakes, in the heart of Upper Bavaria. Not far from the Austrian border, it's an ideal base for exploring the majestic Bavarian Alps, Munich, Salzburg and Lake Chiemsee with Castle Herrenchiemsee and Frauenchiemsee or Chiemgauer Seenplatte, one of the oldest nature reserves in Bavaria. Several cycle routes and hiking trails lead from the campsite up into the wooded hills and through the peaceful valleys.

The camping area is terraced in places, and there are 155 pitches, of which 70 are for touring, with electricity, water & waste facility. An attractive grassy expanse, dotted with trees and popular with sun worshippers, leads down to the lake, where a gently shelving pebble beach allows access to the calm water for swimming and windsurfing.

Key Features

 Book Online

 Pets Accepted

 Play Area

A single heated toilet block. Baby room. Dishwashing area. Laundry. Chemical toilet point. Facility for visitors who are disabled. Motorhome service point. Security barrier. Children's play area. Games room. BBQs allowed. Gas sales. Dogs are allowed in the low season. Various cycle routes. You can swim nearby in a lake/recreational pond. Windsurfing. Fresh bread to order. WiFi charged.

Scan me for
more information.

Capital London
Currency British Pound (£)
Language English, Welsh
Time Zone GMT
Telephone Code +44
Tourism website visitbritain.com

Shops Hours differ between the four nations. Generally 9am to 5pm weekdays and Sat, and 11am to 4pm on Sun. Smaller supermarkets stay open longer.

Money ATMs are widespread and accessible 24hrs a day. Most places accept cards. Amex less widely accepted.

Driving in Britain Driving is on the left, speed is measured in miles per hour. When using motorways, never use the hard shoulder unless instructed to or if you break down. Tailgating, drink-driving, smoking in the car with minors present and using a mobile device whilst driving are illegal. Pedestrians and cyclists have priority.

Public Holidays 1 Jan New Year's Day; Mar/Apr Good Friday; Mar/Apr Easter Monday; May Early May Bank Holiday; 8 May King Charles III Coronation; May/June Late May Bank Holiday; Late Aug August Bank Holiday; 25 Dec Christmas Day; 26 Dec Boxing Day.

Regional holidays are observed, check before travelling.

LEZ Low Emissions Zones in all major cities.

London has ULEZ, ZEZ and congestion charges in place also. Registration is required for all non-UK vehicles.

●●●●○ **Accessible Travel Score**

Mostly well-equipped, most public buildings in cities and major towns are accessible. Efforts to adapt are actively being made.

Wales Boasting a diverse landscape, from lakes, mountains, rivers and valleys to beautiful coastlines and rolling wooded countryside.

Scotland From gently rolling hills and rugged coastlines to dramatic peaks punctuated with beautiful lochs, Scotland is an untamed land steeped in history.

Northern Ireland From wild coastlines to green valleys, rugged mountains and shimmering lakes to the natural phenomenon of the Giant's Causeway, Northern Ireland is crammed full of sights.

Great Britain

View all campsites in Great Britain
alanrogers.com/england
alanrogers.com/northern-ireland
alanrogers.com/scotland
alanrogers.com/wales

See campsite map page 480

Climate Varied. Mild in the summer and cooler and wetter in the winter months.

Emergency services Call 999 or 112 for the police, ambulance and fire and rescue.

Units Britain uses the imperial system for road signs but metric is used elsewhere.

The United Kingdom offers a wealth of extraordinary landscapes set against the backdrop of rich and vibrant history. In terms of character and stunning scenery, it offers an unsurpassed choice of holiday activities from coast to country.

Northern England A beautiful and varied region of rolling hills and undulating moors, along with a wealth of industrial heritage and undiscovered countryside. The Yorkshire Moors, Cumbrian lakes, Northumbrian ancient forts and fairytale castles are all highlights not to be missed.

Southern England Rich in maritime heritage and historical attractions, the southern region comprises tranquil English countryside replete with picture-postcard villages, ancient towns, formidable castles and grand stately homes, coupled with a beautiful coastline, white-faced cliffs and lively Victorian seaside resorts.

Heart of England Spanning central England, from the ancient borders of Wales in the west across to Lincolnshire on the east coast, the Heart of England is rich in glorious rolling countryside, magnificent castles and fine stately homes.

Eastern England A perfect mix of gentle countryside and sleepy villages, it's an unspoilt region with endless skies, inland waterways and traditional beach resorts.

Western England A region of contrasts, with windswept moorlands and dramatic cliffs towering above beautiful sandy beaches.

Alan Rogers Code: UK9830
23 accommodations
GPS: 49.46997, -2.44575
Post Code: GY1 3HR

Herm Island, Herm

www.alanrogers.com/uk9830
reservations@herm.com
Tel: +44 1481 750000
www.herm.com/where-to-stay/
camping

Open (Touring Pitches):
Early April - Late September.

Seagull Campsite

This tiny site, and indeed the island of Herm, will certainly appeal to those who are looking for complete tranquillity and calm. Reached by boat from Guernsey (20 minutes), this beautiful 300-acre island allows no cars, only tractors, on its narrow roads and paths (no bicycles either).

The campsite is a twenty-minute uphill walk from the harbour, although your luggage will be transported for you. There are several ready-erected tents to rent; they are fully equipped except for bedding and lighting, which are not included. Unfortunately, there is no option to use your own equipment.

On-site warden, Free luggage porterage on arrival and departure (on Isle of Herm Ferry Sailings), Shower and toilet facilities refurbished in 2020 – heated coin-operated showers (£1 coins needed), Washbasins and shaver points provided, Freezer for ice packs, Coin operated tumble dryer and washing machine (£1 coins needed), On-site Grocery shop, Camping cots available at no extra charge (subject to advance booking), Please note there isn't a cash machine or cash-back facility on the island, bring plenty of £1 coins for the showers and laundry facilities.

Key Features

 Beach Access

Scan me for more information.

Alan Rogers Code: UK0050
250 pitches
GPS: 50.19618, -5.49102
Post Code: TR26 3LX

Cornwall, South West

www.alanrogers.com/uk0050
reception@polmanter.com
Tel: +44 1736 795640
www.polmanter.com

Open (Touring Pitches):
Late March - End October.

Polmanter Touring Park

A popular and attractively developed park, Polmanter is located high up at the back of Saint Ives with wonderful sea and countryside views. The Osborne family has worked hard to develop Polmanter as a complete family base. Converted farm buildings provide a cosy lounge bar with a conservatory overlooking the heated swimming pool.

The 250 touring pitches (no caravan holiday homes) are well-spaced in several fields divided by established shrubs and hedges, giving large, level, individual pitches with connecting tarmac roads. There is a choice of grass and hardstanding multi-serviced pitches with electricity, water, wastewater and TV point, serviced pitches with 16A electricity and non-serviced tent pitches.

Three modern, fully equipped toilet blocks with underfloor heating include en-suite family rooms. Facilities for disabled visitors. Baby rooms. Fully equipped laundry. Motorhome services. Well-stocked shop. Bar with food and family area (all Whitsun-mid Sept). Takeaway. Heated swimming pool (Whitsun-mid Sept). Some entertainment (peak season). Tennis. Putting. Play area. Sports field. Games room. WiFi (charged).

Key Features

 Pets Accepted

 Disabled Facilities

 Beach Access

 Swimming Pool

 Play Area

 Bar/Restaurant

Scan me for more information.

Alan Rogers Code: UK0085
177 pitches
GPS: 50.20197, -4.97202
Post Code: TR2 5EL

Cornwall, South West

Merrose Farm (CAMC)

www.alanrogers.com/uk0085
UKSitesBookingService@camc.com
Tel: +44 1872 580380
www.camc.com

Open (Touring Pitches):
Early April - Early November.

Merrose Farm Caravan and Motorhome Club site is a 14-acre site with 177 touring pitches (some seasonal) including 73 hardstanding. It consists of five areas surrounding the main facilities block. Set in the beautiful Roseland Peninsular, it is an ideal touring centre.

With the Cornish Coast Path nearby, there are beautiful beaches and traditional fishing villages to explore such as Porthcasco and Port Loe (with the famous Lugger Inn.) St Mawes and King Harry Ferry to Falmouth are a four-mile drive. The beautiful Cathedral City of Truro is a 30 min drive and has several supermarkets, banks, and transport links across the county.

A large single toilet block central to the site has facilities for disabled/wheelchair users and a baby/family room. Showers. Washbasins. Dishwashing and laundry room all facilities are very clean and well maintained. Washers and Dryers require £1.00 tokens from reception. The children's play area is new, well-maintained and of a high standard. The onsite shop/reception is well stocked with Gas available. Information room. Defibrillator. Access to water/waste and chemical disposal points around the site. Motorhome service point. BBQ's allowed. Pets allowed. Dog walk. WiFi average charged. TV reception good. Twin Axle caravans accepted. Late-night arrivals area. Bus stop 200 metres. Co-Op 5 miles. The earliest arrival 13:00. Maximum outfit length 9 metres.

Key Features

 Book Online

 Pets Accepted

 Disabled Facilities

 Beach Access

 Play Area

Scan me for more information.

Alan Rogers Code: UK0006
123 accommodations
282 pitches
GPS: 50.34619, -4.48318
Post Code: PL13 2JR

Cornwall, South West

www.alanrogers.com/uk0006
reception@tencreek.co.uk
Tel: +44 1503 262447
www.dolphinholidays.co.uk

Open (Touring Pitches):
All year.

Tencreek Holiday Park

Situated within walking distance of Cornwall's beautiful south coast, Tencreek is a family-owned campsite with a friendly welcome that rightly justifies its description as a complete holiday park. Of the 350 pitches, about 100 are occupied by mobile homes, but the rest are reserved for touring units and tents, with most hardstanding. The site gently slopes towards the coast and is organised into formal rows, so every pitch has a sea view.

The site is close to many local attractions and offers plenty to offer on-site with a well-stocked shop, a fine heated indoor pool, a new, all-weather multisports pitch, a large bar and a cabaret stage for evening entertainment. The Joce family continues to invest in the park to develop the site and offer a full family holiday experience: the result is a well-kept, organised site with clean and modern facilities.

Two modern, well-kept blocks provide toilets, showers, open-style washbasins, and 12 family washrooms. Facilities for disabled visitors. Full launderette. Licensed camp shop. Camping & Calor Gas. Bar with bar meals (app available to order food for table service or takeaway to your pitch). Large screen TV. Games room. Indoor pool with lifeguard (all year). Multisport pitch. Children's football coaching during the main holiday season. Play area. Organised entertainment for all ages. Free WiFi in Castaways social area (other areas chargeable). Post and parcel delivery or collection to reception. Caravan holiday homes to rent.

Key Features

 Book Online

 Open All Year

 Pets Accepted

 Disabled Facilities

 Beach Access

 Swimming Pool

 Play Area

 Bar/Restaurant

 Scan me for more information.

Alan Rogers Code: UK0819
4 accommodations
50 pitches
GPS: 50.30148, -3.78930
Post Code: TQ7 4AF

Devon, South West

Parkland

www.alanrogers.com/uk0819
enquiries@parklandsite.co.uk
Tel: +44 1548 852723
www.parklandsite.co.uk

Open (Touring Pitches):
All year.

Parkland is in an area of outstanding natural beauty and is perfectly situated for exploring all that the stunning South Hams area of South Devon has to offer. Open all year; the site is set within three acres of mature, landscaped grounds with panoramic views over Kingsbridge and Salcombe and the rolling countryside towards Dartmoor National Park.

Explore the market town of Kingsbridge and the historic towns of Dartmouth and Totnes. Ramble along the picturesque South West Coast path. Relax on fabulous beaches; Bantham, Thurlestone, Bigbury, Slapton Sands and Hope Cove. Enjoy an array of attractions, activities and water sports. Indulge in local produce, quality village pubs and fine dining eateries. The site has 50 grass & hard standing pitches with 16 amp electric hook-up and drinking water points for all pitches. Grey and Black waste disposal points (majority of pitches). The site is for adults only (aged 18 and over), and dogs are not permitted on site.

Key Features

 Adults Only

 Open All Year

 Disabled Facilities

 Beach Access

Two heated amenity buildings with toilets, washbasins and 'wet room' showers. Hand dryers, hairdryer and shaver points. Disabled suite, with large wet room shower, low-level basin, toilet with grab rails, emergency pull cord, and a 'sit in' bath. Laundry. Indoor dishwashing rooms. Onsite shared-use BBQ with outside seating and an indoor dining room. Social room with comfy sofas, complimentary tea and coffee, TV and traditional board games. Mini kitchen with microwave, toaster and kettle, breakfast bar and stools, along with a fridge and a freezer. BBQs allowed. BBQ wash-up. Earliest time for arrival 12:00 noon.

Scan me for more information.

Alan Rogers Code: UK0681
6 accommodations
91 pitches
GPS: 51.20484, -4.06417
Post Code: EX34 9SH

Devon, South West

Mill Park

www.alanrogers.com/uk0681
enquiries@millpark.com
Tel: +44 1271 882647
www.millpark.com

Open (Touring Pitches):
Start March - End October.

Mill Park is a small family-run sheltered touring caravan and camping site set in an attractive wooded valley on the North Devon Coast. It has a shop, a takeaway, a games room, laundry, and many other useful facilities such as gas-changing and ice pack freezing. Several glamping options are available on-site, including three bell tents and three glamping pods.

There is also an on-site pub serving a modest menu. Mill Park is surrounded by attractive woodland and is an ideal family site as it's just a short walk to quiet sand and pebble beaches. Bring your Fishing tackle to Mill Park and enjoy the Lake. A stream fed 1.5-acre coarse fishing lake stocked with carp.

Equally close by is the unspoilt and breathtaking beauty of Exmoor and the nearest village, Berrynarbor, just a five-minute walk from the site. This village dates back to the sixteenth century and earlier. There is a quaint old country pub, village stores and a post office.

Key Features

 Pets Accepted

 Disabled Facilities

 Play Area

 Bar/Restaurant

 Fishing

Two Separate shower blocks - recently refurbished and kept impeccably clean, onsite bar, well-stocked shop, fishing lake, a small river flowing through the park, children's play area, games room, book swap, games library, free Internet in bar and games room. Close to beaches, secluded and quiet, and very peaceful.

Scan me for more information.

Alan Rogers Code: UK1270
122 accommodations
155 pitches
GPS: 50.66020, -3.28051
Post Code: EX9 7BX

Devon, South West

www.alanrogers.com/uk1270
info@ladrambay.co.uk
Tel: +44 1395 568398
www.ladrambay.co.uk

Open (Touring Pitches):
Mid March - Start November.

Ladram Bay Holiday Park

Ladram Bay is a complete holiday village with 755 units, including many lodges and holiday homes for hire, and it even has its own beach. It is quite possible to spend a couple of weeks here without needing to leave the site.

The 155 hardstanding touring pitches are fully serviced and have 16A electricity. They are located on a hillside and have some of the best sea views, and the site tractor tows all units into position. There are extensive on-site facilities - shops, a good restaurant, a café/takeaway and a cabaret bar. A hardworking team provide entertainment every night of the week, with special events at weekends. The sheltered pebble beach is just a short walk through the site.

Two modern toilet blocks are clean and have excellent facilities, including underfloor heating and family bathrooms. Facilities for disabled visitors (steep climb from some pitches). Launderette. Well-stocked shop. Restaurant, snack bar and takeaway. Indoor swimming pool (extra charge). Indoor climbing wall. Adventure play area. Children's club. Themed mini golf. Entertainment. WiFi over site (charged).

Key Features

 Pets Accepted

 Disabled Facilities

 Beach Access

 Swimming Pool

 Play Area

 Bar/Restaurant

 Fishing

Scan me for more information.

Alan Rogers Code: UK1340
49 pitches
GPS: 50.99200, -3.09257
Post Code: TA3 7BS

Somerset, South West

Cornish Farm Touring Park

www.alanrogers.com/uk1340
info@cornishfarm.com
Tel: +44 1823 327746
www.cornishfarm.com

Open (Touring Pitches):
All year.

This neat little park is on level ground and located close to the M5 motorway. There are 49 pitches with 10A electricity, of which 25 are on gravel hardstanding. Most pitches are accessed from a gravel road (one-way system) with plenty of fresh water taps, site lighting and some picnic tables. A separate area for tents is close to the toilet block. A pleasant and quiet site, but there is some background motorway noise.

The maximum length for motorhomes is 30 ft, unless by prior arrangement with the wardens. With its old apple trees, this park makes a pleasant stopover or location for touring the area. Off to the left are the barns that house the Van Bitz workshops producing security systems for motorhomes and accessories for both motorhomes and caravans.

One central block has underfloor heating and modern fittings. Large, dual-purpose room providing facilities for disabled visitors and small children. Dusk to dawn low energy lighting. Laundry room. Motorhome services. Camping supplies are for sale, and plenty of tourist information is available. Calor Gas bottle exchange. Free WiFi.

Key Features

 Open All Year

 Pets Accepted

 Disabled Facilities

Scan me for
more information.

Alan Rogers Code: UK1490
40 pitches
GPS: 51.17237, -2.64188
Post Code: BA4 4HL

Somerset, South West

www.alanrogers.com/uk1490
stay@greenacres-camping.co.uk
Tel: +44 1749 890497
greenacres-camping.co.uk

Open (Touring Pitches):
Late April - Early September.

Greenacres Camping

Greenacres is a rural site in the Somerset countryside for tents, trailer tents and small motorhomes only. Hidden away below the Mendips and almost at the start of the Levels, it is a simple green site – a true haven of peace and quiet. The grass is neatly trimmed over the 4.5 acres and hedged with mature trees, though there is a view of Glastonbury Tor in one direction and of Barrow Hill in the other.

All 40 pitches are around the park's perimeter, leaving a central area safe for children to play. At the site's south side, 13 pitches with 10A electricity are ideal for birdwatchers and those without children. There are now six pitches on the north part of the site with electricity (10A).

The central wooden toilet block is kept very clean and includes facilities for children. Play equipment, football, badminton net, table tennis and playhouses. For hire, a full range of bikes and firepits (with wood and kindling). The park office is across the lane. Cabin with fridges and freezers for campers' use (free), library and tourist information. Mobiles and laptops are charged for a small donation to charity. Dogs are not accepted.

Key Features

 Beach Access

 Play Area

 Bike Hire

Scan me for more information.

Alan Rogers Code: UK1800
400 pitches
GPS: 50.61927, -2.50040
Post Code: DT3 4DW

Dorset, South West

East Fleet Farm

www.alanrogers.com/uk1800
enquiries@eastfleet.co.uk
Tel: +44 1305 785768
www.eastfleet.co.uk

Open (Touring Pitches):
Mid March - End October.

East Fleet Farm has a marvellous situation on part level, part gently sloping meadows leading to the shores of the Fleet, with views across to the famous Chesil Bank with the sea beyond. The Whitfield family has developed this park within the confines of their 300-acre organic arable farm in keeping with its surroundings, yet with modern amenities. It is maturing well as bushes and trees grow.

The 400 pitches (some seasonal) back onto hedges and are of a comfortable size, so there is no feeling of crowding. Of these, 350 are level and marked with 10/16 amp electricity, over 70 also have hardstanding, and some are fully serviced. The large shop has a good range of camping equipment and outdoor gear. The site is a member of the Caravan and Motorhome Club Affiliated Site Scheme, but visitors who are not members of the club are very welcome.

Key Features

 Pets Accepted

 Disabled Facilities

 Beach Access

 Play Area

 Bar/Restaurant

Three fully equipped toilet blocks, the two latest providing en-suite facilities. Unit for disabled visitors. Baby changing facilities. Laundry room. Motorhome services. Reception plus shop with groceries, bread, papers, gas and camping accessories. Bar with terrace (w/ends only in low season). Large play barn with table tennis and gym equipment. Twin Axle caravans accepted. Defibrillator. Fenced play area. Games field. Nature watch boards. Pets allowed. Dog Walk. BBQs allowed. Wi-Fi throughout (charged). TV reception fair. Tents allowed. Bus stop 800 metres. Train station 3 miles. Asda 2 miles. No late-night arrivals area. Earliest arrival time 11:30. Maximum outfit length 9 metres.

Scan me for more information.

Alan Rogers Code: UK2500
60 pitches
GPS: 50.68940, -1.52704
Post Code: PO40 9SH

Isle of Wight, South

www.alanrogers.com/uk2500
web@heathfieldcamping.co.uk
Tel: +44 1983 407822
www.heathfieldcamping.co.uk

Open (Touring Pitches):
Mid April - End September.

Heathfield Farm Camping

Situated between Yarmouth & Freshwater, Heathfield is a pleasant contrast to many of the other sites on the Isle of Wight in that it is a 'no frills' sort of place. Despite its name, it is no longer a working farm. A large, open meadow provides large grass and level pitches with 16A electricity. The large field is divided into three distinct areas by large mature hedges. There is no shop as you are only eight minutes from the centre of Freshwater.

The site, in part, overlooks Colwell Bay and across the Solent towards Milford-on-Sea and Hurst Castle. One of the fields has a children's play area in the middle of a large grass meadow surrounded by pitches. There is also a playing field for ball games and a wildflower meadow with a perimeter mown for dog walking.

The main sanitary facilities are housed in a modern, ingeniously customised, prefabricated unit, including hot showers and baby changing. A second similar unit has WCs and washbasins in cubicles plus facilities for disabled visitors. Laundry facilities. Motorhome services. Gas supplies. Ice pack service. Playing field. Bicycle hire arranged. WiFi throughout (charged). No commercial vehicles are accepted. Gate locked 22.30-07.00.

Key Features

 Pets Accepted

 Disabled Facilities

 Beach Access

Scan me for more information.

Alan Rogers Code: UK2466
60 pitches
GPS: 50.64677, -1.19236
Post Code: PO36 9PJ

Isle of Wight, South

Old Barn Touring Park

www.alanrogers.com/uk2466
mail@oldbarntouring.co.uk
Tel: +44 1983 866414
www.oldbarntouring.co.uk

Open (Touring Pitches):
Start March - End October.

Old Barn is a small friendly park with downland views in a beautiful countryside setting. The park takes its name from the 17th-century thatched barn at the park's entrance. Nowadays, the barn is used as a games and TV room (open Spring Bank Holiday to early September). Landscaping has provided the park with 60 sheltered pitches all with hard road access and electrical hook-up.

The site welcomes tents, motorhomes, caravans and trailer tents. Dogs on leads are welcomed, and from your spacious pitch, you can venture into the countryside on many walks surrounding the park. At the park's reception, you will find ample information on numerous places of interest, beaches and countryside activities that the island has to offer. A supermarket and petrol station are only a 1/4 mile away. A 5-minute drive will take you to Sandown or Shanklin, with their lovely sandy beaches and seaside entertainment.

The fully tiled toilet block has individual cubicles in the ladies for extra privacy. Spacious showers have ample room to change and accept 20p coins. A freezer pack exchange is available using site ice packs. Camping and Calor gas sales. Bus stop 200 metres. WiFi around the reception area. Motorhome service point. TV room. TV reception is good. Pets allowed. Dog walk. Children's play area. Charge for pets and awnings. Tents allowed.

Key Features

 Pets Accepted

 Beach Access

 Play Area

Scan me for more information.

Alan Rogers Code: UK2330
27 pitches
GPS: 50.85208, -0.84811
Post Code: PO18 8DL

West Sussex, South East

www.alanrogers.com/uk2330
contact@conciergecamping.co.uk
Tel: +44 1243 573118
www.conciergecamping.co.uk

Open (Touring Pitches):
Mid January - Early December.

Concierge Camping

Concierge Camping at Ratham Estate opened a luxury touring park in 2015. Each generous pitch is framed with hedging for seclusion and privacy. Originally a working farm until the 1990s, the estate has three Grade II listed properties on-site, which include a chapel, the original water mill and a farmhouse. Hardstanding pitches of three sizes, including Emperor pitches with a day-living Safari tent. Luxury safari-style lodges are also available.

The Ratham Estate is situated in West Ashling near Chichester and is steeped in history; it is mentioned in the Domesday Book and originates from the 15th century. The current owners, Lord and Lady Hodgkin, purchased the estate in 2011 and are bringing it back to its former glory.

All pitches have hardstanding. 16amp power supplies. Fresh & wastewater. Enclosed grass recreation area. Satellite TV sockets. Fully equipped laundry, comprising of a washing machine and tumble dryer. Indoor dish-washing area. Luxury toilet and shower block. 2 late-arrival bays. Pets welcome. Electric bicycles are available to hire from a local supplier.

Key Features

 Pets Accepted

 Disabled Facilities

 Bike Hire

Scan me for more information.

Alan Rogers Code: UK2700
12 accommodations
200 pitches
GPS: 51.54660, -0.82480
Post Code: SL6 5NE

Berkshire, South

Hurley Riverside Park

www.alanrogers.com/uk2700
info@hurleyriversidepark.co.uk
Tel: +44 1628 824493
www.hurleyriversidepark.co.uk

Open (Touring Pitches):
Start March - End October.

On the banks of the Thames, not far from Henley-on-Thames, you will find the picturesque village of Hurley, where some buildings date back to 1086. Just outside the village is Hurley Riverside Park, which has been family-run since 1926 and provides facilities for holiday homes, touring units, tents and moorings for boats.

The touring area is flat and separated into smaller fields. With the pitches arranged around the outside of each field and the centre left free, the park has a spacious feel, even during busy periods. There are 200 touring pitches, 146 with 10-16A Europlug, including 13 fully serviced and some on long hardstandings, especially for American-style RVs. A camping field provides 62 tent pitches, including some with electric hook-ups. A very popular park, and there is also a large rally field.

Three wooden toilet blocks (raised on legs) include a very good unisex block with private bathrooms (shower, washbasin, toilet). The other blocks have been renovated and are well-equipped. Family shower rooms in one block (shower, WC, washbasin). Separate shower and toilet facilities for disabled visitors at reception. Baby area. Launderette. Motorhome services. Well-stocked shop at reception. Play area. Fishing. Electric car charging points. Temporary moorings. Nature and wildlife trail, riverside picnic grounds, slipway and fishing in season. American RVs accepted.

Key Features

 Pets Accepted

 Disabled Facilities

 Play Area

 Fishing

Scan me for more information.

221

Alan Rogers Code: UK2942
1 accommodations
12 pitches
GPS: 50.94855, -0.19245
Post Code: BN6 9EZ

West Sussex, South East

Apollo Sun Club

www.alanrogers.com/uk2942
apollonaturistcamping@gmail.com
Tel: +44 7919 260462
www.apollosunclub.co.uk

Open (Touring Pitches):
Start April - Late September.

This small, well-established, family-orientated, naturist campsite is run by and for its members. It is within ten miles of Brighton and the Sussex coast. The site is ideal for campers wishing to try naturism for the first time without pressure to disrobe until comfortable to do so. The site has extensive sunbathing lawns and many quieter spots in just under six acres of ancient woodland. There is plenty of room for eight caravans or motorhomes (10A electricity), three of them hardstandings, and room around the site for tents. One chalet can be rented. The communal barbecue (most Saturdays), occasional spit roast, solar-heated swimming pool, and clubhouse are all popular gathering points.

Brighton is a lively town, well known for its entertainment and pier. The 45-metre observation wheel has panoramic views over the town and the English Channel. Vineyards offer guided tours and wine-tasting events a little closer to the campsite. The Sussex Downs are full of interesting formal gardens and ancient sites. Nearby are the prehistoric Cissbury Ring hillfort and Neolithic flint mine.

Key Features

  Naturist Site

  Swimming Pool

Two sanitary blocks with mainly open, pushbutton showers, one private cubicle per block. No laundry. Dishwashing and cooking facilities with the use of a fridge-freezer. Clubhouse. Solar-heated swimming pool. Sauna (£1.50). Short tennis court. Snooker. Darts. Barbecue and spit roast. Chalet to rent.

Scan me for more information.

Alan Rogers Code: UK3055
150 pitches
GPS: 51.20073, 0.39333
Post Code: TN12 6PY

Kent, South East

www.alanrogers.com/uk3055
touring@thehopfarm.co.uk
Tel: +44 1622 870838
www.thehopfarm.co.uk/stay

Open (Touring Pitches):
Start March - End October.

The Hop Farm Campsite

Set in 500 acres of the Garden of England, The Hop Farm Touring & Camping Park is a popular family visitor attraction. There are plenty of activities to entertain children, including adventure play areas (indoor and outdoor), a driving school, funfair rides, the Magic Factory and the Great Goblin Hunt.

This is also the venue for many special events throughout the summer, including music festivals & shows. To one side, overlooking all this activity and the attractive cluster of oasts is the touring park, which provides 150 pitches, of which 75 are hardstanding on flat, open fields. Electricity (16A) and water are available. There are also 1000 pitches for tents! The main toilet block is clean and provides straightforward facilities; these are supplemented by prefab units when events bring extra campers.

Brand new state-of-the-art showers and washrooms have been added to the site to enhance guest experiences, providing a luxurious touch to their stay. Small shop (in reception) for essentials. Free entry for campers and caravanners to the Family Park with restaurant and café. Nature walks. Boat launching. Fishing. Dogs are accepted but not permitted inside the visitor attraction. Activities and entertainment at the visitor attraction.

Key Features

 Pets Accepted

 Disabled Facilities

 Play Area

 Bar/Restaurant

 Fishing

Scan me for more information.

Alan Rogers Code: UK3048
5 pitches
GPS: 51.20236, 0.60365
Post Code: ME17 3ED

Kent, South East

www.alanrogers.com/uk3048
hudson2323@me.com
Tel: +44 1622 844491
www.roundoak-hebridean.co.uk

Open (Touring Pitches):
Early May - Late October.

Roundoak Farm Camping

Round Oak Farm is a smaller, CL-style campsite on a working farm that focuses mainly on rare breed sheep and cows. Located in the heart of the Kentish countryside, south of the county town of Maidstone. The grassland farm consists of 180 acres, including 5 acres of a natural oak woodland walk and 9 acres of walking routes open to guests. Dogs are allowed on site but must be kept on a lead at all times.

The site has generously sized touring pitches on the level mowed grass, all with 16 Amp hookups. You can also find two hard-standing pitches located at the back of the campsite near the woodland area. The site has secure-coded access gates and security cameras, and the camping area is gated and fenced away from the main farm buildings.

The yard bar on the main farm site is a unique barn regularly used for functions and entertainment. The campsite has invested in a new sanitary block situated at the back of the yard bar, where you can find two communal showers and two toilets with sinks for washing up.

There is a separate accessible toilet and shower available to guests. Single sanitary building with two showers and two toilets, Shop (small), Reception, BBQ available to hire, Dogs allowed, Adults only.

Key Features

 Book Online

 Adults Only

 Pets Accepted

 Disabled Facilities

Scan me for more information.

Alan Rogers Code: UK3040
25 accommodations
110 pitches
GPS: 51.10647, 0.86809
Post Code: TN26 1NQ

Kent, South East

www.alanrogers.com/uk3040
holidaypark@broadhembury.co.uk
Tel: +44 1233 620859
www.broadhembury.co.uk

Open (Touring Pitches):
All year.

Broadhembury Caravan Park

Broadhembury Caravan & Camping Park is found in the quiet countryside just outside Ashford and within easy reach of London, Dover, Folkestone and the Kent coast. There are areas for family camping with play areas and amenities designed with children in mind and separate quiet meadows just for adults with new luxury facilities.

In total, the park takes 110 touring units of any type. The well-kept pitches are on level grass and backed by tall, neat hedges, 105 with electricity connections (10/16A). In addition, six pitches are fully serviced, and ten more have double hardstanding plus a grass area for an awning. The welcome is friendly at this popular park and is often full in the main season.

Well-equipped toilet block for the family areas and ecologically considered block for the couples meadows. Underfloor heating. Private cabins. High-quality facilities for disabled visitors. Well-equipped laundry room. Good campers' kitchen, fully enclosed with microwaves, fridge and freezer, all free of charge. Motorhome services. Well-stocked shop with local produce, wine and beer (butchers, bakery and papers to order). Internet access. Pool room, games room with video games, table football and table tennis. Two play areas (one for children under 7 yrs), one with an all-weather surface. Playing field adjacent to touring area. Campers' herb garden. WiFi over site (charged). Up to two dogs per pitch are accepted. Large units are accepted if pre-booked.

Key Features

 Adults Only

 Open All Year

 Pets Accepted

 Disabled Facilities

 Beach Access

 Play Area

Scan me for more information.

Alan Rogers Code: UK4177
33 accommodations
72 pitches
GPS: 51.74728, -1.97111
Post Code: GL7 7BH

Gloucestershire, Heart of England

www.alanrogers.com/uk4177
enquiries@mayfieldpark.co.uk
Tel: +44 1285 831301
www.mayfieldpark.co.uk

Open (Touring Pitches):
All year.

Mayfield Touring Park

Mayfield Touring Park is a family-run touring and residential park nestled in the hills on the outskirts of the famous market town of Cirencester, the 'Capital of the Cotswolds'. Spread across twelve acres; the wide-open fields boast views across the Churn Valley, with buzzards and kites circling overhead and a spectacular sunset come nightfall. There is always a friendly face to welcome you and lend a helping hand throughout your stay.

Whether you want a short weekend stay to explore the wonders of the Cotswolds or you are looking for a longer-term stay, this is the place for you. The site has 72 touring pitches (some are seasonal), most with an electric hook-up point. There are also 33 privately owned mobile homes.

The modern heated toilet block has showers, wash basins and WCs. Facility for visitors who are disabled. Laundry room. Dishwashing area. Vegetable preparation area. Chemical toilet point. Pets welcome. Shop. Gas sales. WiFi free. No children's play area. No motorhome service point. Public transport adjacent. Mobile phone signal poor.

Key Features

 Open All Year

 Pets Accepted

 Disabled Facilities

Scan me for more information.

Alan Rogers Code: UK2590
140 pitches
GPS: 51.85754, -1.29142
Post Code: OX5 3BQ

Oxfordshire, South

www.alanrogers.com/uk2590
info@greenhill-leisure-park.co.uk
Tel: +44 1869 351600
www.greenhill-leisure-park.co.uk

Open (Touring Pitches):
Late March - Late October.

Greenhill Leisure Park

Greenhill Leisure Park is situated in the heart of the beautiful Oxfordshire countryside. Nestled between the beauty of the Cotswolds and the scenic Chiltern Hills, the site is well-positioned to explore the attractions in the area. Close to Oxford, it is accessible, being 6 miles from junction 9 of the M40 and 3 miles from the A34. Nearby, you can visit Blenheim Palace, Cotswold Wildlife Park, Waddesdon Manor and Bicester Village Outlet Centre.

For fishermen, there are four well-stocked fishing lakes situated next to Greenhill. There is also access to the River Cherwell/Oxfordshire Canal approx. 400 metres from the site. There are 140 grass or hardstanding pitches. Most have an electric hook-up point, and 12 are serviced pitches (waste & water). There are also two pitches suitable for large motorhomes.

Three toilet blocks provide showers, washbasins and WCs, shaver points, and a hairdryer. Two of which have ramp access to facilities for visitors who are disabled and families. Chemical toilet point. Separate laundry room. Dishwashing area. Campers kitchen. Wet weather shelter. Information area. Well-stocked shop selling camping equipment, groceries and own farm produce between April-Sept. Play area with assault course, football nets and kite flying area. Fishing lakes. Games/meeting room. Well-behaved dogs accepted (on leads while on-farm). Caravan storage. WiFi charged. The earliest time of arrival is 14:00.

Key Features

 Pets Accepted

 Disabled Facilities

 Play Area

 Fishing

Scan me for more information.

227

Alan Rogers Code: UK3210
88 accommodations
34 pitches
GPS: 51.75374, 0.00013
Post Code: EN11 0AS

Hertfordshire, London

www.alanrogers.com/uk3210
dobbsweircampsite@leevalleypark.org.uk
Tel: +44 3000 030619
www.visitleevalley.org.uk/lee-valley-caravan-park-dobbs-weir

Open (Touring Pitches):
Mid April - End January.

Lee Valley, Dobbs Weir

This large (27-acre) camping park is ideally situated in the Lee Valley for fishing, walking and cycling activities. It is divided into two sections: one for private static caravans with a large fenced caravan storage area, the other for touring. The 34 level touring pitches are numbered but not separated; all have 10A electricity, and 22 are hardstanding. There is an area for tents with a field adjacent to the River Lee for tents requiring electricity.

The whole complex is very flat with little shade. There is no public transport, but a 25-minute walk along a towpath takes you to Broxbourne railway station for travel along the Lee Valley to London. Reception has a range of maps showing walking routes. Within a short distance, there is riding and white-water rafting. Many of the villages and towns in the region are of historical interest and worth visiting, along with the close proximity of the Olympic Park and London.

Two modern, heated toilet blocks with controllable showers, open washbasins and facilities for disabled campers. Washing machines and dryers. Motorhome services. Small shop (open all season). Small play area. River fishing. Bicycle hire. WiFi over site.

Key Features

 Pets Accepted

 Disabled Facilities

 Play Area

 Bike Hire

 Fishing

Scan me for more information.

Alan Rogers Code: UK3290
70 pitches
GPS: 51.78996, 0.98460
Post Code: CO5 8FE

Essex, East of England

www.alanrogers.com/uk3290
havefun@fenfarm.co.uk
Tel: +44 1206 383275
www.fenfarm.co.uk

Open (Touring Pitches):
Mid March - Late October.

Fen Farm Campsite

Tents were first pitched at Fen Farm in 1923, and since then, the park has 'grown rather than developed' – something of which owners Ralph and Wenda Lord and their family are proud. There are approximately 120 pitches (many seasonal), with 70 available for touring. They are all unmarked, on level grass and within four fields with a spacious feel. An area for 90 privately owned holiday homes is separate and screened from the touring area. All pitches have 10A electricity connections, and three have hardstanding and are fully serviced.

A limited number of seasonal pitches are available on the smaller field, with outstanding views and direct access to the beach. This is an attractive well laid out site, with trees and two ponds. The site provides facilities for launching boats from the seashore and is popular with water skiers and windsurfers. Jet skis are not allowed. There are also many opportunities for walking, either inland or along the beach.

The very good toilet block in the main touring field includes a family room and shower/toilet for disabled visitors. Laundry room. Gas supplies. Two play areas. Caravan and boat storage. WiFi throughout (charged).

Key Features

 Pets Accepted

 Disabled Facilities

 Beach Access

 Play Area

 Sailing

Scan me for more information.

Alan Rogers Code: UK3365
150 accommodations
55 pitches
GPS: 52.22018, 1.56370
Post Code: IP16 4TE

Suffolk, East of England

www.alanrogers.com/uk3365
reception@cakesandale.co.uk
Tel: +44 1728 831655
www.cakesandale.co.uk

Open (Touring Pitches):
Start April - End October.

Cakes And Ale Park

Cakes and Ale Holiday Park is set amongst beautiful Suffolk scenery between Aldeburgh and Southwold Cakes and is an oasis of tranquillity and quality. Just minutes from the Minsmere bird sanctuary and the ancient monument of Leiston Abbey. It is the ideal place to explore the Suffolk Heritage coast (or to relax and put your feet up).

All pitches are fully serviced with grass and hard standing, water, a 10amp electric hook-up, grey water connections, and free Wi-Fi. The recreation field has a playground, football goals, golf practice range, tennis courts and a boule rink (with equipment available to borrow free of charge). A section of the touring and motorhome area is an Adults only area for those that really value a bit of peace and quiet. The site has 55 hard-standing/grass-touring pitches. There are also 150 privately owned mobile homes.

The heated toilet block has wet rooms, showers and WCs. Facility for guests who are disabled. Laundry with washing machine and tumble dryer. Motorhome service point. Outdoor area to hang washing. Dishwashing area. Chemical toilet point. Gas sales. WiFi charged. Small shop. Bar. Pets allowed. Dog walk. Children's play area. Public transport nearby. Electric car charging points. Tennis courts. Boules area. Golf practice range. Supermarket 3miles.

Key Features

 Pets Accepted

 Disabled Facilities

 Beach Access

 Play Area

 Bar/Restaurant

 Golf

Scan me for more information.

Alan Rogers Code: UK3385
11 accommodations
160 pitches
GPS: 52.44636, 1.02514
Post Code: NR16 2HE

Norfolk, East of England

www.alanrogers.com/uk3385
info@applewoodholidays.co.uk
Tel: +44 1953 715319
www.applewoodholidays.co.uk

Open (Touring Pitches):
All year.

Applewood Country Park

Whether you're looking to explore Norfolk's many historic sights and lively market towns, set out for an adventure to take in the beautiful countryside and stunning coastline or want to relax, Applewood Countryside Park is your perfect choice of campsite.

A tranquil, family-friendly caravan park and campsite set within 13 acres of grassy parkland, it caters for all. Spacious pitches with electric hook-ups are separated by mature laurel hedges allowing plenty of privacy. The park then has a large central area with unmarked pitches for those who do not need electricity. There is a further area with pitches which can be booked exclusively and a large field too, perfect for rallies and larger groups. Six cosy glamping pods and five luxury en-suite Shepherd's Cabins are available for hire.

Launched in April 2019, Applewood now boasts eight contemporary private shower rooms with underfloor heating and adjustable water temperature, plus two fully accessible/ family-friendly bathrooms. Two separate toilet buildings provide clean and adequate facilities. Washing machine and dryer. Gas supplies. Rally field. Children's play area. Free WiFi. Dogs are welcome at no extra charge. Secure storage facility.

Key Features

 Book Online

 Open All Year

 Pets Accepted

 Disabled Facilities

 Beach Access

 Play Area

Scan me for more information.

Alan Rogers Code: UK3435
160 accommodations
180 pitches
GPS: 52.92093, 1.17445
Post Code: NR26 8TU

Norfolk, East of England

Woodlands Caravan Park

www.alanrogers.com/uk3435
info@woodlandscaravanpark.co.uk
Tel: +44 1263 823802
www.woodlandscaravanpark.co.uk

Open (Touring Pitches):
Late March - End October.

This pleasant caravan park is set in parkland in the beautiful surroundings of north Norfolk's protected heathland, next to Sheringham Park (National Trust). There are 180 grass pitches, around half of which are on a gentle slope, and all have 10A electricity. They are in two main areas for caravans and motorhomes (tents are not accepted). Caravan holiday homes (160) occupy the edge of the site on three sides, all privately owned.

A major feature of this site is the superb modern toilet block with electronically controlled showers and underfloor heating. There are many lovely local walks, including one to the beach (1.5 miles). The park is within easy reach of Holt, Cromer and Sheringham, with the major birdwatching areas of Blakeney, Cley and Salthouse also within 30 minutes drive.

One excellent new toilet block provides all the necessary facilities, including those for disabled visitors, baby changing and laundry. Well-stocked shop. Gas supplies. Lounge bar and family bar with musical entertainment most weekends. Barbecues. Play area (fenced and gated). Adjacent Woodlands Leisure Club with an indoor pool, gym, and sauna (all year).

Key Features

 Pets Accepted

 Disabled Facilities

 Beach Access

 Swimming Pool

 Play Area

 Bar/Restaurant

Scan me for more information.

Lucksall Caravan Park

Alan Rogers Code: UK4310
34 accommodations
140 pitches
GPS: 52.02302, -2.63052
Post Code: HR1 4LP

Herefordshire, Heart of England

www.alanrogers.com/uk4310
karen@lucksallpark.co.uk
Tel: +44 1432 870213
www.lucksallpark.co.uk

Open (Touring Pitches):
Start March - End November.

Set in 21 acres and bounded on one side by the River Wye and over 90 acres of woodland on the other, Lucksall Caravan and Camping Site has 140 large, well spaced and level touring pitches (some seasonal), all with 16 amp electricity and 70 with hardstandings. The river is open to the site with lifebelts and safety messages in evidence. Canoes are available for hire, or bring your own (launching facilities); fishing permits may be obtained from reception. A large, fenced playground and a large grassy game area are provided. A well-stocked shop selling various goods is in reception (a mini market is within 1.5 miles), and there is a café/takeaway.

The site is a member of the Caravan and Motorhome Club Affiliated Site Scheme, but visitors who are not members of the club are also very welcome. It is also a member of the Countryside Discovery group.

Key Features

 Pets Accepted

 Disabled Facilities

 Play Area

 Fishing

Three centrally heated toilet blocks provide top-of-the-range facilities, and two separate units with ramped entrances for visitors who are disabled. Family room. Laundry room. Shop and licensed café/takeaway. Gas sales. Free WiFi. Only breathable groundsheets are permitted. No late-night arrivals area. Pets allowed. Dog walk. BBQs allowed. TV reception good. Bus stop adjacent. Train station 4 miles. Tesco 4 miles. Boat launch facility. 4 Glamping Pods. 4 Glamping Huts. 1 Glamping Pavilion. Earliest arrival time 13:00.

Scan me for
more information.

Alan Rogers Code: UK4070
48 pitches
GPS: 52.43930, -1.66947
Post Code: CV7 7PL

Warwickshire, Heart of England

www.alanrogers.com/uk4070
enquiries@somerswood.co.uk
Tel: +44 1676 522978
somerswood.co.uk

Open (Touring Pitches):
All year.

Somers Wood Caravan Park

Somers Wood is a quiet, peaceful park, attractively situated amongst mixed conifers and deciduous trees. A very pleasant park which only accepts adults and does not take tents, it is especially convenient for those visiting shows at the NEC in Birmingham when it can get very busy.

From the reception building at the entrance, an oval gravel road provides access to 48 pitches, all on hardstandings and with 10A electricity hook-ups. Areas of woodland, carpeted with flowers in summer, surround the site and partition it into small intimate areas that create a rural feel. Log buildings blend comfortably into the surroundings providing reception, the owners' home, separate sanitary facilities, new laundry and drying room, and tourist information.

The central, heated, modern sanitary block is fully equipped. Shower cubicles are especially large. A separate block for disabled visitors is located away from the main block. New laundry and drying room. WiFi throughout (charged).

Key Features

 Adults Only

 Open All Year

 Pets Accepted

 Disabled Facilities

 Golf

Scan me for
more information.

Alan Rogers Code: UK3580
282 pitches
GPS: 52.56053, -0.30593
Post Code: PE2 5UU

Cambridgeshire, East of England

Ferry Meadows (CAMC)

www.alanrogers.com/uk3580
UKSitesBookingService@camc.com
Tel: +44 1733 233526
www.camc.com

Open (Touring Pitches):
All year.

Ferry Meadows Caravan and Motorhome Club site lies 3 miles from bustling Peterborough and closer still to the East of England Showground. The immaculate site is an ideal family holiday site occupying 30 acres of the 500-acre Nene Country Park. Open all year; the site provides 282 pitches (16A electricity) – grass pitches on one side of the park, informally laid out in small groups and surrounded by a variety of mature trees, and 132 gravel hardstandings just across the road for caravans and motorhomes.

A very small area (with electricity) is reserved for tents. Families with children may prefer the grass area, where they can keep a watchful eye on the well-equipped playground.

Key Features

 Book Online

 Open All Year

 Pets Accepted

 Disabled Facilities

 Play Area

Two modern, well-appointed and heated toilet blocks are of a high standard, with en-suite facilities for disabled visitors in one block. Baby/toddler washroom. Laundry room. Dishwashing area. Motorhome services. Chemical toilet point. BBQs allowed. Pets allowed. Dog walk adjacent. The office stocks basic provisions, including Gas. Fish and chip van at weekends. Good play areas. TV reception booster system. WiFi fair (charged). Security barrier. Twin Axle Caravans accepted. No late-night arrivals area. Tents allowed. Defibrillator. Information room. Bus stop 900 metres. Train station 4 miles. Earliest time of arrival 13:00. Maximum outfit length 9 metres.

Scan me for more information.

Alan Rogers Code: UK4435
1 accommodations
46 pitches
GPS: 52.69827, -2.86597
Post Code: SY5 9GD

Shropshire, Heart of England

www.alanrogers.com/uk4435
info@cartrefcaravansite.co.uk
Tel: +44 1743 821688
www.cartrefcaravansite.co.uk

Open (Touring Pitches):
Start March - End January.

Cartref Caravan & Camping

This delightful, small, family-run campsite is situated just 5 miles outside of the stunning Medieval market town of Shrewsbury. Surrounded by countryside with views of the Shropshire hills, the site offers easy access from the A5 and is an ideal base to explore Shropshire and the towns and villages on the Welsh border.

Cartref is also the first campsite off the A5 travelling North West, making it an ideal stop-off on your route to North and Mid Wales. Onsite features include a children's play area, a uniquely styled bar, and an adults-only area.

Award-winning amenities include hot showers, privacy cubicles, and a family and disabled washroom. Laundry room with coin-operated washing machine, tumble dryer, iron & ironing board. Unique onsite bar with log burner serving local ales, lager, wines & spirits, including local gin. Pizzas & takeaways. Breakfasts are served at weekends. Onsite shop selling locally sourced produce and campsite essentials. A dog-friendly dedicated off-lead area is available; quiet, friendly dogs are welcome in the bar. Dedicated adults-only area. Children's play area. Free WiFi.

Key Features

 Pets Accepted

 Disabled Facilities

 Play Area

 Bar/Restaurant

Scan me for more information.

Alan Rogers Code: UK5241
1 accommodations
115 pitches
GPS: 53.19743, -2.59872
Post Code: CW7 2QJ

Cheshire, North West

Elm Cottage Touring

www.alanrogers.com/uk5241
booking@elmcottage.co.uk
Tel: +44 1829 760544
www.elmcottage.co.uk

Open (Touring Pitches):
All year.

Elm Cottage has an unusual facility for such a small site – a pizza oven, open most Fridays during July & August and all Fridays on Bank Holiday weekends. Bring along a drink & watch your pizzas being freshly made to order. In 2018 the site commissioned 'Creative Play' to design & build a new children's park.

A dog-friendly park, Elm Cottage welcomes well-behaved dogs and their owners! It has a large, dedicated dog walking area within the grounds where you can let your dog off the lead. Open all year; the site is suitable for caravans, motorhomes and trailer tents. A combination of camping, rally and seasonal pitches are available. The touring park has 35 pitches, all with electric hookups. Hard surfaced access roads lead to a mix of pitch types, including six fully serviced pitches (16 amp EHU) with generous gravelled surfaces, fresh water and grey waste facility, picnic bench, dustbin and night-time low-level lighting.

Key Features

 Open All Year

 Pets Accepted

 Disabled Facilities

 Play Area

The heated toilet block, showers, dishwashing room, laundry room and a disabled/toddler wet room (accessed by a RADAR key). Shop. Calor Gas sales. WiFi charged. Tyre inflation facility. Children's play area. Dog walk.

Scan me for more information.

Alan Rogers Code: UK3846
49 pitches
GPS: 53.20437, -1.82830
Post Code: SK17 9QG

Derbyshire, Heart of England

www.alanrogers.com/uk3846
info@pomeroycaravanpark.co.uk
Tel: +44 1298 83259
www.pomeroycaravanpark.co.uk

Open (Touring Pitches):
Early April - Late October.

Pomeroy Caravan Park

Pomeroy Caravan Park is a small, family-run site on a farm in the heart of the Peak District, perfectly situated for exploring the High Peak Trail and surrounding areas. Set away from the Ashbourne to Buxton Road, it is easy to find yet lovely and quiet. A picturesque location in the Peak District, it provides magnificent views of the High Peaks, a very rural part of the county. Easy access to many local walks, including the High Peak Trail, with no need to go on any roads, so it is a safe option for families and cyclists who want to experience the lovely countryside.

The site is a wonderful place for anyone to stay, suitable for young and old, couples and families, and the perfect base for a weekend break or a longer holiday to explore the Peak District area. The site has 49 grass or hardstanding pitches, most with 16 amp electricity.

A single toilet block has underfloor heating, toilets, showers and washbasins. Family bathroom and disabled wash facilities. Laundry. Dishwashing area. Free WiFi is available throughout the site. Reception/ shop stocking essential items, camping equipment, milk, ice cream, milkshakes, and a small range of other local produce such as meat and baked goods. Fire pit hire available. Ball games field. Dog exercise area – well-behaved dogs on leads are welcome all over the site.

Key Features

Pets Accepted

Disabled Facilities

Scan me for
more information.

Alan Rogers Code: UK3954
30 pitches
GPS: 53.33801, -0.90478
Post Code: DN22 9NJ

Nottinghamshire, Heart of England

www.alanrogers.com/uk3954
info@olivetreecaravanandcamping.co.uk
Tel: +44 1777 703415
olivetreecaravanandcamping.co.uk

Open (Touring Pitches):
All year.

Olive Tree Camping Park

Once settled into your spacious pitch at Olive Tree Caravan and Camping Park, feel free to plan activities such as fishing, historic building visits, and spa days. There are also miles and miles of wonderful walks along the Chesterfield Canal, Clumber Park, or the famed Sherwood Forest.

Should the weather make it possible, you are welcome to fire up a barbecue. For supplies, browse the selection of essentials at the site shop or take the 10-minute drive to the supermarkets in Retford. Several security measures ensure that guests can sleep easily. The smart modern toilet block has heating and accessible facilities.

A single toilet block provides showers, washbasins and WC's. Facility for visitors who are disabled. Chemical toilet point. Dishwashing area. Shop. BBQ's allowed. Electricity metered, tokens from office. Dogs allowed. Dog walk. Security barrier. Pic-Nic tables. Bar, Restaurant, Farmer's market, Fishing, Cycle hire and Public transport nearby. Caravan/Motorhome storage. Earliest arrival is 13.00.

Key Features

 Adults Only

 Open All Year

 Pets Accepted

 Disabled Facilities

Scan me for more information.

Alan Rogers Code: UK3675
20 accommodations
120 pitches
GPS: 53.11666, -0.20665
Post Code: LN4 4JS

Lincolnshire, Heart of England

www.alanrogers.com/uk3675
sales@willowholt.co.uk
Tel: +44 1526 343111
www.willowholt.co.uk

Open (Touring Pitches):
Mid March - Late October.

Willow Holt Camping Park

Willow Holt is a pleasant park with appeal for those who would like a quiet location from which to explore this interesting corner of Lincolnshire. It covers 25 acres of woodland and former gravel pits, with the camping areas on flat land alongside fishing and boating lakes.

There are 60 pitches occupied on a seasonal basis, and a further 60 are available for touring units. All have 10A electricity and water taps close by. An area without electricity is available for tents. Along the lakeside are 20 mobile homes, most are privately owned, but three are available to rent. Facilities are continually improved with roads resurfaced, plus a modern entrance and reception building.

The heated toilet block has showers, washbasins, WCs, shaver points, and mirrors. Facilities for visitors who are disabled. Dishwashing area. Chemical toilet point. Motorhome services. Laundry room with washing machines, dryers and iron/ironing board. Baby change facility. Motorhome service point. Caravan accessory shop. Restaurant. Bar. WiFi. Pets welcome. Children's play area. Ice pack freezer.

Key Features

 Pets Accepted

 Play Area

 Fishing

Scan me for more information.

Alan Rogers Code: UK5360
79 pitches
GPS: 53.58880, -3.04400
Post Code: PR8 3ST

Mersey, North West

www.alanrogers.com/uk5360
info@willowbankcp.co.uk
Tel: +44 1704 571566
www.willowbankcp.co.uk

Open (Touring Pitches):
All year - Excl. February.

Willowbank Touring Park

Well situated for the Sefton coast and Southport, Willowbank Holiday Home & Touring Park is set on the edge of sand dunes amongst mature, -windswept trees. Entrance to the park is controlled by a barrier, with a pass-key issued at the excellent reception building, which doubles as a sales office for the substantial, high-quality caravan holiday home development.

There are 79 touring pitches, 30 on gravel hardstandings, 16 on grass and a further 33 pitches, all with 10A electricity; these are on grass hardstanding using an environmentally friendly reinforcement system. Large units are accepted by prior arrangement. . This is a lovely flat open site which is very well maintained, with large pitches, all with electric, and you have a choice of where you wish to pitch. Facilities were modern and clean in a central block with easy access. If you have mobility issues, this site is ideal as surfaces are smooth and the site is level.

The purpose-built, heated toilet block is of a high standard, including an excellent bathroom for disabled visitors, although the showers are rather compact. Baby room. Laundry. Motorhome services. Play area. A field for ball games. Beauty treatments. WiFi throughout (charged).

Key Features

 Pets Accepted

 Disabled Facilities

 Beach Access

 Play Area

Scan me for
more information.

Alan Rogers Code: UK5331
57 pitches
GPS: 53.81609, -2.91363
Post Code: PR4 3HN

Lancashire, North West

www.alanrogers.com/uk5331
info@littleorchardcaravanpark.com
Tel: +44 1253 836658
www.littleorchardcaravanpark.com

Open (Touring Pitches):
Mid February - End December.

Little Orchard Caravan Park

Little Orchard Caravan Park was given its name as it is located opposite the Johnsons' prize-winning apple orchard. The park has been designed to provide all the facilities required in open and tranquil surroundings whilst not disturbing the adjoining countryside. The 4-acre site is set in open fields with trees all around it. There are 57 pitches, each with an electric hook-up point.

There are some lovely walks in the local area with several public footpaths that can take you across the fields in the heart of the countryside. For the more adventurous, the Trough of Bowland, Pendle Hill and Beacon Fell are only a 40-minute drive away, and the Lake District is only 50 minutes away. The Shell Petrol Station, ¾ mile away from the park, has a shop. A Morrisons and Aldi are in Kirkham, and a Tesco superstore is at junction 4 of the M55.

Toilet block, shower & hairdryer (chargeable). Facilities for ladies, gents and visitors who are disabled. Fresh water supply. Electric hook-up. Chemical toilet disposal point.

Key Features

 Pets Accepted

 Disabled Facilities

 Beach Access

Scan me for more information.

Alan Rogers Code: UK4791
5 accommodations
62 pitches
GPS: 53.58993, -1.77155
Post Code: HD9 7TD

West Yorkshire, Yorkshire

www.alanrogers.com/uk4791
enquiries@holmevalleycamping.com
Tel: +44 1484 665819
www.holmevalleycamping.com

Open (Touring Pitches):
All year.

Holme Valley Camping

Holme Valley Camping & Caravan Park is a family-run park of 3 generations; Owners Philip and Hazel have turned what was once a derelict mill site into a caravan park. This area is a paradise for walkers, horse riders and cyclists with nearby reservoirs, each of them enjoying stunning views. There are also several canal towpaths nearby, ideal for cycling, or for a real challenge, head up Holme Moss, with breath-taking views.

The site is situated just a mile from Holmfirth with its wide range of individual shops, cafes, restaurants and galleries. The site has 62 pitches (some seasonal), most with an electric hook-up point. A selection of camping and glamping cabins are available to hire.

Two toilet blocks (one heated) provide showers, wash basins & WCs. Vanity area with hair dryers. Baby changing facilities. Family bathrooms are available to hire hourly, for the whole or part of the stay. Facilities for wheelchair users. Laundry. Chemical toilet point. Gas sales. Small shop. Ice pack freezer. Children's play area. Archery (chargeable). Bus stop 1 mile. Pets welcome. Dog walk adjacent.

Key Features

 Open All Year

 Pets Accepted

 Play Area

 Fishing

Scan me for more information.

Alan Rogers Code: UK4647
24 pitches
GPS: 53.76882, -0.86049
Post Code: DN14 7LD

East Yorkshire, Yorkshire

www.alanrogers.com/uk4647
fionabrendahouse@outlook.com
Tel: +44 1430 431189
sites.google.com/site/
brendahousetouringcaravanpark

Open (Touring Pitches):
All year.

Brenda House Caravan Park

Brenda House Touring Caravan Site is exclusively for adults, including day visitors. The site is in a tranquil rural location at the foot of the Yorkshire Wolds, enabling visitors to relax and enjoy a peaceful break. The historic market town of Howden, only 1.5 miles away, has a choice of shops, restaurants and public houses. The site has 24 hard-standing and grass pitches.

Fishing and golf facilities are nearby, as are excellent walks and easy cycle rides. Situated 18 miles from York and has local railway links to Leeds, York, Hull, Doncaster, Manchester and Scarborough. Nearby towns of Selby, Beverly and Driffield have superb markets where many a bargain may be found.

Single toilet block provides showers (£1 shower charge for 7 mins), washbasins & WCs. Chemical toilet point. Motorhome service point. Pets welcome. Dog walking and play area. No dishwashing facility. Town Centre 1.5 miles away. Station 5 minutes walk. Supermarket, Co-operative in Howden 1.5 miles. Tesco, Asda, Lidl and Morrisons in Goole 5.7 miles. Earliest arrival time 12 noon.

Key Features

 Adults Only

 Open All Year

 Pets Accepted

Scan me for
more information.

Alan Rogers Code: UK4510
78 pitches
GPS: 54.09382, -0.31250
Post Code: YO25 4JE

East Yorkshire, Yorkshire

www.alanrogers.com/uk4510
caravansite@thorpehall.co.uk
Tel: +44 1262 420393
www.thorpehall.co.uk

Open (Touring Pitches):
Start March - End October.

Thorpe Hall Camping Site

Just outside the village of Rudston, in the grounds of Thorpe Hall, this pleasant small touring park is six miles from the sea at Bridlington. Enthusiastically managed, it is set on flat grass, largely enclosed by the old kitchen garden wall. The 78 large pitches have 16A electrical hook-ups and TV connections. There are no caravan holiday homes or seasonal pitches. Tourist information leaflets on a range of local walks are provided, and visitors can arrange guided walks around the estate.

Bridlington's shops, bars and restaurants are just five miles away, as is its historic Old Town. Other attractions include the harbour with its heritage museum, the Spa Theatre and Ballroom, Sewerby Hall and Gardens and Leisure World.

Key Features

 Pets Accepted

 Disabled Facilities

 Beach Access

 Play Area

 Fishing

Heated toilet and shower block. Some cubicles with washbasins. Separate bathroom for disabled visitors and families with young children. Laundry facilities. Recycling area. Small shop with gas, essentials and local produce. Small play area. Ball games are only permitted in the Games Field (adjacent). Coarse fishing lake (charged). Free WiFi

Scan me for
more information.

245

Alan Rogers Code: UK4720
100 pitches
GPS: 54.10025, -2.28483
Post Code: BD24 0DP

North Yorkshire, Yorkshire

www.alanrogers.com/uk4720
info@knightstainforth.co.uk
Tel: +44 1729 822200
www.knightstainforth.co.uk

Open (Touring Pitches):
Start March - End October.

Knight Stainforth Hall

In a very attractive setting, this park is located in the heart of the Yorkshire Dales, the whole area a paradise for hill-walking, fishing and pot-holing, and it has outstanding scenery. The camping area is on slightly sloping grass, sheltered by mature woodland. There are 100 touring pitches (20 are seasonal), 60 with 16A electricity and water and 25 with hardstanding. A separate area contains 66 privately owned caravan holiday homes.

A gate leads from the bottom of the camping field, giving access to the river bank where the Ribble bubbles over small waterfalls and rocks and whirls around deep pools. This area is not fenced, and children should be supervised, although it is a super location for a family picnic. Settle is only 2 miles away, and train buffs will want to travel on the Settle-Carlisle railway over the famous Ribblehead Viaduct.

A modern, heated amenity block provides toilets and showers and includes some washbasins in cubicles. Facilities for disabled visitors and baby changing. Laundry facilities. Motorhome services. Small shop. Games/TV room. Play area with safety base. Fishing (permit from reception). Security barrier. Deposit for the key to the toilet block and barrier £10. WiFi throughout (charged).

Key Features

 Pets Accepted

 Disabled Facilities

 Play Area

 Fishing

Scan me for more information.

Alan Rogers Code: UK4580
76 pitches
GPS: 54.23745, -0.99033
Post Code: YO62 7SD

North Yorkshire, Yorkshire

www.alanrogers.com/uk4580
info@foxholmesprings.co.uk
Tel: +44 1439 772336
www.foxholmesprings.co.uk

Open (Touring Pitches):
End March - Early January.

Foxholme Springs

Foxholme Springs Touring Park is an adult-only park managed by an on-site warden. It would suit those who want a quiet holiday disturbed only by birdsong and passing deer. There are 76 grass/hardstanding touring pitches set either in an open, slightly sloping field or between trees on grass.

Thirty of the pitches are for seasonal use and are arranged amongst the trees. All the pitches have 10amp electricity (a few need long leads), and six have hardstandings. Some picnic tables are provided. The park is set in quiet countryside and would be a good base for touring, being within striking distance of the moors, the coast and York. There are no on-site activities. There is lighting, but a torch would be useful.

The heated toilet block has showers, washbasins and WCs. Chemical toilet point. Laundry with washing machine and dryer. Dishwashing room. Two further small blocks provide WCs only. Motorhome service point. Caravan storage. Dogs allowed. Dog walk.

Key Features

 Adults Only

 Pets Accepted

 Disabled Facilities

Scan me for
more information.

Alan Rogers Code: UK4532
30 accommodations
30 pitches
GPS: 54.43012, -0.54670
Post Code: YO22 4UF

North Yorkshire, Yorkshire

www.alanrogers.com/uk4532
info@middlewoodfarm.com
Tel: +44 1947 880414
www.middlewoodfarm.com

Open (Touring Pitches):
Start March - End October.

Middlewood Farm

Middlewood Farm Holiday Park is a level park, surrounded by hills and with views of the sea from some of the pitches. A short walk through the farm fields and wildflower conservation areas leads to Robin Hood's Bay's picturesque old fishing village and the sea.

The park has 30 touring pitches for caravans and motorhomes with 10A electricity, 18 with hardstanding and the remainder on grass. There is space for around 130 tents in two areas with 41 electricity connections available and 30 caravan holiday homes to rent. Camping pods are available for hire. A good beach is only ten minute walk through the fields.

Two splendid toilet blocks have clean facilities and are modern, heated and tiled, with free showers and private cabins. Fully equipped laundry room including iron and board. Facilities for babies and disabled visitors. Play area with bark base set amongst the tents. WiFi on part of the site (charged).

Key Features

 Pets Accepted

 Disabled Facilities

 Beach Access

 Play Area

Scan me for more information.

Alan Rogers Code: UK5534
117 pitches
GPS: 54.21552, -2.86422
Post Code: LA11 6RB

Grange-over-Sands, Cumbria

www.alanrogers.com/uk5534
UKSitesBookingService@camc.com
Tel: +44 15395 32912
www.camc.com

Open (Touring Pitches):
All year.

Meathop Fell (CAMC)

Peaceful Meathop Fell Caravan and Motorhome Club site, just outside pretty Grange-over-Sands, is thoughtfully laid out with separate pitching areas attractively divided by shrubs and grass. The site is an ideal base to launch your exploration of North Lancashire and the beautiful Southern Lake District. Brockhole, the National Park Visitor Centre, is a good place to start your exploration as it holds an enormous collection of information, books and audio/visual material about the Lakes under one roof.

The site is open all year and has 117 grass/hardstanding pitches all with 16 amp electricity. The entire area is a walker's paradise with its scenic beauty. Literary associations with famous artists are everywhere - from Wordsworth at Dove Cottage in Grasmere to Beatrix Potter at Sawrey.

A single toilet block provides facilities for visitors who are disabled and children. Laundry. Chemical toilet point. Children's play area. Motorhome service point. WiFi is poor, and charged. BBQs allowed. TV reception booster system. Defibrillator. Information room. Pets allowed. Dog walk adjacent. Dog pit stop. Gas sales. Twin axle caravans accepted. Late-night arrivals area. Tesco 3 miles. No Tents allowed. Earliest time of arrival 1:00pm. Maximum outfit length 11 metres. Train 3 miles.

Key Features

 Book Online

 Open All Year

 Pets Accepted

 Disabled Facilities

 Beach Access

 Play Area

Scan me for more information.

Alan Rogers Code: UK5511
10 accommodations
23 pitches
GPS: 54.78270, -3.10315
Post Code: CA7 8DL

Wigton, Cumbria

www.alanrogers.com/uk5511
enquiry@wallacelanefarm.co.uk
Tel: +44 1697 478188
www.wallacelanefarm.co.uk

Open (Touring Pitches):
All year.

Wallace Lane Farm

Wallace Lane Farm is a 23-acre site with spectacular views. Ideal for families and campers with pets. The fully licenced site offers a range of facilities for tents, caravans, motorhomes and trailer tents with 18 hardstanding pitches, 14 fully serviced with electricity, water and waste and 4 have electric-only with water available nearby. There are five large grass pitches for small to large tents, all with a 10amp electric supply and water (some seasonal). The site also has ten lodges, yurts & cabins for hire.

The site is situated high in the magnificent Northern lakes on the fringe of the Lake District National Park. Local shops and pubs in the villages of Caldbeck and Wigton are within a short drive. Situated on the edge of Caldbeck fells, you can enjoy the beautiful scenery and explore by foot or by bicycle.

Heated toilet block, showers, washbasins & WCs. Laundry. Dishwashing area. Chemical toilet point. Motorhome service point. Public phone. Pets welcome. Dog walk. Children welcome. Drying room. Local shops and Pubs. Electric car charging point. All pitches with 10 or 16-amp electricity. Mobile phone reception is good. WiFi, free.

Key Features

 Open All Year

 Pets Accepted

Scan me for more information.

Alan Rogers Code: UK5753
27 accommodations
70 pitches
GPS: 55.18006, -2.53525
Post Code: NE48 1AX

Northumberland, Northumbria

www.alanrogers.com/uk5753
info@kielderwaterside.com
Tel: +44 01434 251000
www.kielderwaterside.com

Open (Touring Pitches):
Early April - Late September.

Kielder Waterside

Kielder Waterside Caravan Park is nestled in the beauty of Kielder Water & Forest Park. The Park is situated amongst acres of woodland forest, has the largest man-made lake on your doorstep and impeccable dark skies above you at night. You will be in awe from the moment you arrive. The site is the perfect retreat getaway for you and the whole family, including your four-legged friends. Kielder Waterside is a dog-friendly park, with dog walks available on-site and nearby.

The site has 70 touring pitches, both partial Lakeview pitches & Woodland pitches available. Some seasonal caravan pitches. All pitches have electric hookups and all the on-site facilities you may require. There are also ten lodges available to hire. Imagine a magical kingdom with ancient castles, golden beaches, rolling hills, great parks, and wild moorland. Such a kingdom exists, it is Northumberland, and it truly is a magical and inspiring place.

The toilet block has showers, washbasins & WCs. Laundry area with washing machine, dryer and iron. Facility for visitors who are disabled. Restaurant. Food preparation area. WiFi charged. TV aerial points. Waste disposal. On-site shop. Pets welcome. Bike hire adjacent. Indoor swimming pool adjacent. Sauna and gym adjacent. Earliest arrival time is 12 noon. Departure no later than 11 am. If your caravan or motorhome is over 7 metres, please get in touch with site staff before arrival.

Key Features

 Pets Accepted

 Disabled Facilities

 Bike Hire

Scan me for more information.

Alan Rogers Code: UK5746
10 pitches
GPS: 55.57974, -1.67976
Post Code: NE68 7UR

Northumberland, North East

www.alanrogers.com/uk5746
info@westfieldfarmhouse.co.uk
Tel: +44 1665 478988
www.westfieldpaddock.co.uk

Open (Touring Pitches):
All year.

Westfield Paddock

Westfield Paddock Touring Caravan Site is a privately owned adult-only touring site offering facilities within easy walking distance to the village of Seahouses. The nearest dog-friendly pub is open daily and serves food nightly in peak season. Approx. 15-minute walk, you will find the fantastic sandy beach walk from the site to Bamburgh Castle approx. 3 miles. Seahouses shops, pubs and restaurants are a 5-minute drive approx. 20-30 mins walk. The site has ten pitches (8 grass 2 hardstanding), all have electric hook-ups 16amp. N.B. The site does not have a toilet block.

Stick around Seahouses for the golf club, horse riding and afternoons at the spa, or set off for the beach at North Sunderland's shores (all about a five-minute drive). Wildlife-spotting boat trips to the Farne Islands leave from the village, with chances to peer at puffins, seals and dolphins during the tour.

Key Features

(18+) Adults Only

365 Open All Year

🐾 Pets Accepted

⛱ Beach Access

Chemical toilet point. Tourist information. Pets welcome. Dog walk. Dogs must always be on a lead. TV reception good. WiFi free. Earliest arrival time 13:00. Charge for pets and awnings. Co-op 0.5miles. No tents.

Scan me for more information.

Alan Rogers Code: UK5915
40 pitches
GPS: 51.86964, -3.18669
Post Code: NP8 1LP

Powys, Mid Wales

www.alanrogers.com/uk5915
info@glanuskestate.com
Tel: +44 1873 810414
www.glanuskestate.com

Open (Touring Pitches):
Start March - End July / Mid Sept -
End October.

Glanusk Caravan Park

Glanusk Caravan Park is in a secluded part of the Glanusk estate and is perfectly private. Relax on all-weather pitches with the option of electricity in an area that's surrounded by nature. The site reaches out towards the river's banks, where the peaceful waters are ideal for salmon and trout fishing.

Steeped in history, the estate is a beautiful space that began life as a retreat for Sir Joseph Bailey and their family. It features a stretch of the tranquil River Usk, a host of majestic trees, wide meadows and secretive walled gardens. A distinctive tower and bridge add the perfect finishing touch to these surroundings. It is known as The Jewel in the Usk Valley, and this luxurious setting sees more than 200 species of oak and a huge variety of charming flowers, plant life and wildlife. The site has 40 all-weather pitches, and most have an electric hook-up point.

Key Features

 Pets Accepted

 Disabled Facilities

 Fishing

Modern heated toilet block with showers, washbasins and WCs. Dishwashing area. Facility for visitors who are disabled. Washing point for dogs. WiFi charged. Space for washing bicycles. Fishing, shooting and clay pigeon practice are all available on-site. The Nantyffyin Cider Mill with its country inn is a 15-20 minute walk from the site. Two miles from the park is Crickhowell village with its bars and restaurants.

Scan me for more information.

Alan Rogers Code: UK5928
170 pitches
GPS: 51.43156, -3.50292
Post Code: CF71 7PB

Vale of Glamorgan, South Wales

www.alanrogers.com/uk5928
info@llandowcaravanpark.com
Tel: +44 1446 794527
llandowcaravanpark.com

Open (Touring Pitches):
Start February - End November.

Llandow Caravan Park

Llandow Caravan Park is in a fairly secluded rural area in the beautiful Vale of Glamorgan. You will receive a warm welcome from the park wardens, Julie and Alan. The site is divided into two areas separated by a road. The main area comprises 100 level pitches, some on hardstanding, whilst across the road is the new area with 70 mainly grass pitches.

This quiet site is suitable for couples, families and visitors with disabilities. The owners work very hard to maintain the highest standard of cleanliness for all facilities. The laundry room is spacious and bright, with seating and local tourist information literature. The site has a purpose-built storage compound and has been commended for its high standards in security. All visitors are issued with a security pass upon arrival.

Two sanitary blocks, one on the 'new' (2012) field has good facilities for disabled visitors. Coin-operated showers. Good quality laundry facilities. Well stocked shop in reception. Play area. Dog walking area. Tourist information leaflets. Free WiFi throughout. 10/16 Amp Electricity dependent upon which part of the site you are sited on.

Key Features

 Pets Accepted

 Disabled Facilities

 Play Area

Scan me for more information.

Alan Rogers Code: UK5995
25 accommodations
107 pitches
GPS: 51.87298, -5.25690
Post Code: SA62 6QT

Pembrokeshire, West Wales

Caerfai Bay

www.alanrogers.com/uk5995
info@caerfaibay.co.uk
Tel: +44 1437 720274
www.caerfaibay.co.uk

Open (Touring Pitches):
Start March - Mid November.

Caerfai Bay Caravan & Tent Park is about as far west as one can get in Wales. Located near St Davids, Britain's smallest city, noted for its cathedral and Bishop's Palace. This cliff-top park, just a 15-minute walk from St Davids, has direct access to the Pembrokeshire Coastal Path and a magnificent sandy beach. Family run with an emphasis on peace, quiet and relaxation, the perfect spot for walkers, rock climbers, water sports enthusiasts, star gazers & wildlife lovers.

There are 107 touring pitches (inc.78 for tents) and, 59 electric hook-ups (10A), & 33 hardstandings. The site is spread over three open fields with magnificent sea views, one for caravans and motorhomes with hardstanding and electric as well as accommodation to rent; two for tents with some electric points. The main access roads are tarmac.

Key Features

 Pets Accepted

 Disabled Facilities

 Beach Access

Three main buildings house the sanitary facilities (two are heated), one by reception contains facilities for disabled visitors and families, dishwashing, laundry, and cooking facilities (hot plate, microwave and fridge). A small block offers three unisex cubicles (WC and basin). The third, in the tent field, includes four family rooms, dishwashing, microwave, fridge, toaster, wet suit washing and drying area. Motorhome services. Bicycle storage. Gas. Dog walking area (there is a non-dog camping area in tent field 3). WiFi (charged). Secure charging points for phones/tablets. Lounge with tourist information, maps & book exchange.

Scan me for
more information.

255

Alan Rogers Code: UK6007
50 accommodations
75 pitches
GPS: 52.39766, -4.06655
Post Code: SY23 4DX

Ceredigion, West Wales

www.alanrogers.com/uk6007
enquires@midfieldcaravanpark.co.uk
Tel: +44 1970 612542
www.midfieldcaravanpark.co.uk

Open (Touring Pitches):
Start March - End October.

Midfield Caravan Park

Midfield Holiday & Residential Park is a small family-run site and is situated on a hilltop overlooking Aberystwyth, with uninterrupted panoramic views of the surrounding countryside, town, Cardigan Bay and the Rheidol Valley. It is just over a mile from the railway station, town and Beach. It is well placed as a touring centre, surrounded as it is by the beautiful countryside of mid-wales.

The Ceredigion Coastal Path, the Ystwyth Cycle path and forestry trails ideal for walking & cycling are also close by. There are seventy-five pitches for touring caravans, tents and motor homes, with some level and some sloping, sixty of which have electrical hookups. The site also has thirty mobile homes, which are privately owned and a further twenty available to hire.

A spacious toilet block has showers, toilets, and washbasins. Washroom for clothes and dishes. Laundry with washing machine and dryer. Chemical toilet point. Motorhome service point. Children's Play area with a large climbing frame. Freezer for ice packs. Public phone. WiFi free. Gas sales. Dogs allowed. Dog walk. Earliest arrival time 14:00.

Key Features

 Pets Accepted

 Beach Access

 Play Area

Scan me for more information.

Alan Rogers Code: UK6691
30 accommodations
153 pitches
GPS: 52.92314, -4.13933
Post Code: LL49 9UR

Gwynedd, North Wales

www.alanrogers.com/uk6691
info@tyddynllwyn.com
Tel: +44 1766 512205
www.tyddynllwyn.com

Open (Touring Pitches):
Mid March - End October.

Tyddyn Llwyn Caravan Park

Tyddyn Llwyn Caravan Park is situated in a large area of partially wooded countryside. Nestled in a secluded location in the lea of Moel-Y-Gest. The privately owned estate extends to some 53 acres in total, 18 acres of which are used as a touring and static caravan park. The site has plenty of space for anyone staying in touring caravans, motor homes, campervans or trailer tents to relax.

"Tŷ Mŵg" Beer & Brisket Smokehouse is situated within the park. There's also an outdoor patio area to sit and enjoy views over the countryside. All pitches have an "all-weather" surface along with electric, water and grey waste point. Premium pitches are also available. The park benefits from the proximity of the harbour town of Porthmadog, as well as the picturesque bayside village of Borth-Y-Gest, both of which are within easy walking distance.

Three toilet blocks provide showers, washbasins & WCs. Family room. Digital TV reception. Disabled toilet/shower/wet room. Dishwashing area. Chemical toilet point. Public telephone. Information area. Children's play area. Games room. Licenced bar and restaurant. Second-hand book library/exchange. Calor gas bottle exchange. Freezer block hire. Laundrette. Small shop. Pets welcome. WiFi charged.

Key Features

 Pets Accepted

 Beach Access

 Play Area

 Bar/Restaurant

Scan me for
more information.

257

Alan Rogers Code: UK6633
2 accommodations
55 pitches
GPS: 53.28456, -4.09271
Post Code: LL58 8LR

Isle of Anglesey, North Wales

www.alanrogers.com/uk6633
info@kingsbridgecaravanpark.co.uk
Tel: +44 1248 490636
www.kingsbridgecaravanpark.co.uk

Open (Touring Pitches):
Start March - End October.

Kingsbridge Camping Park

Family-owned and run, Kingsbridge Caravan & Camping Park is a haven for nature lovers and within easy reach of several beaches. It has family and adult-only areas to take full advantage of the spacious 14-acre site. Being in an Area of Outstanding Natural Beauty, there are many opportunities to observe wildlife, including owls and woodpeckers.

Of the 90 level or gently sloping pitches, 55 are for tourers (all 10A electricity) and 35 for tents. Twenty-five hardstandings are included in the touring pitches, and two mobile homes are available to rent. An energy-saving ethos means site lighting is kept to a minimum, all the better for star gazing and encouraging the owls.

Two modern, clean heated sanitary units serve the two touring areas and have controllable hot showers, some private cabins and a baby room. No designated facilities for disabled visitors, but access is good. Motorhome services (by arrangement with reception). Shop with basics, beach items and essential caravan accessories. Play area. Torches essential. WiFi (charged).

Key Features

 Pets Accepted

 Beach Access

 Play Area

Scan me for more information.

Alan Rogers Code: UK6870
2 accommodations
39 pitches
GPS: 54.94218, -3.82016
Post Code: DG5 4NE

Dumfries and Galloway,
Lowlands

www.alanrogers.com/uk6870
glenearlycaravan@btconnect.com
Tel: +44 1556 611393
glenearlycaravanpark.co.uk

Open (Touring Pitches):
All year.

Glenearly Caravan Park

Rurally located, Glenearly has been tastefully developed from farmland into a touring and mobile home, all-year park. There are 115 marked, open pitches (39 for touring), all with 16A Europlug and TV, most on hardstandings. Seasonal units use some pitches. Walls and shrubs divide the touring section from the caravan holiday homes (two to rent), with mature trees around the perimeter. There are attractive views over the hills and forest of Barhill and buzzards, yellow wagtails, woodpeckers and goldfinch are some of the birds that can be seen, along with the park's own donkeys and ponies.

This is a very well-kept and well-designed park, which would suit those looking for a quiet site in the country. The large games room, converted from an old barn, is excellent – heated and with plenty of chairs and tables for parents to supervise the activities.

Situated in the centre of the touring area, the toilets and showers are fitted out to a high standard. Unit for disabled visitors and families. Laundry room with washing machines and dryer and an outside drying area. Motorhome services. Large games room. Play area. Max. 2 dogs accepted.

Key Features

 Open All Year

 Pets Accepted

 Disabled Facilities

 Beach Access

 Play Area

Scan me for
more information.

Alan Rogers Code: UK7029
50 pitches
GPS: 55.71544, -2.73820
Post Code: TD2 6RU

Borders, Lowlands

www.alanrogers.com/uk7029
info@thirlestanecastlepark.co.uk
Tel: +44 1578 718884
www.thirlestanecastlepark.co.uk

Open (Touring Pitches):
Start April - Early October.

Thirlestane Castle Park

Family-run Thirlestane Castle Park is beautifully situated on the outskirts of the Royal Burgh town of Lauder, within the historic parklands of Thirlestane Castle. It is just five minutes walk from local shops and hotels and equally well located for those wishing to find a central base for exploring the Scottish Borders. The park was established over twenty years ago and has an enviable reputation as a quiet, friendly and welcoming site.

The 50 touring pitches, 22 on hardstanding, are fairly level, and all have electricity connections (10A). Very large motor homes cannot be accommodated, but twin-axle caravans are welcome. The area has numerous activities, including fishing and golf, and the Southern Upland Way is only 300 m. away. There is a direct bus service to Edinburgh (1 hour).

The modern toilet block can be heated and has controllable showers, but currently no facilities for disabled visitors. Washing machine. Motorhome services. A torch might be useful.

Key Features

  Pets Accepted

Scan me for more information.

Alan Rogers Code: UK7250
1 accommodations
10 pitches
GPS: 55.59731, -5.68606
Post Code: PA29 6XD

Argyll and Bute, Heart of Scotland

www.alanrogers.com/uk7250
info@westlochshores.com
Tel: +44 1583 421207
www.muasdaleholidays.com

Open (Touring Pitches):
Mid April - End September.

Muasdale Holiday Park

Muasdale Holiday Park has a beachside location with fine sea views and islands between Campbeltown and Tarbert on Kintyre's west coast. This is a small, friendly site with just ten pitches for touring units, five for tents and one used for a caravan holiday home to rent.

The pitches are situated on a level grass field, all with unobstructed sea views. All have electrical connections. You are advised to anchor tents and awnings securely as the winds are sometimes strong and gusty. The beach is a magnificent expanse of white sand with rock pools and an abundance of wildlife. The sunsets are frequently breathtaking. Sea canoeing and sea fishing are both popular.

The newly built toilet block is clean and heated. Laundry facilities. Games room. Direct beach access. Sea swimming and fishing. Canoeing. WiFi (free). Accommodation to rent.

Key Features

 Pets Accepted

 Beach Access

 Fishing

Scan me for more information.

Alan Rogers Code: UK7815
150 pitches
GPS: 56.38929, -5.51722
Post Code: PA34 4QH

Argyll and Bute, Heart of
Scotland

www.alanrogers.com/uk7815
info@obancaravanpark.com
Tel: +44 1631 562425
obancaravanpark.com

Open (Touring Pitches):
Start April - Early October.

Oban Caravan and Camping

Oban Caravan and Camping Park enjoys an idyllic situation amidst the magnificent scenery of the Scottish West Highlands. Just a stone's throw from the sea, with views of the island of Kerrera, it is in a truly peaceful setting, yet only three miles from the centre of Oban. The pitches are mainly grassy, with a few hardstandings for motorhomes. Electricity hook-ups are available on some pitches, including the tent pitches.

A range of rental accommodations is offered - lodges, caravans (all with sea views,) a farm cottage and camping pods with cooking facilities. This site is ideal for families and couples who wish to enjoy the area's natural beauty, and campers are encouraged to keep noise to a minimum. Children will enjoy the free-range hens and the duck pond, whose residents may pay you a visit!

Three sanitary blocks, one refurbished in March 2017 and the other two refurbished in 2014, all have free hot showers and open washbasins. Laundry facilities. Campers' kitchen with gas hob, microwave and freezer. Small licensed shop in reception (end May-early Sept). Hot and cold drinks and soup are sold in the reception. Vending machines in the laundry room. TV/games room. Swings in a fenced area. Bricks are provided for barbecues. WiFi in the reception area (free). Dogs are accepted (max. 2).

Key Features

 Pets Accepted

 Beach Access

 Play Area

Scan me for
more information.

Alan Rogers Code: UK7585
6 accommodations
97 pitches
GPS: 57.00186, -3.39362
Post Code: AB35 5YQ

Aberdeenshire, Grampian

www.alanrogers.com/uk7585
info@braemarcaravanpark.co.uk
Tel: +44 1339 741373
www.braemarcaravanpark.co.uk

Open (Touring Pitches):
All year.

Braemar Caravan Park

Braemar Caravan Park and Camping Pods are the perfect base for walking, hiking, cycling, photography, snow sports, history, arts and crafts and much more. Braemar Caravan Park is situated In the beautiful village of Braemar, Royal Deeside, at the heart of the Cairngorms National Park. Operated by the Invercauld Estate, managed for wildlife, sport, recreation and community. The Estate hosts Scotland's highest 18-hole golf course at Braemar and the Glenshee Ski Centre, which can offer some of the best skiing and snowboarding in the UK. The Estate also provides salmon fishing and mile upon mile of glorious walks.

The site has 97 touring pitches, each with an electric hook-up point. Please note some pitches are slightly smaller than others and are more suitable for VW-size campervans and small motorhomes without awnings. These pitches are not large enough for most awnings and are unsuitable for caravans with awnings and cars. The site also has 6 Glamping pods available for hire.

The heated toilet block has showers, washbasins and WCs. Easy access toilet and shower room. Laundry. Dishwashing areas. WiFi charged. Gas sales. Information room and book exchange. Chemical toilet points. Motorhome service point. Ski lockers. Dogs welcome. Children's play area. Shop. Drying room. Boot cleaning sink.

Key Features

 Open All Year

 Pets Accepted

 Disabled Facilities

 Play Area

Scan me for more information.

Alan Rogers Code: UK7760
45 pitches
GPS: 57.28313, -5.62652
Post Code: IV40 8DH

Highland, Highlands and Islands

www.alanrogers.com/uk7760
reraigbooking@gmail.com
Tel: +44 7342 878776
www.reraigcamping.com

Open (Touring Pitches):
Start May - End September.

Reraig Caravan and Camping

This is a small, level park close to Loch Alsh with a wooded hillside behind (crisscrossed with woodland walks). Set mainly on well-cut grass, it is sheltered from the prevailing winds by the hill and provides just 45 numbered pitches. There are 10A electrical connections and 35 hardstandings (two without electricity). Tents you can stand in are not accepted. Small tents are permitted at the owner's discretion, so it would be advisable to telephone first if this affects you.

Awnings are not permitted during July and August to protect the grass. The ground can be stony, so rock pegs are recommended. Reraig makes a good base from which to explore the Isle of Skye and the pretty village of Plockton with palm trees (remember Hamish Macbeth on TV?)

The single sanitary block is kept immaculately clean. Children have their own low washbasins. Controllable hot showers accept free tokens for guests (1 token for 2 minutes). Sinks for laundry and dishwashing. A slope replaces the small step into the ladies and sink rooms. Motorhome drainage point. WiFi throughout.

Key Features

 Pets Accepted

 Beach Access

Scan me for
more information.

Alan Rogers Code: UK7662
10 accommodations
60 pitches
GPS: 57.43186, -5.81172
Post Code: IV54 8ND

Highland, Highlands and Islands

www.alanrogers.com/uk7662
enquiries@visitapplecross.com
Tel: +44 1520 744258
visitapplecross.com

Open (Touring Pitches):
Start March - End October.

Applecross Camping

The campsite itself is handily located on the road that slaloms down towards the village from the mountain pass. Go past the first field by the reception as the views are better from the 'overflow' field, and there are no caravans there. Both fields are relatively flat with soft ground to pitch on and occupy great positions overlooking Applecross Bay. The campsite has its own beautiful café, where you will be delighted to see the wooden bar area opening out into a long flower tunnel, with neat tables, a small fountain and a children's play area.

An essential deer fence may detract from the view slightly. From here, you will get some of the finest views you will ever see of Scotland's largest island, Skye, with its world-famous and unmistakable Cuillin Mountains. The site does have a few static caravans, a Bed & Breakfast establishment and ten camping huts (eight wishbones cabins and two wigwams) to go along with the space for 60 tents, but aside from the height of summer, it doesn't usually get too crowded.

There is a fully functional hot water shower block, children's facilities, a laundry room with a washing machine, tumble dryer and a payphone, electric hook-up points, Children's play area, Restaurant, WiFi, Pets allowed.

Key Features

 Pets Accepted

 Beach Access

 Play Area

Scan me for more information.

Alan Rogers Code: UK7720
30 pitches
GPS: 58.08027, -4.44705
Post Code: IV27 4DN

Highland, Highlands and Islands

www.alanrogers.com/uk7720
woodendcaravanpark@yahoo.com
Tel: +44 7979 487064
www.facebook.com/
WoodendShinness

Open (Touring Pitches):
Start April - End September.

Woodend Camping Park

Woodend Camping & Caravan Park is a delightful, small park overlooking Loch Shin and perfect for hill walkers and backpackers. Peaceful and simple, it is owned and run by Alan Ross, who provides a wonderfully warm Scottish welcome to visitors. The large camping field is undulating and gently sloping with some reasonably flat areas on a hill with open, panoramic views across the Loch to the hills beyond and all around.

The park is licensed to take 55 units, and most of the 30 electrical hook-ups (16A) are in a line near the top of the field. There are opportunities for fishing and hill walking. The famous Falls of Shin, with a visitor centre (about ten miles) is an ideal place to see the salmon leap.

The sanitary facilities are of old design but kept very clean and are quite satisfactory. Laundry with a washing machine and a dryer. Kitchen with dishwashing sinks and eating room for tent campers. Reception is at the house, Sunday papers, daily milk and bread may be ordered. Fishing licences for the Loch (your catch will be frozen for you).

Key Features

 Pets Accepted

Scan me for
more information.

Alan Rogers Code: UK7920
6 accommodations
19 pitches
GPS: 58.22738, -6.39254
Post Code: HS2 0DR

Isle of Lewis, Highlands and Islands

www.alanrogers.com/uk7920
info@laxdaleholidaypark.com
Tel: +44 1851 706966
www.laxdaleholidaypark.com

Open (Touring Pitches):
Start March - End October.

Laxdale Holiday Park

Whilst not in the most scenic of locations, this good park is well-placed for touring. Surrounded by trees, it is on the edge of Stornaway (ferry port) and is well laid out, with a tarmac road running through the centre. A level area has 19 touring pitches, all with electricity hook-ups (10A), plus five for tents, and a grassy area (no electricity) for tents gently slopes away to the trees and boundary. There is a choice of rental accommodation on offer: caravans, wigwams, a lodge, a bungalow and a bunkhouse.

The site is centrally situated in an ideal spot for touring the Isle of Lewis, with easy access to all parts of the island. The Butt of Lewis, the Callanish standing stones and the Black House Village are all within easy reach and many other attractions. Some parts have rocky coastal scenery, but there are some lovely beaches around the island.

The well-maintained and modern sanitary block is heated and raised above the hardstanding area. Access is via steps or a gravel path to the ramp. Good (but narrow) showers with dividing curtain (on payment). Well-equipped laundry with washing machine, dryer, iron and board, sink and clothesline. Telephone. WiFi in reception (charged). Glamping-style pods are available to rent.

Key Features

 Pets Accepted

 Disabled Facilities

Scan me for more information.

Alan Rogers Code: UK7950
48 pitches
GPS: 58.95443, -3.30041
Post Code: KW16 3DN

Orkney, Highlands and Islands

www.alanrogers.com/uk7950
leisure.culture@orkney.gov.uk
Tel: +44 1856 873535
www.orkney.gov.uk

Open (Touring Pitches):
Start April - End September.

Point of Ness

Point of Ness Caravan & Camping Site is in an idyllic position bounded by the sea on one side (an entrance to the harbour). It is sheltered by the land from the open sea and has views of the mountains and the island of Hoy. There is a rocky beach close by and walks from the site. There are 48 pitches (12 with 10A electricity hook-ups) on this level, firm grassy site protected from the small drop to the sea by a low fence.

Access to the steps to the sea is via a gate in the fence. While being located at one end of Orkney, it is still easy to visit the Churchill Barriers and the Italian Chapel as well as the closer Maes Howe and Skara Brae sites. Regular ferries come into Stromness from Thurso. Do not be surprised if the seals come to watch you. Ferries to other islands go from various ports, and it is sometimes necessary to book in advance.

The well-maintained traditional-style toilet block has good-sized showers (on payment) with curtains separating the changing area. Well-equipped laundry. A lounge for campers is at one end of the block.

Key Features

 Pets Accepted

 Disabled Facilities

 Beach Access

 Scan me for more information.

Alan Rogers Code: UK8420
71 pitches
GPS: 54.22630, -5.93449
Post Code: BT33 OPW

Newcastle, Co. Down

www.alanrogers.com/uk8420
Tel: +44 28 4372 2428
nidirect.gov.uk/articles/tollymore-forest-park

Open (Touring Pitches):
All year.

Tollymore Forest Caravan Park

This popular park, for touring units only, is located within the parkland of Tollymore Forest, which is noted for its scenic surroundings. The forest park is approached by a majestic avenue of Himalayan cedars and covers an area of almost 500 hectares. Situated two miles from the beaches and resort of Newcastle, it is backed impressively by the Mourne mountains.

The open grassy site is attractively laid out with 71 hardstanding pitches, all of which have 10A electricity. The Forestry Service Rangers are very helpful and ensure that the caravan site is efficiently run and quiet, even when full. Exploring the park is part of the pleasure of staying here, and the stone bridges and entrance gates are particularly interesting. The picturesque Shimna and Spinkwee rivers rise in the Mournes and flow through the park. Tree lovers appreciate the arboretum with its many rare species.

The timbered toilet blocks have wash cubicles, showers, dishwashing and a laundry area. Fishing (permit required, available from the Four Seasons Tackle Shop in Newcastle).

Key Features

 Open All Year

 Pets Accepted

 Disabled Facilities

 Beach Access

 Fishing

Scan me for more information.

Alan Rogers Code: UK8350
48 pitches
GPS: 55.17103, -6.57114
Post Code: BT57 8UJ

Bushmills, Co. Antrim

Bush Caravan Park

www.alanrogers.com/uk8350
info@bushcaravanparkni.com
Tel: +44 28 2073 1678
www.bushcaravanparkni.com

Open (Touring Pitches):
Easter - End September.

A good base for touring the North Antrim Coast, this family-run park is only minutes from two renowned attractions, the Giant's Causeway and the Old Bushmills Distillery. It is located just off the main Ballymoney-Portrush Road (B62) and is approached by a short drive. Mature trees and hedging partly surround the park, but views across the countryside can still be appreciated. Tarmac roads lead to 48 well-laid out and spacious pitches with hardstanding and 16A electricity or a grass area for pup tents.

Unique features on site are murals depicting the famed scenery, sights and legends of the Causeway Coast. The enthusiastic owners may organise occasional barbecues, tours to the distillery and coastal trips.

The toilet block (opened by keypad) is modern, clean and equipped to a high standard. Facilities include controllable showers with excellent provision for visitors with disabilities (they can also be used by families). Washing machine and dryer. Central play area.

Key Features

 Pets Accepted

 Disabled Facilities

 Beach Access

 Play Area

Scan me for more information.

Alan Rogers Code: UK8515
38 pitches
GPS: 54.30658, -7.89505
Post Code: BT93 5DU

Enniskillen, Co. Fermanagh

www.alanrogers.com/uk8515
enquiries@rushinhouse.com
Tel: +44 28 6638 6519
www.rushinhouse.com

Open (Touring Pitches):
Mid March - Late October.

Rushin House Caravan Park

Although situated in Northern Ireland, this park opened in 2007 and is almost on the border with the Republic of Ireland. It has been carefully landscaped from farmland that sloped down to the tranquil Lough MacNean. There are 38 fully serviced, terraced pitches on hardstanding. They form a friendly circle surrounding a fairy thorn tree and have an added bonus of a wonderful view of the loch. There is also a small camping area. The toilet block, boat jetty, picnic tables and play areas are only a short walk away from the pitches.

The helpful owners live on-site and are on call most of the time. This park provides a peaceful haven to relax after returning from days out in lovely Fermanagh. At the farm entrance are the stark ruins of Templerushin Church, and nearby is Saint Patrick's Holy Well.

Key Features

 Pets Accepted

 Disabled Facilities

 Play Area

 Fishing

Heated toilet block, beautifully appointed, with laundry and adjoining kitchen area. Separate facilities for disabled campers. Motorhome services. Payphone. Boat jetty. Play area. All-weather sports facility. Picnic area. WiFi throughout.

Scan me for more information.

Capital Athens
Currency Euro (€)
Language Greek
Time Zone EET (GMT+2)
Telephone Code +30

Shops Hours vary throughout the year, with many shops operating on shorter hours in low and shoulder seasons. In high season 8am to 2pm Mon, Wed, Sat and 8am to 2pm and 5pm to 9pm Tues, Thurs, Fri.

Money ATMs are widespread, mostly 24/7 and have multilingual instructions. Credit/debit cards are accepted in urban areas but it's handy to have cash.

Travelling with children Greece has plenty of green spaces, historical attractions and sandy beaches. Greek culture is all about sharing so restaurants will always be accommodating towards children.

Public Holidays 1 Jan New Year's Day; 6 Jan Epiphany; Mar Orthodox Ash Monday; 25 Mar Independence Day; Apr/May Orthodox Good Friday; Apr/May Orthodox Easter Sunday; Apr/May Orthodox Easter Monday; 1 May Labour Day; Jun Orthodox Whit Sunday; Jun Orthodox Whit Monday; 15 Aug Assumption; 28 Oct Ochi Day; 25 Dec Christmas Day; 26 Dec Boxing Day

LEZ Low Emissions Zones in Athens. Foreign vehicles do not need to register.

● EU Member | ● Schengen Area

Tourism website visitgreece.gr

●●○○○ **Accessible Travel Score**

Although improving, especially so in cities, much of Greece is difficult to navigate due to its historic nature. Public buildings such as museums will often cater for wheelchair users and those who are less able.

Driving in Greece Road signs are written in Greek and English. Some roads have distance-based tolls. In Athens, parking is prohibited within the Green Zone unless signposts state otherwise. Drink-driving, using you mobile whilst driving are illegal. Dashcams are legal but using footage for insurance purposes is prohibited.

 Dashcams are legal

 Speed camera detectors are legal

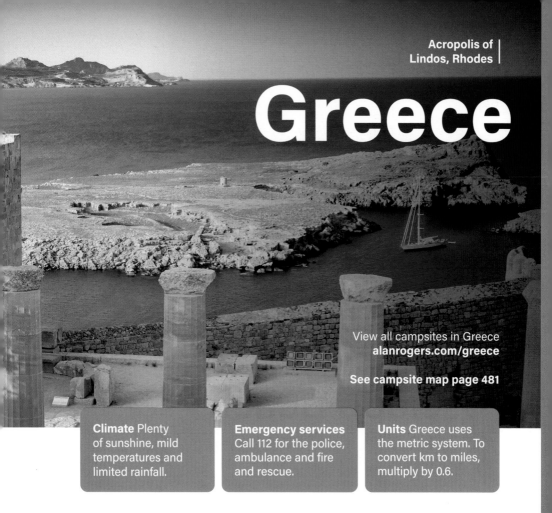

Greece

View all campsites in Greece
alanrogers.com/greece

See campsite map page 481

Climate Plenty of sunshine, mild temperatures and limited rainfall.

Emergency services Call 112 for the police, ambulance and fire and rescue.

Units Greece uses the metric system. To convert km to miles, multiply by 0.6.

Greece is made up of clusters of islands with idyllic sheltered bays and coves, golden stretches of sand with dunes, pebbly beaches, coastal caves with steep rocks and black volcanic sand and coastal wetlands. Its rugged landscape is a monument to nature with dramatic gorges, lakes, rivers and waterfalls.

Nestling between the Aegean, Ionian and Mediterranean waters, Greece has over 13,000 km of coastline. A largely mountainous country, its backbone is formed from the Pindus range, which extends as far as Crete, the largest of Greece's 6,000 islands, themselves peaks of the now-submerged landmass of Aegeis.

Mount Olympus in the north of the country, known from Greek mythology as the abode of the gods, is the highest mountain (2,917 m).

The Greek islands have something to offer every visitor – the vibrant nightlife of Mykonos, the 'honeymoon' island of Santorini, Rhodes, where the modern city sits alongside the medieval citadel, and Corfu with its Venetian and French influences. The mainland is home to some of the most important archaeological sites, including the Acropolis, the Parthenon and Delphi.

Scan QR code to browse more campsites on our website

Alan Rogers Code: GR8120
37 accommodations
27 pitches
GPS: 40.01297, 22.59050
Post Code: GR-60065

Neos Panteleimonas, Central Macedonia

Camping Poseidon Beach

www.alanrogers.com/gr8120
info@poseidonbeach.com
Tel: +30 23 52 04 16 54
www.facebook.com/
campingposeidon

Open (Touring Pitches):
Early April - End October.

Mount Olympus towers are an iconic backdrop to this region, and its slopes run down to the shores of the Aegean, where Camping Poseidon Beach is to be found. This rural area is just off the E75 motorway, which follows the coast from Thessalonica to Athens. The area is known for its sandy beaches, and this campsite enjoys direct access to the sea with windsurfing, snorkelling and waterskiing all available. Head inland to Mount Olympus National Park and take to the hiking and biking trails to explore the rugged majesty of these wooded slopes.

The touring pitches are on level ground, well-shaded by mature trees and various colourful shrubs, and all have 16A electricity. There is a good restaurant, which is open for most of the season. Off-site a principal attraction is the 13th-century castle of Platamon, set on a high point to the south and standing watch over the azure waters of the Aegean. Enjoy the sensational wraparound views from this dramatic vantage point. There may be some noise from the nearby railway and motorway.

Two modern and one refurbished sanitary blocks with mainly British style WCs (one Turkish toilet per block), open washbasins and controllable showers. Washing machines and dryers. Shop. Beachside bar. Fishing. WiFi.

Key Features

 Pets Accepted

 Beach Access

 Bar/Restaurant

 Fishing

Scan me for
more information.

Alan Rogers Code: GR8130
75 pitches
GPS: 40.38975, 23.89317
Post Code: GR-63075

Lerissos, Central Macedonia

www.alanrogers.com/gr8130
campingdelphini@hotmail.com
Tel: +30 23 77 02 22 08
www.facebook.com/Campingdelphini

Open (Touring Pitches):
Start May - End September.

Camping Delphini

Just 27 km south of the birthplace of Aristotle is the small town of Lerissos, on the peninsula of Agio Oros, famous for Mount Athos and several Byzantine monasteries. Mount Athos has been revered as a mystical and religious centre since 800 AD, prompting the creation of the places of worship. Simonos Petras monastery, founded in the 13th century, is notable for its clifftop setting with dramatic sea views and a famed chanting choir. Lerissos offers all the usual useful shops, restaurants, amenities, and a long sandy beach.

Camping Delphini offers a very simple, quiet campsite surrounded by fields in a rural area, set back a few hundred metres from the nearest beach. This is a place to visit if you are looking for a restful break and are not seeking all the facilities of the bigger beach-front sites. There are 75 pitches which are all for touring units, in a wooded area. The dense trees provide ample shade, so there are none of the horizontal screens found on many other Greek campsites. The restaurant and bar provide simple Greek meals and a place to chat with the locals in the cool shade of the terrace or under a parasol.

The toilet block includes showers, WCs (some Turkish) and washbasins. Kitchen with sinks, electric hobs and fridges. Laundry with washing machines. Bar and simple restaurant.

Key Features

 Beach Access

 Bar/Restaurant

Scan me for
more information.

Alan Rogers Code: GR8415
5 accommodations
150 pitches
GPS: 38.67303, 20.71088
Post Code: GR-31100

Vlicho, Ionian Islands

www.alanrogers.com/gr8415
camping.desimi@gmail.com
Tel: +30 26 45 09 53 74
ar.camp/desimi-beach

Open (Touring Pitches):
Start April - End October.

Desimi Beach Camping

Desimi Beach is a small, family-run campsite on the Island of Lefkada near the town of Nydri. It's located in a pretty, south-facing bay next to a narrow pebble beach with direct access to the warm waters of the Ionian Sea. Wooded slopes rise up from the azure sea, which gently laps the shoreline. The island of Lefkada is one of the few Ionian islands that is accessible without needing a ferry and is reached by driving from the mainland and then crossing the unique 'floating' swing bridge in Lefkada town.

The pitches are set amongst olive trees, some offering shade, and are laid out along the length of the beach on flat ground, all with water and electricity ranging from 4 to 16 amp.The campsite has a restaurant and bar where you can enjoy continental breakfasts and traditional homemade Greek specialities. There is also a shop with fresh bread and many local products, including olive oil produced by the owner's own olive press. You don't have to venture far for more food options as you will find another taverna a short stroll from the campsite on the other side of the cove. Another supermarket, bakery and more tavernas are 3km away.

Key Features

 Pets Accepted

 Beach Access

 Bar/Restaurant

Fishing

Toilet block with hot showers. Restaurant, Bar, Shop. Bakery. Boat hire, pedal boats, kayaks and jet ski hire. Free boat mooring. Dogs permitted. WiFi.

Scan me for more information.

Alan Rogers Code: GR8500
90 pitches
GPS: 38.82350, 22.71663
Post Code: GR-35009

Molos, Central Greece

www.alanrogers.com/gr8500
Camping@venezuela.gr
Tel: +30 22 35 04 16 92
www.venezuela.gr

Open (Touring Pitches):
Start May - End September.

Camping Venezuela

Camping Venezuela is a comfortable and well-maintained campsite located in Maliak Bay, right on the beach of Agios Seraphim and at the foot of Mount Knimis. Athens is a couple of hours away and makes a memorable day trip. This region is known for its beaches, mountain scenery and thermal springs. Take a boat trip to the neighbouring islands, enjoy snorkelling, explore the archaeological monuments and go hiking and cycling in the Oitis National Park. Visit the thermal springs near Kamena Vourla and the Monument of Leonidas, just 10 km from the campsite, commemorating the legendary battle of Thermopylae in 480 BC.

Hedges and colourful shrubs separate the 90 well-demarcated pitches, and all have 5 amp electricity connections with some shade offered by the eucalyptus, poplar and olive trees dotted around the campsite. The campsite has a mini market on-site and a 'campers kitchen' if you wish to prepare a quick meal. Alternatively, you can visit the on-site taverna 'L Holevaina', which has a good menu offering local Mediterranean cuisine and seasonal grills.

Key Features

 Pets Accepted

 Beach Access

 Play Area

 Bar/Restaurant

 Fishing

Toilet blocks with hot and cold water. Washing machines. Campers kitchen. Shop. Restaurant. Bar. Takeaway meals. Small children's play area. Maximum 2 dogs per pitch. WiFi.

Scan me for more information.

Alan Rogers Code: GR8285
120 pitches
GPS: 39.31083, 23.10910
Post Code: GR-38500

Kato Gatzea, Thessaly

www.alanrogers.com/gr8285
info@campinghellas.gr
Tel: +30 24 23 02 22 67
www.campinghellas.gr

Open (Touring Pitches):
All year.

Camping Hellas International

There is a warm welcome from the English-speaking brother and sister team whose family has owned and run Camping Hellas since the sixties. It's in a beautiful setting in a 500-year-old olive grove, right next to the beach and the calm blue waters of the Pagasitikos gulf. There are around 120 pitches, all with 16A electricity. Pitch sizes vary, and some parts are all level, and shade is plentiful thanks to the olive trees.

Everything is kept spotlessly clean, and the owners have many plans for further improvements. The restaurant is a traditional Greek taverna serving local seafood and there is also a bar conveniently located next to the beach. The surrounding area has plenty to explore, including the picturesque villages of Mount Pelion or the island of Skiathos. At weekends a steam train departs from the nearby village of Ano Lechonia on a trip through spectacular mountain scenery.

Two modern sanitary blocks, both very clean with British style toilets and open washbasins. Very good facilities for disabled visitors. Laundry room with sinks and washing machines, Dryers, ironing facilities. Motorhome services. Shop, bar, restaurant and takeaway from 1 May. TV room. Dogs are allowed on the beach as long as they are on a lead. WiFi over site (free).

Key Features

 Open All Year

 Pets Accepted

 Disabled Facilities

 Beach Access

Scan me for more information.

Alan Rogers Code: GR8330
9 accommodations
210 pitches
GPS: 37.83662, 21.13380
Post Code: GR-27050

Vartholomio Ilias, Peloponnese

www.alanrogers.com/gr8330
ionionfl@otenet.gr
Tel: +30 26 23 09 68 28
www.ionion-camping.gr

Open (Touring Pitches):
All year.

Camping Ionion Beach

This is a very attractive and well-kept site in a beautiful location by the Ionian Sea, created from former farmland by the Fligos family. Much has changed since they welcomed their first guests in 1982 when they still left plenty of space for growing potatoes. Now it is a modern site with a large pool and a paddling pool, and two blocks of apartments to rent. Separated by various trees and oleander bushes, there are 210 pitches of 80-100 sq.m, all with 16A electricity. Those at the front of the site enjoy views over the sea and the island of Zakinthos.

The campsite has its own beach bar for snacks and exotic cocktails, and there is also a delightful restaurant with a good menu serving Greek specialities. Motorhome owners should be aware that public transport in the area is poor, but it is possible to arrange car and motorcycle hire at the site.

Three excellent sanitary blocks with British style WCs, and showers with washbasins in cabins. Facilities for disabled campers. Motorhome services. Turkish style chemical disposal point. Laundry room. Shop, bar, restaurant (approx April-October). Swimming pool (no depth markings) and paddling pool (approx May-October). Excellent play area. WiFi over site (charged).

Key Features

 Open All Year

 Pets Accepted

 Disabled Facilities

 Beach Access

 Swimming Pool

 Play Area

 Bar/Restaurant

 Sailing

Scan me for more information.

Alan Rogers Code: GR8605
167 pitches
GPS: 38.04000, 23.02000
Post Code: GR-20300

Schinos, Peloponnese

Camping Alkioni

www.alanrogers.com/gr8605
campingalkioni@yahoo.gr
Tel: +30 27 44 05 72 94
www.campingalkioni.gr

Open (Touring Pitches):
All year.

Camping Alkioni is situated about 50 km west of Athens in the bay of Agia Sotira and provides a beachside location with a backdrop of tree-clad mountains. It offers a relaxing escape from everyday life with pleasant walks around the craggy headland and wonderful views out to sea. Explore further along the coast and discover enticing little coves and secret bays.

There are 167 pitches for touring units and tents, accessed by a winding tarmac road which slopes down to the small shingle beach. Pitches are flat and on terraces at various levels. Facilities include four good toilet blocks, a beach bar, a restaurant and a shop.

The restaurant, with a covered terrace set among palm trees, is a popular haunt over lunchtimes and provides excellent views of the Alkionides islands. Away from the beach, there is plenty of scope for cycling and hiking through the wooded hills of the interior.

Key Features

🗓 Open All Year

⛱ Beach Access

🍸 Bar/Restaurant

Four toilet blocks include showers, WCs and washbasins. Solar panels together with a new gas installation for hot water. Electric hobs for cooking. Lounge area. Small shop. Restaurant. Beachside bar. Volleyball. Basketball. Direct beach access. Free WiFi.

Scan me for
more information.

Alan Rogers Code: GR8590
10 accommodations
66 pitches
GPS: 38.00861, 23.67194
Post Code: GR-12136

Peristeri-Athens, Attica

Camping Athens

www.alanrogers.com/gr8590
info@campingathens.gr
Tel: +30 21 05 81 41 14
www.campingathens.gr

Open (Touring Pitches):
All year.

Camping Athens is an all-year site, located in the west of the city and convenient for visiting Athens. In fact the Acropolis is only 10 km away, with a bus stop opposite the site entrance (public transport works well, so don't plan to drive into the city centre yourself). It may be a city campsite but the pitches are of a reasonable size and are generally well shaded by olive, cypress and palm trees, which create the feeling of being in a kind of lush oasis within the city. Be sure to plan your visit programme in advance as the city can be hot during mid afternoon in summer and the traffic may be heavy.

The site prides itself on friendly Greek hospitality and offers 66 touring pitches, all with 16A electricity connections. Smaller pitches are available for tents. The two toilet blocks are of modern design and well maintained. The site's restaurant is most welcoming after a day's sightseeing, and a selection of Greek starters, helped along by chilled wine, can be thoroughly recommended.

Key Features

 Open All Year

 Pets Accepted

 Beach Access

Two modern toilet blocks. Washing machines. Shop. Bar. Takeaway food and restaurant (all May-Oct). Excursions can be arranged. Barbecues and open fires are forbidden. Free WiFi over site.

Scan me for
more information.

Capital Dublin
Currency Euro (€)
Language English and Gaelic
Time Zone GMT
Telephone Code +353

Shops 9.30am to 6pm Mon to Sat (to 8pm Thurs in cities), noon to 6pm Sun.

Money ATMs are widespread and accessible 24hrs a day. Visa/Mastercard are widely accepted, Amex only by major retailers and Diners/JCB rarely accepted. Rural areas are often more reliant on cash.

Travelling with children
Children are welcomed in Ireland, although family facilities aren't always accessible in rural spots. Most restaurants accept children although some high-end establishments may not. Children under five travel free on all public transport.

Public Holidays 1 Jan New Year's Day; 17 Mar St Patrick's Day; Mar/Apr Easter Monday; Early May May Day; Early Jun June Bank Holiday; Early August Bank Holiday; Late Oct October Bank Holiday; 25 Dec Christmas Day; 26 Dec Boxing Day

♻ **LEZ** Low Emissions Zones in most major cities. Registration required.

● **EU Member** | ○ **Schengen Area**

Ireland is part of the Common Travel Area, an agreement between Ireland, Northern Ireland and the rest of the UK allowing free movement between the countries.

Tourism website ireland.com

●●●●○ **Accessible Travel Score**

All new buildings are wheelchair-friendly. In cities, most buses have low-floor access and trains are accessible.

Driving in Ireland Driving is on the left-hand side, and roads are generally well maintained. Tolls exist on some routes, although most toll stations don't accept cards, so make sure to carry change. Signposts are in both Gaelic and English in most areas. Drink-driving and using your mobile whilst driving are illegal.

 Dashcams are legal

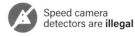 Speed camera detectors are **illegal**

**Cliffs of Moher,
County Clare**

Ireland

View all campsites in Ireland
alanrogers.com/ireland

See campsite map page 480

Climate Cool to mild summers. Winters are cold rarely freezing, often rainy.

Emergency services Call 112 for the police, ambulance and fire and rescue.

Units Ireland uses the metric system. To convert km to miles, multiply by 0.6.

Ireland is made up of four provinces: Connaught, Leinster, Munster and Ulster, comprising 32 counties, 26 of which lie in the Republic of Ireland.

Famed for its folklore, traditional music and friendly hospitality, the Republic of Ireland offers spectacular scenery within a relatively compact area. With plenty of beautiful areas to discover and a relaxed pace of life, it is an ideal place to unwind.

Ireland is the perfect place to indulge in a variety of outdoor pursuits while taking in the glorious scenery. There are plenty of waymarked footpaths which lead through woodlands, across cliffs, past historical monuments and over rolling hills. With its headlands, secluded coves and sandy beaches, the dramatic coastline is fantastic for watersports or for just simply relaxing

and watching the variety of seabirds that nest on the shores.

The Cliffs of Moher, in particular, is a prime location for birdwatching and Goat Island, just offshore, is where puffins make their nesting burrows.

In the south, the beautiful Ring of Kerry is one of the most visited regions. This 110-mile route encircles the Inveragh Peninsula and is surrounded by mountains and lakes. Other sights include the Aran Islands, the Rock of Cashel and the bustling cities of Dublin, Galway and Cork.

Scan QR code to browse more campsites on our website

Alan Rogers Code: IR8640
60 accommodations
50 pitches
GPS: 55.18292, -7.61148

Portsalon, Co. Donegal

www.alanrogers.com/ir8640
enquiries@knockallacaravanpark.com
Tel: +353 74 915 9108
knockallacaravanpark.com

Open (Touring Pitches):
Mid March - Mid September.

Knockalla Caravan Park

What adds to the popularity of this site is its location, nestling between the slopes of the Knockalla Mountains and Ballymastocker Bay amidst the breathtaking scenery of County Donegal. The fact that the beach here has been named 'the second most beautiful beach in the world' is not surprising. Approached by an unclassified but short road, Knockalla's elevated situation commands a panoramic view of the famed Bay, Lough Swilly, Inishowen Peninsula and Dunree Head.

A newer area, with excellent beach views, has been created for touring units. These all have electrical hook-ups and hardstanding, with space for an awning and room to park a car. There are two areas for tents, one of which has views of the mountains, and the other is near the outdoor play area, ideal if you have children. The family-run park is partly terraced, giving an attractive, orderly layout with reception, shop and restaurant in a central position. Specialities at the shop and café are homemade scones, apple cakes, jams, etc., with a takeaway or table service. Full Irish breakfasts are served.

Key Features

 Beach Access

 Play Area

Y Bar/Restaurant

The main toilet block is kept clean and fresh and can be heated. Showers (with token, €1). Laundry service operated by staff. Motorhome services. Gas available. Shop and café (both July/Aug, plus B.H. w/ends). Campers' kitchen with hot water. Play area. TV/games room. No Mobile home accommodation for rent.

Scan me for more information.

Alan Rogers Code: IR8695
55 pitches
GPS: 54.27242, -8.60448

Strandhill, Co. Sligo

Strandhill Park

www.alanrogers.com/ir8695
strandhill@sligocaravanandcamping.ie
Tel: +353 71 916 8111
www.sligocaravanandcamping.ie

Open (Touring Pitches):
Easter - Late September.

This seaside park is located on 20 acres of undulating grass on a sandy base, with natural protection from the coastal breezes of the famous Strandhill beach. The megalithic tombs at Carrowmore, older than the Pyramids at Giza, are 5 km. away and the flat beach at Culleenmore is 2 km. Strandhill provides an excellent touring base for the Benbulban, Yeats' Country and Lough Gill's Isle of Innisfree, combining nature, heritage, and fable.

There are 55 hardstanding pitches for caravans and motorhomes, with electricity and ample water points, and two camping areas for tents, one with views of the sea and the second more sheltered. Throughout the site, many hollows provide ideal pitches for tents. Strandhill, world-renowned as a surfing hotspot, also offers activities for all the family. There are miles of sandy beaches and dunes, and Knocknarea Mountain is popular for walkers. The epic views from the summit are a suitable reward.

Key Features

 Pets Accepted

 Disabled Facilities

 Beach Access

The toilet block (keys provided on deposit) is clean and fresh with hot showers (token €1.50), electric hand dryers and hairdryer. Reception building, including a TV room, games room, campers' kitchen, laundry and a well-equipped facility for disabled visitors. WiFi over part of the site (charged). Automatic gate and door control.

Scan me for more information.

Alan Rogers Code: IR8770
95 pitches
GPS: 53.80530, -9.53950

Westport, Co. Mayo

www.alanrogers.com/ir8770
camping@westporthouse.ie
Tel: +353 98 277 66
www.westporthouse.ie/caravan-camping-mayo

Open (Touring Pitches):
Start April - Early September.

Westport House Caravan Park

Located in the grounds of an elegant country estate, this is a popular park. In an attractive, sheltered area of the parkland, set in the trees, are 95 pitches, 70 with hardstanding and 10/12A electricity. Outside the peak season, the site may not be fully open, and some facilities, such as the bar and café, may not be available.

Westport House, an 18th-century historic home with original architecture, antiques and art, is on the doorstep, offering tours and tea rooms. There's an adventure park in the grounds with features like the Pirates' Plunge log flume, Treasure Island Express miniature railway and other runs and rides. Campsite visitors get a 20 per cent discount on all tickets, and there are also special family rates for three days of camping, along with an annual pass to the adventure park. Outdoor enthusiasts enjoy the Great Western Greenway bike and pedestrian trail, which runs from Westport to Achill Island, passing magnificent scenery.

Toilet facilities are provided at various points on the site, plus a 'super-loo' located in the farmyard buildings. Facilities for disabled visitors. Laundry facilities. Café and bar with food and musical entertainment at weekends. Fishing. Westport House and Pirate Park. Dogs are not accepted in July/Aug. Bell tents available to rent. Free WiFi over site.

Key Features

 Pets Accepted

 Disabled Facilities

 Play Area

 Bar/Restaurant

 Fishing

Scan me for more information.

Alan Rogers Code: IR8790
20 pitches
GPS: 53.79950, -9.21699

Castlebar, Co. Mayo

Carra Caravan Park

www.alanrogers.com/ir8790
info@carracaravanpark.com
Tel: +353 94 907 2895
www.carracaravanpark.com

Open (Touring Pitches):
Mid January - Late November.

This is an ideal location for those seeking a real Irish village experience in a 'value for money' park. Small, unpretentious and family-run, it is located in Belcarra, a regular winner of the Tidiest Mayo Village award. Nestling at the foot of a wooded drumlin, it is surrounded by rolling hills and quiet roads, which offer an away from it all feeling, yet Castlebar, the county's largest town, is only 8 km away. The owner, Pat, and her daughter, Deirdre, are proud of their locality and give occasional talks on the area.

On the pleasant 1.5-acre park, the 20 unmarked touring pitches, 15 with electric hook-up (13A Europlug), are on flat, grassy ground enclosed by ranch fencing and shaded in parts by trees. A novel accommodation offering here are the traditional horse-drawn caravans for hire. It's an idyllic, rural location surrounded by fields and country lanes, so recommended walks are plentiful, and maps are provided. The National Museum of Country Life at Turlough (8 km) which is a super attraction.

The new toilet block has well-equipped showers (€1). En-suite facility for disabled visitors. Combined kitchen with fridge/freezer, sink, table, chairs, washing machine and dryer. Comfortable lounge with TV, books and magazines located at reception. Horse-drawn caravans for hire.

Key Features

 Pets Accepted

 Disabled Facilities

 Beach Access

 Bar/Restaurant

Scan me for more information.

Alan Rogers Code: IR8960
60 pitches
GPS: 53.44815, -7.88992

Athlone, Co. Westmeath

www.alanrogers.com/ir8960
loughreeeastcamping@gmail.com
Tel: +353 90 647 8561
loughreeeastcamping.wixsite.com

Open (Touring Pitches):
Early April - End September.

Lough Ree Camping

This touring park sits alongside the Breensford River, screened by trees but reaching the water's edge. It's a pleasant rural spot, peaceful and surrounded by fields, woodland and a few houses. The top half of the site is in woodland, and beyond the reception and sanitary block, Lough Ree comes into view, and the remaining pitches run down to the shoreline. There are 60 pitches, most on hardstanding and all with 6A electricity. With fishing right on the doorstep, there are boats for hire locally, and the site has private mooring buoys, plus a dinghy slip and harbour. A restaurant and a 'singing' pub are close by.

Situated midway between Galway and Dublin, linked by the M6, the park is easily accessible. Nearby attractions include the Kilbeggan Distillery Experience, but the main appeal is Lough Ree and the navigable Shannon river flowing into and out of the lough on its way to the sea. There are pleasure cruises based in Athlone.

The toilet block is clean, and the refurbished ladies' toilets, unisex showers (€1) and facilities for disabled visitors are all excellent. Dishwashing sinks outside. Laundry room (wash and dry €8). A wooden chalet houses a pool room with an open fire and a campers' kitchen (no cooking facilities).

Key Features

 Pets Accepted

 Disabled Facilities

 Play Area

 Fishing

 Sailing

Scan me for more information.

Alan Rogers Code: IR8900
15 pitches
GPS: 53.71575, -6.57334

Slane, Co. Meath

Slane Farm Camping

www.alanrogers.com/ir8900
info@slanefarmhostel.ie
Tel: +353 41 988 4985
www.slanefarmhostel.ie

Open (Touring Pitches):
Start March - End October.

Slane Farm Camping is a friendly, family-run campsite situated on a large working farm in a rural setting in the heart of the historic Boyne Valley, 16 km. West of Drogheda. This small campsite has a sunny field for tents and a separate stony area for motorhomes and caravans. Electricity (6A Europlug) is available, but long leads may be needed. It is an ideal base for concerts in the grounds of Slane Castle, only 5 minutes walk away, so can be quite busy. A well-equipped kitchen is available for use by campers, and the reception area is well-stocked with local information. The owners are always on hand to offer help and advice about the area.

Fresh produce from the adjacent vegetable garden is available, and visits can be made to the dairy and the farm animals. There is a donkey and two goats for the children to see on site. There are many marked walks around Slane Farm for those seeking to explore the immediate surroundings. Areas recommended for visits are the Boyne valley, County Louth, County Neath and County Kildare. Dublin, 50 km, is easy to reach by car using the M1 motorway.

Key Features

 Pets Accepted

 Beach Access

Well maintained, but very basic toilet facilities in nearby farm building. Kitchen. Laundry room. Barbecue. Bicycle hire (delivered to site). WiFi (free). 6 cottages to rent. Hostel accommodating 42 people in private rooms. Twin-axle caravans are not accepted.

Scan me for more information.

Alan Rogers Code: IR9465
3 accommodations
99 pitches
GPS: 53.01677, -9.40200

Doolin, Co. Clare

www.alanrogers.com/ir9465
ken@doolincamping.com
Tel: +353 65 707 4458
www.doolincamping.com

Open (Touring Pitches):
Mid March - Mid October.

Nagle's Doolin Camping Park

This neat and tidy seaside site is located just one kilometre from the dramatic cliffs of Moher, a UNESCO Global Geopark, and just a few metres from the ferry, which zips across to the sparsely populated Aran Islands in 20 minutes. The nearby village of Doolin, famed for its traditional music, has a good range of shops, restaurants and pubs with lively, impromptu music sessions. Walkers and nature lovers will be in their element here, with wonderful trails and signposted coastal walks along the eight-kilometre headland. From here, there are magnificent panoramic views out to the Aran Islands and spectacular seascapes over the bay to Connemara.

The site has 99 pitches, including 76 level hardstandings (all with 10A electricity and 21 also with water and drainage) and grass pitches for tents. They are not separated by hedges, but the site is divided into bays by limestone walls. Three new camping pods are available for hire. There is excellent WiFi coverage over the whole site.

One modern, well equipped toilet block is unheated but has good facilities including hot showers (€1) and en-suite unit for disabled visitors. Laundry facilities (charged). Kitchen with cooking rings (charged), fridge/freezer and sinks with hot water. Motorhome services. Shop (June-Aug). Gas. Games room. Play area. WiFi throughout.

Key Features

 Book Online

 Pets Accepted

 Disabled Facilities

 Beach Access

 Play Area

Scan me for more information.

Alan Rogers Code: IR9462
20 pitches
GPS: 52.73535, -9.53414

Doonbeg, Co. Clare

Strand Camping

This is a small site facing resolutely out to sea on the beautiful Doonbeg Bay and just a short walk from Doonbeg village. The site owners are happy to advise on walking routes and book fishing and dolphin-watching trips, and the Trump Golf Complex is just a short drive away. The scenery is wild and spectacular, with numerous paths and trails, especially along the coast, so boots and bikes are popular accessories. Others come for kayaking, riding, golf and surfing.

A bus service connects Doonbeg with the towns of Kilrush, Kilkee, Lahinch and Ennis, all worthy of a visit or further afield around the Loop Head peninsula. Just 20km away is the Shannon Ferry terminal for easy access to County Kerry.

The 20 level pitches, some with sea views, vary in size and are mainly on hardstanding. They are separated by shrubs and wildflowers, and each has a 16A electricity hook-up; there are four water points on site. The village has a choice of bars, restaurants and takeaways.

One heated sanitary block has free hot showers. No facilities for disabled visitors. Well equipped laundry block. Motorhome services (a chemical disposal is planned). Small dishwashing and kitchen area. Bicycle hire. Free WiFi over site.

www.alanrogers.com/ir9462
strandcampingdoonbeg@gmail.com
Tel: +353 65 905 5345
www.strandcampingdoonbeg.com

Open (Touring Pitches):
Mid March - Early September.

Key Features

 Pets Accepted

 Beach Access

 Fishing

Scan me for more information.

291

Alan Rogers Code: IR9455
28 pitches
GPS: 52.53867, -8.79290

Adare, Co. Limerick

www.alanrogers.com/ir9455
adarecc@gmail.com
Tel: +353 61 395 376
www.adarecamping.com

Open (Touring Pitches):
Start April - End September.

Adare Caravan Park

This attractive family-run park is ever popular due to its location just 3 km from Adare, often referred to as Ireland's prettiest village. The thatched cottages and bucolic surroundings are charming, making this an ideal overnight halt when travelling to or from the country's southwest. Stay a while and explore the heritage, notably the 13th century Desmond Castle, Franciscan Abbey (1464 AD), Augustinian Abbey (1315 AD) and Trinitarian Abbey (1215 AD). Limerick lies 20 km away, with bright lights and King John's imposing 13th-century castle. And as for sports, Adare plays host to the 2027 Ryder Cup.

It's a small site, set back from the road, with an open layout, shrubs and mature trees. There are 28 level pitches of about 80-100 sq.m. Of these, 15 have hardstanding with 16A electricity, whilst the remainder are on grass and used mainly for tents. There are picnic tables, and a farm walk provides scenic views and good dog walking. A modern building at the entrance houses the reception.

The heated toilet block is well tiled and houses spacious well fitted showers, washbasins and hand/hair dryers. Baby changing room and facilities for disabled visitors (washbasin and WC). Laundry room. Campers' kitchen with cooker and sandwich toaster. Hot tub (charge). Play area. Night lighting.

Key Features

 Pets Accepted

 Disabled Facilities

 Play Area

Scan me for more information.

Alan Rogers Code: IR9400
2 accommodations
48 pitches
GPS: 52.41998, -8.18787

Glen of Aherlow, Co. Tipperary

The Glen of Aherlow

www.alanrogers.com/ir9400
rdrew@tipperarycamping.com
Tel: +353 62 565 55
www.tipperarycamping.com

Open (Touring Pitches):
All year.

The owners of one of Ireland's newest parks, George and Rosaline Drew, are campers themselves and have set about creating an idyllic park in an idyllic location. This three-hectare park is set in one of Ireland's most picturesque valleys and is open all year. There are beautiful views of the wooded and hilly areas of Slievenamuck and the Galtee Mountains.

There are 48 large and level touring pitches, on both hardstanding and grass, each pair sharing a double 10 amp Europlug post and water point. The Drew family welcomes large groups and rallies, and large units can be accommodated. The new stone-built reception and shop beside the gate is a super addition to the site and includes a coffee shop. The excellent facilities are located in a purpose-built toilet block. The site is a member of the Caravan and Motorhome Club Affiliated Site Scheme, but visitors who are not members of the club are also very welcome.

Key Features

 Book Online

 Open All Year

 Pets Accepted

 Disabled Facilities

 Bike Hire

The modern toilet block includes free showers and facilities for visitors who are disabled. Motorhome services. Laundry room with ironing facility. Campers' kitchen. Recreation and TV rooms. Shop. Gas sales. Coffee shop. Bicycle hire (delivered to site). WiFi (free). Chemical toilet point. Ice pack freezing facility. BBQs allowed. The TV reception is good. Late-night arrivals area. Battery charging facility. Tents allowed. Train station 5 miles. Tesco 5 miles. The earliest arrival time is 12 noon.

Scan me for more information.

Alan Rogers Code: IR9240
30 pitches
GPS: 52.64270, -7.22199

Kilkenny, Co. Kilkenny

Treegrove Camp

www.alanrogers.com/ir9240
info@kilkennycamping.com
Tel: +353 86 830 8845
www.kilkennycamping.com

Open (Touring Pitches):
Early March - Mid November.

This park lies just outside the historic town of Kilkenny, voted Europe's friendliest city by Condé Nast Traveller. It's a short walk away, and there's much to see with the Medieval Mile stretching along cobbled streets from the castle to the cathedral.

The Smithwick's Experience traces the history of brewing here back to the 18th century. County Touring Routes are worth following, and the Nore Valley is popular with cyclists for its trails and unspoilt scenery with abundant wildlife.

The site is terraced with 30 hardstanding pitches for caravans, all with 10A electricity hook-ups and plenty of water points. There are 13 full-service pitches. A grassy area is reserved for hikers and cyclists, with further caravan and tent pitches sited on grass near the elevated sanitary block. It's an attractive setting, with mature trees and floral plantings and shrubs at the entrance. There is some occasional road noise, which can be distracting.

Family room with shower, WC and washbasin which can be used by disabled campers. Laundry room. Open, covered kitchen for campers with fridge, worktop, sink and electric kettle adjoins a comfortable games/TV room with pool table, and easy chairs. Bicycle hire. Riding. Tents to rent. Free WiFi.

Key Features

 Pets Accepted

 Disabled Facilities

 Bike Hire

 Horse Riding

Scan me for
more information.

Alan Rogers Code: IR9340
56 accommodations
40 pitches
GPS: 52.14763, -7.17274

Tramore, Co. Waterford

www.alanrogers.com/ir9340
info@newtowncove.com
Tel: +353 51 381 979
www.newtowncove.com

Open (Touring Pitches):
Late April - Late September.

Newtown Cove Camping

Well-run and friendly, this attractive small park is only five minutes walk from the beautiful Newtown Cove. It offers views of the famous and historic Metal Man and is 2.5 km from Tramore beach and 11 km south of Waterford. The busy holiday resort of Tramore offers a wide range of shops and eateries, and there are many delightful cliff walks close by. The historic town of Waterford is attractive, and the Waterford Crystal Centre is a popular visit. The Copper Coast towards Dungarvan is popular for its craggy cliffs, secret coves and windswept sandy beaches.

Some 40 pitches are neatly laid out on gently sloping grass, with 30 of these on hardstanding. They are open and sunny, all with 10A Europlug, and access is by well-lit, tarmac roads. There are around 56 privately owned caravan holiday homes. A modern building at the entrance houses reception, amenities and additional sanitary facilities.

The main sanitary block at the bottom end of the site provides good, clean facilities including a bathroom. Showers on payment (token from reception). Additional toilet facilities in reception. Excellent motorhome services. Campers' kitchen with cooking facilities, sheltered eating area, lounge and small laundry. Small shop (July/Aug). TV room. Games room. Small play area. WiFi throughout (charged).

Key Features

 Pets Accepted

 Beach Access

 Play Area

Scan me for more information.

Alan Rogers Code: IR9150
29 accommodations
120 pitches
GPS: 52.88840, -6.14528

Redcross Village, Co. Wicklow

River Valley Park

www.alanrogers.com/ir9150
info@rivervalleypark.ie
Tel: +353 40 441 647
www.rivervalleypark.ie

Open (Touring Pitches):
Mid March - Late September.

In the small country village of Redcross, in the heart of County Wicklow, this is a first rate, family run park. It is within easy reach of beauty spots such as the Vale of Avoca (Ballykissangel), Glendalough and Powerscourt, plus Brittas Bay, a 3.5 mile stretch of beautiful white sand dunes and clean beaches.

Celestine Bar and Restaurant on the site offers traditional Irish music, log fires and weekly entertainment. The 120 touring pitches (some serviced) are divided into separate, well landscaped areas with an adults-only section. All have 6/10 amp electricity connections and offer a choice of hardstanding or grass – you select your pitch.

Key Features

 Book Online

 Pets Accepted

 Disabled Facilities

 Beach Access

 Play Area

 Bar/Restaurant

 Golf

Modern, high-quality toilet blocks. Excellent facilities for visitors who are disabled. Showers (€1 token). Baby & toddler washroom. Laundry area. Campers' kitchen. Motorhome services. Gas supplies. Full bar and restaurant. Entertainment twice per week. TV and games room. Three tennis courts. Beer garden with entertainment for children (July/August). Sports complex. Foot-golf course. Go-kart track. Remote control boats and cars. Movie nights. Adventure and toddlers' playgrounds. Caravan storage. WiFi (free). Archery range. Mini wildlife walk. Glampotel onsite. Late-night arrivals area. Pets allowed. Dog walk. BBQs allowed. Tents allowed.

Scan me for more information.

Alan Rogers Code: IR9660
70 accommodations
27 pitches
GPS: 52.23813, -9.97128

Tralee, Co. Kerry

www.alanrogers.com/ir9660
info@greenacrespark.com
Tel: +353 66 713 9158
www.greenacrespark.com

Open (Touring Pitches):
Easter - Start October.

Green Acres Caravan Park

This small, family run site is situated close to the village of Castlegregory, Co. Kerry. With direct access to an Atlantic Coast beach, just metres away, it is ideal for campers who enjoy watersports, as well as those just wishing to relax in a coastal setting. Set in an Area of Outstanding Natural Beauty, with the mountains to the east and the sea to the west, there is plenty of interest for campers who enjoy the great outdoors. Moreover, it is an easy drive to some well known tourist spots such as Tralee, Dingle and Killarney.

It's a friendly, simple site, within walking distance of shops and restaurants and the local bar has live music twice a week. There are 27 unmarked, level, grassy pitches for tourers, each with a 10A electricity hook-up and a water point. Three extra large pitches are available for American-style motorhomes. There are some 70 privately owned units on the site.

Basic sanitary facilities include hot showers (€1.50/6 mins). Baby changing. No facilities for disabled visitors. Laundry room with washing machine and dryer. Fridge/freezer. TV/games room with pool table and air hockey. Adventure-style play area (2-12 yrs). Direct beach access. Excursions can be organised in the reception. Dogs are not accepted. Multi Universal Games Area on the beach. WiFi over site (charged).

Key Features

 Beach Access

 Sailing

Scan me for more information.

Alan Rogers Code: IR9600
6 accommodations
37 pitches
GPS: 52.05887, -9.93198

Curraheen Little, Co. Kerry

www.alanrogers.com/ir9600
glenross@eircom.net
Tel: +353 66 976 8451
www.campingkerry.com

Open (Touring Pitches):
Early April - Early October.

Glenross Camping Park

With a location set right in the heart of Co. Kerry, Glenross Caravan, Camping & Motorhome Park is situated on the spectacular Ring of Kerry and the Kerry Way footpath. It's an ideal base for touring Killarney and Dingle and the scenery is epic as Glenbeigh is approached. The park commands stunning views of Rossbeigh Strand (within walking distance) and the Dingle Peninsula.

With a peaceful location on the edge of the village, the park is well screened from the road and has 37 hardstanding touring pitches, mostly with 10 amp electricity (Europlug). There's a dedicated small tent area. Village shops are near as is the Kerry Bog Village, a reconstructed pre-famine village. Watersports, fishing, riding and fell walking are all within a short distance, and there's golf at the Dooks and Killorglin courses.

Well maintained and modern toilet block with showers (€1) includes facilities for visitors who are disabled. Laundry facilities. Motorhome services. Shelter for campers and dining area. Bar and restaurant next to site gates. Games room. Free Wi-Fi throughout. Late-night arrivals area. BBQs allowed. Pets allowed. Dog walk adjacent. TV reception good. Bus stop adjacent. Shop 100 metres. Tents allowed. Earliest arrival time 12 noon. Maximum outfit length 9.5 metres.

Key Features

 Book Online

 Pets Accepted

 Disabled Facilities

 Beach Access

 Bike Hire

Scan me for more information.

Alan Rogers Code: IR9640
105 pitches
GPS: 52.04304, -9.49954

Killarney, Co. Kerry

www.alanrogers.com/ir9640
info@killarneyfleskcamping.com
Tel: +353 64 663 1704
www.killarneyfleskcamping.com

Open (Touring Pitches):
Early April - End September.

Killarney Flesk Camping Park

At the gateway to the majestic National Park and Lakes, near Killarney town, this family-run, seven-acre park offers high quality. Pitches vary in size and spacing and have 10A electricity. Many pitches have a good grass area for awnings, and 21 also have dedicated electricity, water and drainage. The grounds are neat and tidy, with a feeling of space.

Killarney Flesk Caravan & Camping is ideally situated at the start of the Kerry Way and is well located for visiting Killarney and the famous Ring of Kerry. Walking and cycle paths lead directly from the park to Killarney National Park and the adjacent lakes, providing access to Killarney's world-famous woodlands and mountain scenery and flora and fauna. A short stroll away is the brooding Ross Castle and its pier, where you can embark on a pleasant lake cruise and enjoy the landscape slipping past you. Nearby is Muckross Abbey, burned down by Oliver Cromwell in 1652, two centuries after its founding but now a notable landmark of historical interest.

Modern, clean toilet blocks are well designed and equipped. Baby room. En-suite facility for disabled campers (key operated). Laundry room. Campers' kitchen. Night time security checks. WiFi throughout.

Key Features

 Pets Accepted

 Disabled Facilities

 Bar/Restaurant

 Bike Hire

Scan me for more information.

Alan Rogers Code: IR9580
15 accommodations
15 pitches
GPS: 51.82790, -9.73560

Tuosist, Co. Kerry

www.alanrogers.com/ir9580
info@bearacamping.com
Tel: +353 64 668 4287
www.bearacamping.com

Open (Touring Pitches):
Mid April - Mid October.

Beara Camping

Five minutes from Kenmare Bay, The Peacock is a unique location for campers who appreciate the natural world, where disturbance to nature is kept to a minimum. This five-acre site offers simple camping facilities with a variety of accommodation including a hostel, caravan holiday homes, secluded hardstanding pitches with electricity and level grass areas for tenting. The site is run by a Dutch couple, Bert and Klaske van Bavel, who are almost more Irish than the Irish, having made Ireland their home for their family.

The campsite is located on the Ring of Beara, an iconic 92-mile circular route around the Beara Peninsula along the Atlantic Ocean in the southwest of Ireland. It's wild and rugged, spectacular but safe, and the scenery of the counties of Cork and Kerry is simply incredible. The Gleninchaquin park is a highlight with its great walking routes and the unique Uragh Stone Circle. Elsewhere popular visits include the Healy Pass, Ardea Castle, Derreen Gardens and the fishing town of Castletownbere.

Key Features

 Play Area

Three small and basic blocks provide toilets, washbasins and free hot showers. Laundry service for a small fee. Campers' kitchens and sheltered eating area. Restaurant and takeaway (July/Aug). Pets are not accepted. WiFi on part of site.

Scan me for
more information.

Alan Rogers Code: IR9515
7 accommodations
6 pitches
GPS: 51.66875, -9.26105

Drimoleague, Co. Cork

Top of the Rock

www.alanrogers.com/ir9515
david@topoftherock.ie
Tel: 353 86 173 5134
www.topoftherock.ie

Open (Touring Pitches):
All year.

Top of the Rock Pod Páirc & Walking Centre is a family site located in the heart of West Cork, near the Atlantic coast and amid nine miles of beautiful walking trails in an area rich in folklore, history and culture. The working farm provides space for tents (six 6A Europlug electricity sockets and water) and a dedicated area for six camper vans (no caravans) on gravel, with full facility access. There are seven pods to rent, dispersed throughout the farm, their design inspired by early Christian structures. This beautiful rural environment includes farmland, woodland, water, flora and fauna.

The quaint West Cork market town of Clonakilty is just a 45-minute drive away: children love the Model Railway Village here, and nearby is Inchidoheny Beach. Alternatively, a 15-minute drive away is the ferry at Baltimore, where you can embark on the short crossing to Sherkin Island with three unspoilt beaches.

Sanitary facilities with provision for disabled visitors (showers 5 mins. for €1). Laundry room with drying area, dryer and washing machine. Self-catering campers' kitchen with fridge, cookers, kettles etc. Breakfast delivered to pitches. Campfire area. Playground. Grass area for football and volleyball. Games room with table tennis, pool (€1), board games. Barbecue and grill for hire. WiFi in reception (free).

Key Features

 Open All Year

 Pets Accepted

 Disabled Facilities

 Beach Access

 Play Area

Scan me for
more information.

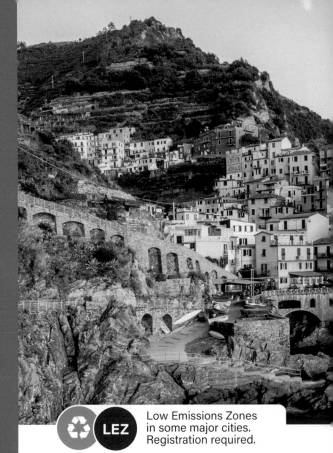

Capital Rome
Currency Euro (€)
Language Italian
Time Zone CET (GMT+1)
Telephone Code +39

Shops Hours vary throughout the year, with many shops operating on shorter hours in low and shoulder seasons. In high season 9am to 1pm and 3.30pm to 7.30pm Mon to Sat. Outside of cities, most close on Sun. Some also close on Mon morning.

Money ATMs are widespread and are accessible 24hrs a day, some have multilingual instructions. Credit/debit cards are widely accepted, some smaller shops and trattorias may not take them.

Travelling with Children Very kid-friendly. Beaches are generally safe. State-run attractions are often free to EU citizens under 18 years of age. Few restaurants open before 7.30pm although pizzerias usually open earlier.

Public Holidays 1 Jan New Year's Day; 6 Jan Epiphany; Mar/Apr Easter Sunday; Mar/Apr Easter Monday; 25 Apr Liberation Day; 1 May International Workers' Day; 2 Jun Republic Day; 15 Aug Assumption; 1 Nov All Saints; 8 Dec Immaculate Conception; 25 Dec Christmas Day; 26 Dec Boxing Day.

LEZ Low Emissions Zones in some major cities. Registration required.

● **EU Member** | ● **Schengen Area**

Tourism website italia.it

●●○○○ **Accessible Travel Score**

Not as well-equipped for wheelchair users as some of its European neighbours. Public buildings are slowly upgrading. Awareness is growing and museums offer reduced rates.

Driving in Italy Tolls are payable on the autostrada network. A pre-paid Via card can be used to pay, or an electronic tag called Telepass can be purchased. An overhanging load must be indicated by a large red/white hatched warning square. An unladen weight of over 50% of the weight of the towing vehicle must have service brakes on all wheels. Drink-driving and using your mobile whilst driving are illegal.

 Dashcams are legal

 Speed camera detectors are **illegal**

Italy

View all campsites in Italy
alanrogers.com/italy

See campsite map page 482

Climate Hot summers, mild winters in the south. Cooler with snow in the north.

Emergency services Call 112 for the police, ambulance and fire and rescue.

Units Italy uses the metric system. To convert km to miles, multiply by 0.6.

Once the capital of the Roman Empire, Italy was unified as recently as 1861; thus, regional customs and traditions have not been lost. Its enviable collections of art, literature and culture have had worldwide influence and continue to be a magnet for visitors who flock to cities such as Venice, Florence and Rome.

In the north, the vibrant city of Milan is the fashion capital of the world and home to the famous opera house, La Scala, as well as Da Vinci's 'The Last Supper. It is also a good starting-off point for the Alps; the Italian Lake District, incorporating Lake Garda, Lake Como and Lake Maggiore; the canals of Venice and the lovely town of Verona.

The hilly towns of central Italy are especially popular, with Siena, San Gimignano and Assisi among the most

visited. The historic capital of Rome with its Colosseum and Vatican City is not to be missed.

Naples is an ideal base for visiting Pompeii and the breathtaking scenery of the Amalfi coast. The city also has a charm of its own – winding narrow streets and crumbling façades inset with shrines sit alongside boutiques, bars and lively street markets amid chaotic traffic and roaring scooters.

Scan QR code to browse more campsites on our website

303

Alan Rogers Code: IT65030
90 accommodations
137 pitches
GPS: 44.25076, 7.38994
Post Code: I-12010

Entracque, Piedmont

www.alanrogers.com/it65030
info@campingvallegesso.com
Tel: +39 0171 978 247
www.campingvallegesso.com

Open (Touring Pitches):
All year.

Camping Valle Gesso

Valle Gesso is situated in Entracque, a village near Cuneo in southern Piedmont. It borders on the Parco Naturale delle Alpi Marittime, the largest protected area in Piedmont and one of the biggest in Italy. It's a picturesque spot surrounded by imposing tree-clad mountains. A little away from the site, hot springs gush out in the spa complex of Terme di Valdieri, and nearby is a centre for the conservation of wolves, which may be spotted from a lookout. A secure nature walkway runs through the woods to the river.

There are 137 touring pitches, 70 of which have 3-6A Europlug, water and drainage, and a dedicated area with up to 70 tents. It's a site which offers something for everyone with a magnificent pool, football and volleyball field, hiking and cycling for the more active, while also maintaining a totally natural mountain retreat for those seeking a more restful break away from the bustle of everyday life at home.

There are three sanitary blocks, all kept very clean and offering a mixture of British and Turkish style WCs. Motorhome services. Laundry. Basic shop and bar (July/Aug). Three section swimming pool and whirlpool (July/Aug). Large screen TV. Video games. Billiard table. Playground and woods for exploring. Football. Volleyball. Communal barbecue. Bicycle hire. WiFi over site (free).

Key Features

 Pets Accepted

 Disabled Facilities

 Swimming Pool

 Play Area

 Bar/Restaurant

 Bike Hire

Scan me for more information.

Alan Rogers Code: IT62436
41 accommodations
32 pitches
GPS: 45.73649, 8.57577
Post Code: I-28040

Dormelletto, Piedmont

Camping Röse

www.alanrogers.com/it62436
booking@campingrose.it
Tel: +39 0322 497 979
www.campingrose.it

Open (Touring Pitches):
Start April - End September.

Camping Röse enjoys a particularly favourable position, located directly on Lake Maggiore in the Canneti di Dormelletto Nature Reserve, just a few kilometres from Arona. Milan is around 50 km away and makes a great day trip, with its design and fashion heritage and magnificent Gothic cathedral. The campsite is small and friendly with a welcoming atmosphere and is well laid out with large, grassy pitches, well shaded by mature plane trees with electricity and water.

Camping Röse has its own lake beach with umbrellas and deckchairs on the grassy area leading down to it. It's perfect for swimming and watersports and is close to the bar and the adjacent sports field where youngsters can run around freely. A swimming pool with Jacuzzi allows you to relax and take in the scenery of Lake Maggiore as you soak in the warm waters. The onsite restaurant-pizzeria is popular, with a decent menu offering local specialities, and has a large terrace overlooking the lake. For children there is a convenient play area equipped with table football, table tennis and video games.

Key Features

 Book Online

 Pets Accepted

 Beach Access

 Swimming Pool

 Play Area

 Bar/Restaurant

 Fishing

Sanitary units with token-operated hot showers. Disabled facilities. Bar, restaurant. Reception. Laundry area with washing machine and dryer. Boat mooring and haulage and boat rental. Table football, table tennis. Multisport field. Children's play area. WiFi. Pets allowed.

Scan me for more information.

Alan Rogers Code: IT62610
157 accommodations
149 pitches
GPS: 45.65708, 10.03740
Post Code: I-25049

Iseo, Lombardy

www.alanrogers.com/it62610
info@campingdelsole.it
Tel: +39 0309 80 288
www.campingdelsole.it

Open (Touring Pitches):
Mid April - Late September.

Camping del Sole

Camping del Sole is, in our opinion, one of Italy's best family sites, in a wonderful setting and offering high-quality facilities. It lies on the southern edge of Lake Iseo, just outside the pretty lakeside town of Iseo and to the north of Brescia. The ancient city of Bergamo is to the west.

The site has 306 pitches, of which 149 are for touring, all with 3A electricity and some fine views of the surrounding mountains and lake. Pitches are generally flat and reasonably sized, but cars must park in the car park, as is often the norm. The site has its own sandy beach and a large grassy expanse for sunbathing (with its own lakeside bar with wonderful views). A wide range of excellent leisure amenities includes a large swimming pool and a bar/restaurant with a pizzeria near the pool, which serves excellent local cuisine and features local wines.

Sanitary facilities are modern and well maintained, with special facilities for children and disabled visitors. Washing machines and dryers (€4). Bar, restaurant, pizzeria, snack bar and excellent shop. Motorhome services. Bicycle hire. Swimming pool with children's pool (High season). Tennis. Football pitch. Fitness area. Canoe and pedal boat hire. WiFi. Dog exercise area. Entertainment in high season.

Key Features

 Book Online

 Pets Accepted

 Disabled Facilities

 Swimming Pool

 Play Area

 Bar/Restaurant

 Bike Hire

 Fishing

Scan me for
more information.

Alan Rogers Code: IT62860
46 accommodations
145 pitches
GPS: 45.56155, 10.55352
Post Code: I-25080

Manerba del Garda, Lake Garda

www.alanrogers.com/it62860
info@campingbaiaverde.com
Tel: +39 0365 651 753
www.campingbaiaverde.co.uk

Open (Touring Pitches):
Mid April - Mid October.

Camping Village Baia Verde

Baia Verde is a smart, well-equipped and peaceful campsite located in the attractive village of Manerba on the southwestern corner of Lake Garda, backed by the Valtenesi hills. The site leads down towards the lake and overlooks the large sandy expanse of beach, making this an appealing campsite for families with young children.

The 145 touring pitches are in regular rows on flat, open ground with young trees giving some shade. They are all fully serviced (16A electricity), and 12 have superb private facilities. The remaining 46 pitches are used for mobile homes to rent, and there are apartments available too. The excellent restaurant block and the building housing the other facilities were both designed by an architect, showing the attention to detail and loving care that has gone into Baia Verde. This is an excellent, well-run campsite in an enviable location that ensures plenty of repeat visitors.

Full range of high quality sanitary facilities in an impressive three storey building in the style of an Italian villa. Rooms for babies and children. Superb facilities for disabled visitors. Washing machines and dryers. TV lounge. Rooftop sunbathing area with jacuzzi. Entertainment and activity programme (high season). WiFi over site (charged). Only some breeds of dog accepted.

Key Features

 Book Online

 Pets Accepted

 Disabled Facilities

 Swimming Pool

 Play Area

 Bar/Restaurant

Scan me for more information.

Alan Rogers Code: IT62660
113 accommodations
363 pitches
GPS: 45.45539, 10.70170
Post Code: I-37010

Cavalcaselle, Lake Garda

www.alanrogers.com/it62660
info@gasparina.com
Tel: +39 0457 550 775
www.gasparina.com

Open (Touring Pitches):
Start April - Mid October.

Camping Gasparina

At the southern end of Lake Garda and just a few kilometres west of Verona, Gasparina is in a peaceful location and has the feeling of being in the countryside. Verona is lovely, featuring the Roman arena and Juliet's balcony, made famous by Shakespeare, while the vineyards of Bardolino are close by. There's plenty of easy going cycling and walking to be enjoyed as well as trips around the beautiful lake, perhaps via elegant Sirmione, and days out at the various theme parks so popular with the youngsters.

As the site slopes gently towards the lake, levellers are needed in some parts. There are 363 grassy touring pitches in back-to-back rows separated by gravel roads. Many trees and flowers adorn the site, with shade in most parts courtesy of mature plane trees. The fenced and supervised busy swimming pools are separated from the restaurant terraces by a neat, well-clipped hedge. Loungers and umbrellas can be hired by the day from Reception.

Two toilet blocks have the usual facilities with warm water. Facilities for disabled visitors. Washing machines and dryer. Shop. Bar/restaurant with terrace. Swimming pool (High season). Playground. Watersports. Entertainment in high season. Dogs and other pets are not accepted in rentals.

Key Features

 Pets Accepted

 Disabled Facilities

 Swimming Pool

 Play Area

 Bar/Restaurant

 Bike Hire

 Fishing

Scan me for more information.

Camping Village Paradiso

Alan Rogers Code: IT66135
205 accommodations
90 pitches
GPS: 43.84819, 10.26016
Post Code: I-55049

Viareggio, Tuscany

www.alanrogers.com/it66135
info@campingparadisoviareggio.com
Tel: +39 0584 392 005
www.campingparadisoviareggio.it

Open (Touring Pitches):
Start April - End September.

Just 20 km north of Pisa and its famous leaning tower and a 90-minute drive from gorgeous Florence, Camping Village Paradiso enjoys a prime location. Even better, it's just a short walk through the woodland path among the pine trees and sand dunes to the long sandy beach. It's a large family-friendly site with excellent facilities that evolve around a central courtyard containing the campsite shop, restaurants and bar.

Cycling or walking into nearby Viareggio is easy. You'll find a lovely traditional beachfront with long sandy beaches, plenty of shops, and useful supermarkets. Back on the site, there's a good swimming pool, fully supervised, and the 90 pitches are well laid out, clearly marked, and of average size. There's good shade to some, thanks to the variety of mature trees, cypress and colourful oleander shrubs and hedging. Some 80 pitches are equipped with electric hook-up points.

Three sanitary blocks all clean with baby change and disabled facilities, as well as a laundry room. Shuttle bus to beach July/Aug, Evening entertainment Bar/Restaurant, shop, bazaar - selling beach/camping equipment. Children's playground. Outdoor swimming pool. WiFi. Bicycle rental. Pets allowed. 'Quiet time' in operation between 2-3pm.

Key Features

 Pets Accepted

 Disabled Facilities

 Beach Access

 Swimming Pool

 Play Area

 Bar/Restaurant

 Bike Hire

Scan me for
more information.

Alan Rogers Code: IT66114
80 accommodations
111 pitches
GPS: 43.44650, 11.61873
Post Code: I-52021

Capannole, Tuscany

www.alanrogers.com/it66114
info@campinglachiocciola.com
Tel: +39 0559 95 776
www.campinglachiocciola.com

Open (Touring Pitches):
Early April - Early November.

Camping la Chiocciola

You will receive a warm welcome from Hans & Francesca and English is spoken by all in reception. This site is in an ideal location for touring Tuscany and visiting Sienna and Florence. Getting into Florence is just a ten minute drive to Bucine and a one-hour train journey takes you right into the centre of this beautiful city. Sienna is about a 45 minute drive away. The setting of this site is perfect in the centre of Chianti country, with beautiful views across the Tuscany countryside and some amazing sunsets.

The site consists of 111 individual touring pitches with shade and separated by low hedging, all have hook-up and a small sink unit. There are also 76 mobile homes and four Safari Tents for hire. There are three pools for campsite guests, surrounded by a sun terrace with many sun loungers. For the active, there are tennis courts, a volleyball court, a football field, ping pong tables, bike hire and a scenic network of paths that runs around the campsite.

Two modern sanitary blocks on site with showers and baby facilities. Laundry with large family washers for 4€. Well-stocked shop. Bar and terrace area. Family restaurant within walking distance. Bicycle hire. Children's play area. Tennis. Table tennis. Superb pool complex with three pools, one especially for children.

Key Features

 Book Online

 Pets Accepted

 Swimming Pool

 Play Area

 Bar/Restaurant

 Bike Hire

Scan me for more information.

Alan Rogers Code: IT66020
92 accommodations
120 pitches
GPS: 44.52366, 11.37410
Post Code: I-40127

Bologna, Emília-Romagna

www.alanrogers.com/it66020
info@hotelcamping.com
Tel: +39 0513 25 016
www.hotelcamping.com

Open (Touring Pitches):
Early January - Mid December.

Camping Città di Bologna

This spacious city site was established in 1993 on the edge of the Trade Fair Centre of this ancient and historic city and is very clean and modern. The 120 pitches, with 6A electricity, are numbered and marked out in an orderly manner and shaded by trees. The level grass pitches are edged with "grasscrete" on the roadside, to aid car parking. There are two main areas plus a separate section for very long units. You should always find space here as there appears to be over capacity.

There is an unassuming restaurant and bar and the swimming pool is very welcome after a day of exploring the city. The site is ideal for an overnight stop, due to its proximity to the motorway, or as a base for exploring the most attractive and lively city of Bologna. A regular bus service operates from reception into the City Centre. Visit the Piazza Maggiore with its arched colonnades, the Fountain of Neptune and the Basilica di San Petronio and medieval towers.

Modern sanitary blocks include excellent provision for disabled visitors (with British-style WCs, free showers and alarms that ring in reception). Washing machines. Motorhome services. Restaurant and bar with adjoining terrace. Large swimming pool with shallow area for children. Basic play area. Minigolf. Fitness centre. Free WiFi over site. EV charging point.

Key Features

 Book Online

 Pets Accepted

 Disabled Facilities

 Swimming Pool

 Play Area

 Bar/Restaurant

Scan me for more information.

Alan Rogers Code: IT60730
109 accommodations
376 pitches
GPS: 44.46641, 12.28499
Post Code: I-48122

Marina di Ravenna, Emília-Romagna

Piomboni Camping Village

www.alanrogers.com/it60730
info@campingpiomboni.it
Tel: +39 0544 530 230
www.campingpiomboni.it

Open (Touring Pitches):
Mid April - Mid September.

The pine forest which is home to Piomboni forms part of the Po Delta National Forest and has been spared the frantic commercial development of other parts of the Adriatic coast. The site, still family-owned and run, maintains a totally natural feel with pitches located between the ancient, tall pines and younger, dividing trees. There are 376 pitches for everything from tiny tents to motorhomes up to 8 metres, all with 4-10A electricity. Access to the beach is just 100 metres from the site gate and there are large, free public areas along with sunbeds for hire.

Early in the evening, the children's singing and dancing near the restaurant makes for a happy family atmosphere and the youngsters are certainly kept active with a busy programme in high season. The restaurant offers fixed menus and à la carte, and is very reasonably priced. Other hostelries line the road a short walk from the site.

Seven toilet blocks, two with hot and cold showers. Baby rooms. Facilities for disabled visitors. Washing machines and dryer. Dog bath. Well stocked shop. Bar, restaurant and takeaway (seasonal). Dancing and entertainments area. TV room with library. Games and play area with boules pitch. Children's activities programme. Archery. Bicycle hire. Free WiFi. Excursions arranged.

Key Features

 Book Online

 Pets Accepted

 Disabled Facilities

 Beach Access

 Bar/Restaurant

 Bike Hire

Scan me for more information.

Alan Rogers Code: IT60135
96 accommodations
300 pitches
GPS: 45.19164, 12.30255
Post Code: I-30015

Chioggia Sottomarina, Veneto

www.alanrogers.com/it60135
info@campeggioatlanta.com
Tel: +39 0414 91 311
www.campeggioatlanta.com

Open (Touring Pitches):
Mid April - Early September.

Atlanta Mediterraneo

This is a great location for visiting Venice, a destination which never fails to excite. Take a short walk into Sottomarina, where you can catch a bus or water bus (16€ return) direct to Venice. The site is only a short drive to old Chioggia (little Venice), and the local town offers a large selection of shops, bars, restaurants and supermarkets and a very long, busy beachfront.

This is a large but very spacious campsite with direct access to the Adriatic from a private supervised beach. There is a restaurant and bar overlooking the two swimming pools, so you can relax while keeping an eye on the children. The site has a total of 300 pitches available for caravans, motorhomes or tents, all with 6 amp electric hook-up and water, and all approximately 70 m2. There is also a variety of luxury mobile homes to rent.

Key Features

 Book Online

 Disabled Facilities

 Beach Access

 Swimming Pool

 Bar/Restaurant

Supervised activities occur throughout the day for children and a modern play area and wading pool. The four sanitary blocks are all modern, clean, and spacious and have facilities for the disabled. Two swimming pools (bathing caps must be worn). Well-equipped laundry room. 24-hour security. Local cycle hire. Well-stocked shop. Supermarkets and town nearby. Direct access to a supervised beach. Entertainment. Bar/Restaurant. WiFi throughout the site (chargeable). No pets.

Scan me for more information.

Alan Rogers Code: IT60055
220 accommodations
331 pitches
GPS: 45.69467, 13.45255
Post Code: I-34073

Grado, Friuli - Venézia Giúlia

www.alanrogers.com/it60055
info@puntaspin.it
Tel: +39 0431 80 732
www.puntaspin.it

Open (Touring Pitches):
Early April - End September.

Camping Punta Spin

Punta Spin is a large, well-maintained site set between the road and a soft sand beach. About 300 flat touring pitches vary in size (65-100 sq.m), all with 6A electricity and with some on the beachfront (book early for these). A bicycle is an asset here to access the furthest sanitary blocks. The comprehensive amenities are clustered near the entrance and include three pools, one of which is a sophisticated paddling complex, and another is covered and heated. The restaurant and bar terraces overlook the illuminated pools, making a great setting for dinner.

This site has a distinctly Italian feel and a thoroughly family-friendly atmosphere. A professional team organises all manner of entertainment in high season, and an impressive Kids' Club is in full swing all day. Of course, a day trip to Venice is a memorable day out.

Three modern sanitary blocks have free hot water throughout. Mostly British style toilets. Facilities for disabled campers. Washing machines and dryers. Motorhome services. Large supermarket and other shops. Bars and restaurant (April-Sept). Pizzeria. Takeaway. Three swimming pools. Beauty and fitness centre. Minigolf. Disco. Entertainment team in high season. Beach bar. Playground. Tennis. WiFi (charged). Bicycle hire. Bungalows and mobile homes for hire.

Key Features

 Book Online

 Pets Accepted

 Disabled Facilities

 Beach Access

 Swimming Pool

 Play Area

 Bar/Restaurant

 Bike Hire

Scan me for more information.

Alan Rogers Code: IT66540
59 accommodations
260 pitches
GPS: 43.18103, 12.01630
Post Code: I-06061

Castiglione del Lago, Umbria

www.alanrogers.com/it66540
info@badiaccia.com
Tel: +39 075 965 9097
www.badiaccia.com

Open (Touring Pitches):
Start April - End September.

Camping Badiaccia

A lakeside site, Camping Badiaccia Village, has a relaxed atmosphere and excellent views of the surrounding hills and the islands of the lake. Being directly on the lake, with a long sandy beach, gives an almost seaside atmosphere.

The 260 numbered and well-tended pitches (4-12A electricity) vary in size and are shaded and separated by trees and bushes. English is spoken by the friendly staff. A very pleasant, large pool is by the restaurant, and a children's pool is in the beach area. There is a protected swimming area along the beach with lots of sunbathing space, sun loungers with some reed areas close by, a jetty for fishing, and a protected mooring for small boats. The site offers a range of sporting opportunities with organised activities for children and adults in the high season.

Three excellent sanitary blocks with hot showers, provision for children and superb units for disabled visitors. Washing machines and dryer. Motorhome services. Gas supplies. Restaurant, snack bar and shop. Health and wellness centre. Swimming and paddling pools (High season). Play areas. Tennis. Fitness room. Bicycle hire. Boules. Minigolf. Watersports. Fishing. Boat hire. Entertainment and excursions in high season. Free WiFi over part of site. Barbecue area by lake. Torches required in places. Boat trips around the lake.

Key Features

 Book Online

 Pets Accepted

 Swimming Pool

 Play Area

 Bar/Restaurant

 Bike Hire

Scan me for more information.

Alan Rogers Code: IT66560
33 accommodations
104 pitches
GPS: 42.88800, 13.01464
Post Code: I-06047

Castelvecchio di Preci, Umbria

www.alanrogers.com/it66560
info@ilcollaccio.com
Tel: +39 0743 939 005
www.ilcollaccio.com

Open (Touring Pitches):
Start April - End September.

Camping Il Collaccio

Castelvecchio di Preci is tucked away in the tranquil heights of the mountainous Umbrian countryside, as is Camping Il Collaccio, which is set on a hillside. The 100 or so terraced touring pitches, with shade and 6A electricity, have stunning views. The friendly family have run the business well for over 30 years, planting thousands of trees here in the process.

A dip in the pools is wonderfully cooling in summer, and an evening meal in the campsite's own restaurant, whilst taking in the views of the lush green vegetation of the surrounding hills, is a must (try the wild boar!). It's a foodie heaven, with homemade gastronomic treats available in the shop on-site, including excellent local wines. This is a relaxed, charming campsite in an idyllic spot with so much to recommend it. A really authentic campsite with plenty to see and do in the surrounding area.

Four modern sanitary blocks spaced through the site have mostly British style WCs, cold water in washbasins and hot, pre-mixed water in showers and sinks. Facilities for disabled visitors. Washing machine. Motorhome services. Bar. Restaurant and takeaway. Shop (basics, seasonal). Two swimming pools (Seasonal). Play area. Tennis. Boules. Entertainment in high season. Excursions. WiFi over part of site (charged). Bungalows and chalets to rent.

Key Features

 Book Online

 Pets Accepted

 Disabled Facilities

 Swimming Pool

 Play Area

 Bar/Restaurant

Scan me for more information.

Alan Rogers Code: IT66230
89 accommodations
200 pitches
GPS: 43.95957, 12.46126
Post Code: I-47893

Repubblica di San Marino,
Emília-Romagna

www.alanrogers.com/it66230
info@centrovacanzesanmarino.com
Tel: +39 0549 903 964
www.centrovacanzesanmarino.com

Open (Touring Pitches):
All year.

Centro Vacanze San Marino

Centro Vacanze San Marino, at 400 m. above sea level and positioned on an attractive hillside, has lovely views of the Adriatic. You'll arrive via twisting mountainous roads winding through dramatic scenery and will discover an excellent, modern site with a variety of well-tended trees offering welcome shade. Make sure you visit the ancient city of San Marino at the top of the mountain (4 km).

On level terraces, the main grass pitches are roomy and accessed from tarmac or gravel roads. Separated by hedges, all have electricity (5A). Smaller pitches on lower terraces are for tents. There is a pleasant open feel to this site. Mobile homes and bungalows are available to rent, and the site is used by a tour operator (30 pitches). The large swimming pool has a section for children and a broad sunbathing terrace.

Four high quality, heated toilet blocks are kept very clean and have British and Turkish style WCs. Facilities for disabled visitors at the upper level to avoid slopes. Laundry facilities. Motorhome services. Gas supplies. Shop (April-Sept). Kitchen. TV room (satellite). Restaurant/pizzeria. Large swimming pool (High season) with jacuzzi and solarium. Large enclosed play area. Games room. Free WiFi over part of site. Tennis. Bicycle hire. Mini zoo. Entertainment programme for children (high season).

Key Features

 Book Online

 Open All Year

 Pets Accepted

 Disabled Facilities

 Swimming Pool

 Play Area

 Bar/Restaurant

 Bike Hire

Scan me for more information.

Alan Rogers Code: IT67790
65 accommodations
150 pitches
GPS: 41.70608, 12.34011
Post Code: I-00122

Lido di Ostia, Lazio

www.alanrogers.com/it67790
info@romacampingcastelfusano.it
Tel: +39 3289 71 894
www.romacampingcastelfusano.it

Open (Touring Pitches):
End March - Mid November.

Internazionale Castelfusano

This site is ideally situated for a beach holiday, with easy access across the road to a lovely, long sandy beach. Ostia is just 3 km away, and as a change of scene, Rome is only an hour's journey with the Colosseum, Vatican City, Piazza Venezia, and much more, making it a day to remember. Take the bus or train for convenience.

There are a total of 350 pitches, 150 of which are for touring, interspersed on undulating ground among mature trees. Although they offer plenty of shade, there are many low-hanging branches, and, as a result, some pitches are small and inappropriate for larger units. However, tents and smaller units can tuck themselves away in interesting nooks and crannies. The soil is sandy, but the access roads are mostly tarmac and gravel. Most of the pitches have 3A electricity. An access road to the beach provides an area for larger units to park.

Three toilet blocks with functional facilities including hot showers but mainly cold water for dishwashing and laundry. Unit for disabled visitors. Washing machine and dryer. Motorhome services. Well stocked shop (Apr-Oct). Bar/restaurant (Feb-Oct) with terrace. Live music (high season). Outdoor pool (June-Sept). Playground. Games area. Entertainment for children twice a week (July/Aug). Internet access and information in reception. Communal barbecue area.

Key Features

 Book Online

 Pets Accepted

 Disabled Facilities

 Beach Access

 Swimming Pool

 Play Area

 Bar/Restaurant

Scan me for more information.

Alan Rogers Code: IT68080
4 accommodations
105 pitches
GPS: 41.74267, 13.98867
Post Code: I-67030

Barrea, Abruzzo

www.alanrogers.com/it68080
info@campinglagenziana.it
Tel: +39 0864 88 101
www.campinglagenziana.it

Open (Touring Pitches):
Mid April - Mid October.

Camping la Genziana

This is the place to get away from it all – situated in the middle of Italy, high in the peaceful Abruzzo mountains with magnificent views over the Barrea lakes. It's an uncomplicated site, an hour from Rome and Pescara, and it could be another world in terms of peace and quiet. The site has limited facilities, but swimming, riding and fishing are all possible nearby. The 105 touring pitches (4A electricity) are set on a hillside amongst wildflowers and grasses and are relatively open, with wraparound views of the surrounding mountains.

The ebullient owner Tomasso Pasetta d'Amico and his family make everyone welcome to this peaceful, natural site. Tomasso is an expert in Alpine walking and a great raconteur. Ask him about 'calling wolves' – he really does and has appeared on BBC World talking about this. If mountain walking is for you, Tomasso will also give sound advice on the many trails starting from the site, of different gradients, each with its unique appeal. English is spoken.

Single clean, modern sanitary block with hot water throughout (honesty payment in high season). Mainly British style toilets. Laundry facilities. Motorhome services. Bar, coffee bar and small shop. WiFi (free). Torches are essential.

Key Features

 Book Online

 Pets Accepted

 Disabled Facilities

 Play Area

 Bar/Restaurant

Scan me for
more information.

Alan Rogers Code: IT67985
50 accommodations
50 pitches
GPS: 42.15431, 14.71578
Post Code: I-66050

Vasto, Abruzzo

www.alanrogers.com/it67985
info@grottadelsaraceno.it
Tel: +39 0873 310 213
www.grottadelsaraceno.it

Open (Touring Pitches):
Early June - Mid September.

Camping Grotta del Saraceno

Set on a beautiful stretch of the Adriatic Coast, Camping Village Grotta del Saraceno is on a promontory overlooking an attractive bay with stunning views. The soft sand beach is down 100 steps; halfway down, there is a charming 'ristopub' which sits alongside the famous grotto. If you are at all unsteady on your feet, this location is probably not for you.

The site has rows of pitches with 6A electricity, most with artificial shade, others with shade provided by trees. Unfortunately, the few pitches with sea views are occupied by permanent units. This is a family-friendly campsite with plenty of organised activities, especially for children. The trio of pools, including fountains, is very pleasant and is floodlit at night, and there is a choice of restaurants and a pizzeria.

Well maintained sanitary facilities with both British and Turkish style toilets and showers. Laundry. Motorhome services. Bazaar. Bar/snack bar. Ristopub. Central and beach bars. Supermarket. News stand. Greengrocer. Swimming pool complex. Restaurants and pizzeria. Beautician. Hairdresser. Sports fields. Beach volleyball. Auditorium. Games room. Fitness area. Entertainment and activities for children and families. Fishing. Bicycle hire. Torches useful. WiFi on part of site (free). Dogs are not accepted.

Key Features

 Book Online

 Disabled Facilities

 Beach Access

 Swimming Pool

 Play Area

 Bar/Restaurant

 Bike Hire

 Fishing

Scan me for more information.

Alan Rogers Code: IT68390
82 pitches
GPS: 40.47328, 14.99729
Post Code: I-84047

Capaccio-Paestum, Campania

www.alanrogers.com/it68390
Info@campingdesiderio.com
Tel: +39 0828 851 135
www.campingdesiderio.com

Open (Touring Pitches):
Start April - End October.

Villaggio Desiderio

Villaggio Camping Desiderio is located on the beautiful coast of Paestum, a city known worldwide for its archaeological importance to the extent that it is designated a UNESCO World Heritage Site. Pompeii, Vesuvius, Naples, Salerno, and the Amalfi Coast are no more than 100 km away and offer a fascinating insight into the history of this beautiful region. The shops and amenities in the village of Laura di Paestum are just 4 km, easily reached on a bike via the handy cycle path direct from the campsite.

The pitches for tents, camper and caravans are large and shady and located under poplars, eucalyptus, palms, olive trees and acacias. They are surrounded by lush vegetation, well-demarcated and equipped with a private washbasin with drinking water. Each one has its own parking place and an electricity connection. There are two toilet blocks with washbasins and hot showers, and the distance from most pitches is unlikely to exceed 100 metres. A path leads through shady pine forest and shifting dunes to the sandy beach 400 metres away, a board expanse of soft sand gently shelving into the water.

Private sanitary facilities available. Bar and shop (Jun-Sept). Swimming pool (Jun-Sept). Tennis court/football pitch. Private beach (Jun-Sept). Baby club (Jul-Aug). Children's playground. Table tennis. Bicycle rental. WiFi.

Key Features

 Book Online

 Pets Accepted

 Beach Access

 Swimming Pool

 Play Area

 Bar/Restaurant

 Bike Hire

 Fishing

Scan me for more information.

Alan Rogers Code: IT68738
7 accommodations
102 pitches
GPS: 41.55526, 15.89319
Post Code: I-71043

Manfredonia, Puglia

www.alanrogers.com/it68738
info@lidosalpi.it
Tel: +39 8845 71 160
www.campinglidosalpi.it

Open (Touring Pitches):
All year.

Camping Lido Salpi

Camping Lido Salpi is a peaceful and simple campsite located in the province of Foggia, on the Adriatic coast between Manfredonia and Margherita Di Savoia. There's plenty of interest here, with some useful suggestions for excursions (heritage, nature, gastronomy and so on) provided by the campsite. A short walk from the campsite takes you right onto a beautiful white sandy beach, part of a huge expanse running along this coastline. At the bus stop outside the campsite entrance, you can take a ride into the town of Manfredonia, where you'll find a lovely marina and plenty of shops and restaurants.

This is a good family site, relaxed and informal, where everyone can get on with enjoying the beach life. All pitches are well spaced, offer plenty of shade under the pines and plane trees, and have 6 amp electricity connections. The campsite is split into two areas; the first is adjacent to the beach with a basic toilet block. A short walk away is the second area with two additional toilet blocks with hot showers. All are clean, if a little dated.

Toilet blocks with hot and cold water, disabled facilities. Washing machines and dryers. Shop. Restaurant/pizzeria. Bar. Large children's play area. Evening entertainment. Beach adjacent. Children's entertainment (high season). Games room. Maximum two dogs per pitch (allowed on the beach). WiFi.

Key Features

 Pets Accepted

 Disabled Facilities

 Beach Access

 Play Area

 Bar/Restaurant

 Fishing

 Sailing

Scan me for more information.

Alan Rogers Code: IT68660
82 accommodations
600 pitches
GPS: 39.99832, 18.02650
Post Code: I-73014

Gallipoli, Puglia

www.alanrogers.com/it68660
info@baiadigallipoli.com
Tel: +39 0833 273 210
www.baiadigallipoli.com

Open (Touring Pitches):
Start April - End September.

Camping Baia di Gallipoli

Down on the 'heel' of Italy, the western shoreline of Puglia offers beaches of excellent quality, interspersed with small villages and some holiday complexes. The Baia di Gallipoli campsite is in a quiet rural area on a minor coast road to the southwest of the town. It's a very pleasant location for a traditional beach holiday.

The campsite offers 600 pitches, all with 6A electricity, under pine and eucalyptus trees. Cars are parked in a separate area, and vehicle access is strictly controlled, giving the site a quiet, peaceful ambience. Although 800 metres from the gently shelving beach, in partnership with other campsites, it provides regular shuttle buses to the beach car park. The 'campsite collective' also runs a bar and restaurant on the beach with toilets and showers. The short walk to the beach from the car park is along a timber walk, and site staff clear rubbish from the beach and the pine wood daily.

Five clean, modern toilet blocks include facilities for disabled visitors on the site and at the beach. Motorhome services. Washing machines. Shop. Bar and restaurant. Swimming pool. Tennis. 5-a-side football. Volleyball. Bocce. Fitness trail. Bicycle, car and fridge hire by arrangement. Children's clubs (4-12 yrs, 13-17 yrs). Entertainment. WiFi in the bar and pool area (free). Shuttle bus to the beach.

Key Features

 Book Online

 Pets Accepted

 Disabled Facilities

 Beach Access

Scan me for more information.

Alan Rogers Code: IT69205
4 accommodations
45 pitches
GPS: 36.81746, 14.46606
Post Code: I-97017

Santa Croce Camerina, Sicily

www.alanrogers.com/it69205
info@campingluminoso.com
Tel: +39 0932 918 401
www.campingluminoso.com

Open (Touring Pitches):
All year.

Camping Luminoso

Camping Luminoso is a high-quality site situated on the southern shores of Sicily, with direct access to a superb private sandy beach with sun loungers and parasols. An ideal site for families seeking a relaxing beach holiday under clear blue skies. The small villages around the site offer many opportunities to sample the local produce, especially the local wines, which are highly recommended. The old hill town of Ragusa is part of the Val di Noto UNESCO Heritage site, devastated by an earthquake in 1693 and today featuring 18 buildings protected by UNESCO patronage. It's a very popular excursion for its narrow streets and pleasant cafés.

There are 45 pitches for touring, some close to the soft, sandy beach, on marked hard standings and with easy access and man-made wooden canopies offering some shade. All have 6A electricity, and there are four accommodation units for hire. A relaxing spot beside a lovely beach lapped by turquoise waters.

Modern toilet block with all necessary facilities, including those for disabled campers. Washing machine/dryer. Small shop (all year). Bar with shady terrace. Bread and fresh food delivery. Games room/TV. Table tennis. Playground. Bowling alley. Bicycle hire. Car wash. Entertainment for children (July/Aug). WiFi throughout (charged). Shady parking is available for hire.

Key Features

 Open All Year

 Pets Accepted

 Disabled Facilities

 Beach Access

 Play Area

 Bar/Restaurant

 Bike Hire

 Sailing

Scan me for more information.

Alan Rogers Code: IT69158
10 accommodations
40 pitches
GPS: 37.74800, 12.49614
Post Code: I-91025

Marsala, Sicily

www.alanrogers.com/it69158
info@lilybeovillage.it
Tel: +39 0923 998 357
www.lilybeovillage.it

Open (Touring Pitches):
All year.

Camping Lilybeo Village

Close to the coastal town of Marsala in western Sicily, best known for its fortified wine, Lilybeo Village is a small, family-friendly campsite within easy reach of the attractive coastline, vineyards, and olive groves of Trapani Province. There are just 40 spacious, grassy pitches with shade provided by mature trees. The area for motorhomes is more open, yet with some shade from olive trees. The beach of Lido Signorino is easily accessible by bicycle or car, as is the historic town of Marsala. Several nature reserves and archaeological sites are along the coast to the north and east.

Marsala has an archaeological museum with a preserved Phoenician warship, a range of shops, bars and restaurants, and a 'cantine' selling local wines directly from the vat. You can take a twenty-minute boat trip from Marsala to the beautiful Egadi Islands. Along the Tyrrhenian coast, you can visit the city of Trapani, the medieval town of Erice, the ancient hilltop site of Segesta and bustling Palermo with its vibrant street markets.

Sanitary block with hot showers and hairdryers. Washing machine, iron and ironing board. Campers' kitchen. Motorhome services. Children's pool. Football field. Bowling. Playground. Bicycle hire. Bungalows for hire. Airport transfer. Car hire. WiFi. Organised visits on Fridays.

Key Features

 Book Online

 Open All Year

 Pets Accepted

 Disabled Facilities

 Beach Access

 Swimming Pool

 Play Area

 Bike Hire

Scan me for more information.

Alan Rogers Code: IT69315
8 accommodations
100 pitches
GPS: 38.00997, 14.23297
Post Code: I-98079

Castel di Tusa, Sicily

www.alanrogers.com/it69315
info@loscoglio.eu
Tel: +39 0921 334 345
www.loscoglio.eu

Open (Touring Pitches):
Start April - End September.

Camping Lo Scoglio

Direct access to the sea and a private pebble beach are the main attractions at this family-friendly campsite, along with lovely views of the Aeolian Islands. The Blue Flag beach shelves gently into the crystal clear sea, making it an ideal spot for campers of all ages who enjoy pottering about in the shallows. Lo Scoglio would suit couples looking for a base for exploring the north coast of Sicily and for families with older children.

The campsite has a thoroughly relaxed atmosphere, even in high season, with a conscious decision not to offer organised entertainment or discos. The campsite has the necessary facilities for a relaxing beach holiday, which is sufficient for most guests who come for rest and relaxation. That said, there are plenty of off-site excursions, with the site providing transport to the nearby railway station. Day trips to colourful Palermo and the ancient town of Cefalu are popular. Lovers of nature enjoy visiting the Tiberio Gorges, located 16 kilometres from Camping Lo Scoglio.

Sanitary block with hot showers. Laundry. Motorhome services. Shop. Bar. Restaurant. Swimming pool. Playground. Direct sea access. Free shuttle to train station. Car hire. Charcoal barbecues only. WiFi throughout (charged).

Key Features

 Pets Accepted

 Beach Access

 Bar/Restaurant

 Fishing

Scan me for
more information.

Alan Rogers Code: IT69630
196 accommodations
600 pitches
GPS: 41.13020, 9.43870
Post Code: I-07021

Cannigione di Arzachena,
Sardinia

www.alanrogers.com/it69630
info@isuledda.it
Tel: +39 078 986 003
www.isuledda.it

Open (Touring Pitches):
Start April - End October.

Isuledda Holiday Centre

This large, high-quality campsite is part of the Baia group and has something for everyone, with an amazing choice of activities and entertainment. The site's coastline includes three kilometres of beaches, one with a busy marina. There is also an excellent dive school and a good choice of watersports and activities available.

Some of the 600 good-sized gravel pitches (with 4A electricity) have magnificent views over the Archena Gulf. We loved the outstanding pitches perched directly over the sea and the various beaches. Other pitches enjoy shade from eucalyptus trees and are flat. Cars must be parked outside the entrance. The central area buzzes with activity, although it is possible to find a quiet area to relax. This well-run, efficient campsite offers a very high standard of holiday.

Five sanitary blocks include British and Turkish-style toilets and facilities for disabled visitors. Another block offers family rooms for hire. Showers. Washing machines. Motorhome services (charged). Large supermarket. Restaurant, pizzeria and snack bar. Aerobics. Gym with bar. Play areas. Boat, car, bicycle and scooter hire. Windsurfing. Sailing. Sub-aqua. Marina. Miniclub, Entertainment. Excursions. Disco and beer bar (can be noisy until late). WiFi (charged). Dogs are accepted in one area.

Key Features

 Book Online

 Pets Accepted

 Disabled Facilities

 Beach Access

 Play Area

 Bar/Restaurant

 Bike Hire

 Fishing

Scan me for
more information.

Alan Rogers Code: IT69900
60 accommodations
143 pitches
GPS: 39.90300, 8.53010
Post Code: I-09170

Torre Grande, Sardinia

Camping Village Spinnaker

www.alanrogers.com/it69900
info@spinnakervacanze.com
Tel: +39 0783 22 074
www.spinnakervacanze.com

Open (Touring Pitches):
Start April - End September.

Spinnaker Village is a smart, purpose-built, modern beach site set on the undulating foreshore under tall pines, with a superb beach frontage to the camping area. Whilst there are no sea views from the pitches, it is an easy 60-metre stroll to the fine white sand where there are free sun loungers and parasols. It is a pleasant walk along the beach to the resort of Marina Torre Grande, and excursions from the site could include a visit to the marine reserve of Sinis Isola di Maladentre or the ruins of Tharros and Santa Christina – a Nuraghe village.

The 143 pitches are level and sandy, with 90 for touring. All have 6A electricity, and there are plenty of water taps. Cars must be parked in a car park outside the site. There are many neat, white buildings on site – the restaurant, a café and the inviting swimming pool with loungers are cleverly set around a large square, where family entertainment takes place.

Toilet blocks are modern, with British-style toilets and facilities for disabled campers. Showers are transponder operated (€ 0.50 per shower). Washing machine. Motorhome services. Small shop. Restaurant and small snack bar. Swimming pool and pool bar. Play area. Bicycle hire. Miniclub and entertainment in high season. Excursions. Torches essential. WiFi throughout. English spoken.

Key Features

 Book Online

 Pets Accepted

 Disabled Facilities

 Beach Access

 Swimming Pool

 Play Area

 Bar/Restaurant

 Bike Hire

Scan me for
more information.

Alan Rogers Code: IT69780
36 accommodations
214 pitches
GPS: 39.12320, 9.51266
Post Code: I-09049

Villasimius, Sardinia

www.alanrogers.com/it69780
campriso@tiscali.it
Tel: +39 0707 91 052
www.villaggiospiaggiadelriso.it

Open (Touring Pitches):
Late April - End October.

Spiaggia Del Riso

Villaggio Spiaggia Del Riso is well kept and professionally run. It is split by a public road, but there is an underpass for campers. Pitches on both sides of the site are mostly flat, some shaded and all with 3A electricity. The area beside the beach has open pitches for caravans and motorhomes with sea views but with a low artificially shaded area alongside. The beaches are reached directly from the site, the main being a fine sandy bay between rocky outcrops and a marina close by. Parents can relax whilst their children swim here.

The well-designed restaurant is fabulous with local specialities, and waiters will fillet the freshest of local fish at your table. Entertainment is provided for children and adults, and a range of sports activities is available. This very pleasant site is wonderful for families especially and gives value for money.

Four modern sanitary blocks provide both British and Turkish-style toilets. Only cold water at washbasins. €0.50 tokens (July/Aug). Pristine locked facilities for disabled campers. Washing machines and dryers. Motorhome services. Cafeteria. Restaurant and bar. Pizzeria/snack bar. Shop. Archery. 5-a-side football. Bicycle hire. Entertainment (high season). Communal barbecue area only. Internet and WiFi over part of the site (charged). Torches useful.

Key Features

 Pets Accepted

 Disabled Facilities

 Beach Access

 Swimming Pool

 Play Area

 Bar/Restaurant

 Bike Hire

 Fishing

Scan me for more information.

Capital Luxembourg City
Currency Euro (€)
Language Letzeburgesch, French and German
Time Zone CET (GMT+1)
Telephone Code +352

Shops 9am to 6pm Mon to Sat. Shops are closed Sun except on the run up to Christmas. Supermarkets and shopping centres often stay open for longer hours. Some shops are closed Mon morning.

Money ATMs are widespread and are accessible 24hrs a day. Credit/debit cards are widely accepted.

Travelling with children A very family-friendly country. Some attractions will offer free admission for young children. Most restaurants will cater for children. Public transport is free to use across the country.

Public Holidays 1 Jan New Year's Day; Mar/Apr Easter Monday; 1 May Labour Day; 9 May Europe Day; May Ascension; May/Jun Whit Monday; 23 Jun National Day; 15 Aug Assumption; 1 Nov All Saints; 25 Dec Christmas Day; 26 Dec Boxing Day.

There are no Low Emission Zones currently in place.

● EU Member | ● Schengen Area

Tourism website visitluxembourg.com

●●●●● **Accessible Travel Score**

Although hilly, Luxembourg is generally wheelchair-friendly. Buses and trams are fitted with ramps, check before using trains.

Driving in Luxembourg There are no road tolls. Many holidaymakers travel through Luxembourg to take advantage of lower fuel prices, thus creating traffic congestion, especially in summer. Blue zone parking exists in the capital, but we suggest using the free park and ride or public transport. Dipped headlights are recommended during the day. Drink-driving and using your mobile whilst driving are illegal.

 Dashcams are **illegal**

 Speed camera detectors are legal

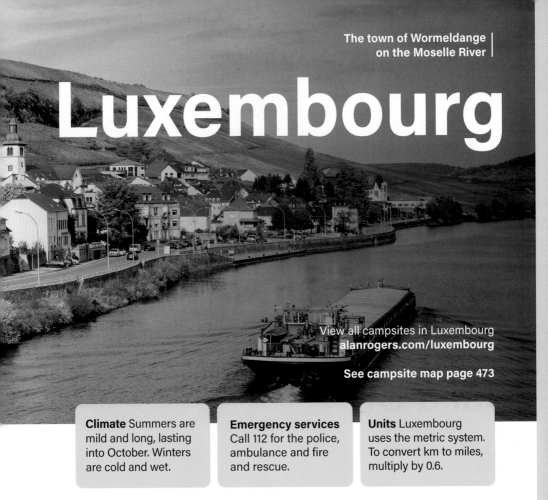

Luxembourg

View all campsites in Luxembourg
alanrogers.com/luxembourg

See campsite map page 473

Climate Summers are mild and long, lasting into October. Winters are cold and wet.

Emergency services Call 112 for the police, ambulance and fire and rescue.

Units Luxembourg uses the metric system. To convert km to miles, multiply by 0.6.

The Grand Duchy of Luxembourg is a sovereign state lying between Belgium, France and Germany. Divided into two areas: the spectacular Ardennes region in the north and the rolling farmlands in the south, bordered on the east by the wine-growing area of the Moselle Valley.

Most attractions are within easy reach of Luxembourg's capital, Luxembourg-Ville, a fortress city, perched dramatically on its rocky promontory overlooking the Alzette and Petrusse Valleys. The verdant hills and valleys of the Ardennes are a maze of hiking trails, footpaths and cycle routes – ideal for an activity holiday.

The Moselle Valley, famous for its sweet wines, is just across the river from Germany; its charming hamlets can be discovered by bicycle or by boat. Popular wine tasting tours take place from late spring to early autumn. Echternacht is a good base for exploring the Mullerthal region, known as 'Little Switzerland'. Lying on the banks of the River Sûre, its forested landscape is dotted with curious rock formations and castle ruins, notably those at Beaufort and Larochette. The pretty Schießentümpel cascade is worth a visit.

Scan QR code to browse more campsites on our website

Alan Rogers Code: LU7770
27 accommodations
76 pitches
GPS: 50.00017, 5.99106
Post Code: L-9747

Enscherange, Diekirch

www.alanrogers.com/lu7770
valdor@pt.lu
Tel: +352 92 06 91
www.valdor.lu

Open (Touring Pitches):
Early April - Late October.

Camping Val d'Or

Camping Val d'Or is one of those small, family run, countryside sites where you easily find yourself staying longer than planned. Set in lush meadowland under a scattering of trees, the site is divided into two by the tree-lined Clerve river as it winds its way slowly through the site. A footbridge goes some way to joining the site together and there are two entrances for vehicles. There are plenty of cycle routes and hiking trails to explore in this rural region.

There are 76 marked, level grass touring pitches, mostly 100 square metres, all with electricity (6A Europlug) and with some tree shade. Some are adjacent to the river. Cars are parked away from the pitches which leaves more room and a quieter, more peaceful atmosphere among the pitches. There are open views of the surrounding countryside with its wooded hills. The site's Dutch owners speak good English and are happy to give advice and local tips.

Next to the reception is a heated sanitary block where some facilities are found, others including some showers are located under cover, outside. Showers are token operated. Laundry room. Gas supplies. Bar (all day in high season). Takeaway (high season except Sundays). Swimming and paddling in river. Three play areas (one with waterways, waterwheel and small pool). Bicycle hire. WiFi (free). Max. 1 dog.

Key Features

 Book Online

 Pets Accepted

 Beach Access

 Play Area

 Bar/Restaurant

 Bike Hire

Scan me for more information.

Alan Rogers Code: LU7440
50 accommodations
150 pitches
GPS: 49.90690, 5.94263
Post Code: L-9650

Esch-sur-Sûre, Diekirch

Camping Im Aal

www.alanrogers.com/lu7440
info@camping-im-aal.lu
Tel: +352 83 95 14
www.campingaal.lu

Open (Touring Pitches):
Mid February – End December.

Lying some 50 km north of Luxembourg, this community-owned site is situated alongside the River Sûre, only a 500-metre stroll from the pretty village of Esch-sur-Sure. It is located in a nature reserve with a man-made lake that runs along the valley and is overlooked by the wooded hills. It's a peaceful spot, even in high summer, when visitors come to enjoy this green oasis.

The area near the bar/restaurant contains mainly seasonal pitches, while a large touring area is across a road bridge within the site, on the opposite side of the river. This contains 150 good-sized level grass pitches with 10A electricity. Adjacent to the site are comprehensive children's play facilities, also belonging to the community. The enthusiastic manager organises a full activity programme for all the family in high season; at other times, it will suit those seeking a quiet retreat in a beautiful location.

Key Features

 Pets Accepted

 Disabled Facilities

 Play Area

 Bar/Restaurant

 Bike Hire

 Fishing

 Horse Riding

Two heated sanitary blocks are well equipped with free hot water for showers and sinks. Facilities for disabled visitors in one block. Laundry and dishwashing building. Shop (high season). Attractive bar with a panoramic view over the river. Play area for children with books and games in the lounge area. Fishing (permit for over 14s). Bicycle hire. Riding. Sailing and boat launching. Entertainment (July/Aug). WiFi.

Scan me for more information.

Alan Rogers Code: LU7520
150 pitches
GPS: 49.92655, 6.22013
Post Code: L-9415

Vianden, Diekirch

www.alanrogers.com/lu7520
info@campingdumoulin.lu
Tel: +352 83 45 01
www.visit-vianden.lu

Open (Touring Pitches):
Late April – Early September.

Camping du Moulin

A popular site set on lightly wooded, level ground alongside the River Our, Camping & Camperpark du Moulin Vianden is conveniently located with good road access just outside Vianden in the Luxembourg Ardennes. We received a very friendly welcome from the attentive staff at reception. The site lies about 50 km north of Luxembourg. A pleasant 1.5 km. walk, mostly alongside the river, takes you into Vianden's charming and historic town with its cobbled streets, castle and cable car. Further afield, there is a vast network of hiking trails through the unspoilt nature of the surrounding area.

The 150 touring pitches (all with 10A connections, four with hardstanding) are numbered but not separated. They are good-sized, grassy, mostly shaded by attractive mature trees and neatly clipped hedging. One terrace of about 20 pitches is alongside the river, with the remainder on a level grassy area slightly above. The site has a snack bar, a service station, and a small supermarket nearby.

Two modern, clean sanitary blocks with free hot showers and hot water to sinks. Private bathroom (€7/day). Facilities for disabled visitors. Laundry facilities. Shop. Snack bar. Games room with TV, snooker, darts and books. Play area. Daily activities with dedicated team (July/Aug). Fishing. Free WiFi (around reception area).

Key Features

 Pets Accepted

 Disabled Facilities

 Play Area

 Bar/Restaurant

 Fishing

Scan me for more information.

Alan Rogers Code: LU7690
137 pitches
GPS: 49.85039, 6.13468
Post Code: L-9161

Ingeldorf, Diekirch

www.alanrogers.com/lu7690
info@camping-gritt.lu
Tel: +352 80 20 18
www.camping-gritt.lu

Open (Touring Pitches):
Start April - End October.

Camping Gritt

Located on the banks of the River Sûre, in the small village of Ingeldorf, Camping Gritt offers around 140 level and marked pitches, all with 6A electricity, in an attractive setting. You will receive a warm welcome from the Dutch manager of this lovely site with its delightful river frontage and the spectacular backdrop of hills and forest providing a view from every pitch. Mature trees provide shade, and the meandering river adds to the peace and tranquillity. It really is a charming spot.

The site has a bar and restaurant serving full meals, snacks and drinks, with indoor seating and an outside terrace. There is no shop on site, but the village is within walking distance. With all its attractions, Diekirch is just 5 km away, and Luxembourg's beautiful 'Little Switzerland' hiking area is popular, with various routes and trails of different lengths and arduousness. There are also numerous castles and hilltop villages to explore. A visit to the city of Luxembourg is a must, easily reached by public transport, all for free.

Two heated sanitary blocks, one older with updated facilities, one new with individual, spacious showers. Baby rooms (ladies and men). Provision for disabled visitors. Laundry. Bar (with TV), restaurant and takeaway. Playground. River fishing. Entertainment is organised in the high season.

Key Features

 Book Online

 Pets Accepted

 Play Area

 Bar/Restaurant

 Fishing

Scan me for more information.

Alan Rogers Code: LU7580
17 accommodations
136 pitches
GPS: 49.74357, 6.08978
Post Code: L-7572

Mersch, Luxembourg District

www.alanrogers.com/lu7580
contact@campingkrounebierg.lu
Tel: +352 32 97 56
www.campingkrounebierg.lu

Open (Touring Pitches):
Start April – End October.

Camping Krounebierg

Situated on a hillside with views over the Mersch valley this is an attractive site for stopovers or more extended stays. It is close to the town of Mersch with good facilities and transport links, but the site has a pleasant rural ambience. There are 177 pitches, 136 for touring, including 12 hardstandings. All are level, grassy and of a good size, with 10A electricity, moderately shaded and separated by neatly maintained hedges.

A stylish, modern building at the site entrance houses reception, shop, bar and restaurant and has an excellent elevated terrace overlooking the open-air children's pool. Everything is fresh and spotlessly clean, and we received a warm and friendly welcome from the managers. Campers can also use the town's indoor pool, adjacent to the site, at a reduced rate. Off site, there are many cycle and hiking routes, with the Valley of the Seven Castles or the unspoilt beauty of Park Mersch being popular. A guided tour of Luxembourg is a great day out.

Five traditional, clean sanitary blocks are heated and have free hot showers. Facilities for disabled visitors. Well stocked shop. Modern bar and restaurant/takeaway. Outdoor paddling pool. Play area. Games room with TV. Football field. Badminton. Daily activity programme (July/Aug). Free WiFi throughout. Max 3 Dogs allowed. BBQs permitted.

Key Features

 Pets Accepted

 Disabled Facilities

 Swimming Pool

 Play Area

 Bar/Restaurant

Scan me for more information.

Alan Rogers Code: LU7620
32 accommodations
359 pitches
GPS: 49.78472, 6.16519
Post Code: L-7465

Nommern, Luxembourg District

www.alanrogers.com/lu7620
info@nommerlayen-ec.lu
Tel: +352 87 80 78
www.nommerlayen-ec.lu

Open (Touring Pitches):
Start March - Early November.

Europacamping Nommerlayen

Situated in the lovely wooded hills of central Luxembourg, this is a top-quality site with fees to match, but it has everything! A large, central building housing most of the services and amenities opens onto a terrace around an excellent swimming pool complex with a large fun pool and an imaginative water playground. This peaceful area has many excellent walking and cycle trails, and day trips to Luxembourg, Vianden castle and the Mosel Valley are easy from here.

The 359 pitches (100 sq.m) are on grassy terraces, all with electricity (2/16A) and water taps. Pitches are grouped beside age-appropriate play areas, and the campsite facilities reflect the attention given to families in particular. Interestingly enough, the superb sanitary block is called Badtemple (having been built in the style of a Greek temple).

A large, high-quality sanitary unit provides washbasins in cubicles, facilities for disabled visitors, family and baby rooms and a sauna. Twelve private bathrooms for hire. Laundry. Motorhome services. Supermarket, restaurant, snack bar, bar (all usually Mar-Nov). An excellent swimming pool complex and heated pool with a sliding roof (High season). Fitness programmes. Bowling. Playground. Large screen TV. Entertainment in the high season. Bicycle hire. WiFi (free over part of the site).

Key Features

 Book Online

 Pets Accepted

 Disabled Facilities

 Swimming Pool

 Play Area

 Bar/Restaurant

 Bike Hire

Scan me for more information.

Alan Rogers Code: LU7590
90 accommodations
175 pitches
GPS: 49.81937, 6.34750
Post Code: L-6551

Luxembourg, Grevenmacher

www.alanrogers.com/lu7590
campbv2000@gmail.com
Tel: +352 79 06 35
www.campingbellevue.lu

Open (Touring Pitches):
All year.

Camping Belle-Vue 2000

Located in a beautiful location in the Müllerthal, Camping Belle-Vue 2000 is suitable for all ages, particularly those seeking peace and tranquillity. The little town of Berdorf in Luxembourg is known for its sensational scenery and variety of outdoor activities. There are natural climbing walls, over 150 climbing routes, and countless meandering trails for cyclists and hikers. The renowned Mullertal trail runs over a length of 112 km and will take you through extensive forests, high plains and deep valleys. It really is a paradise for active nature lovers. Berdorf is located close to various castles and museums, most of which can easily be reached by bike.

The site is occupied by 90 privately owned mobile homes with 12 accommodation units to hire and 175 spacious touring pitches with 10A electricity and water. There is a play area with a zip line for the children, and the adjacent forest, Echternach, is popular with families on bikes. There are several restaurants and a handy supermarket in the centre of Berdorf, which is within walking distance.

Well-appointed en-suite sanitary block in the touring area. Facilities for disabled visitors. Children's facilities, Laundry facilities, Bicycle hire, Children's play area, Pets allowed, WiFi, Shop (small).

Key Features

 Open All Year

 Pets Accepted

 Disabled Facilities

 Play Area

Scan me for more information.

Alan Rogers Code: LU7700
48 accommodations
150 pitches
GPS: 49.48492, 5.98657
Post Code: L-4001

Esch-sur-Alzette, Luxembourg
District

www.alanrogers.com/lu7700
info@gaalgebierg.lu
Tel: +352 54 10 69
www.gaalgebierg.lu

Open (Touring Pitches):
All year.

Camping Gaalgebierg

Occupying an elevated position on the edge of town, near the French border, this site is run by the local camping and caravan club. It's set on a hilltop and shaded by a variety of trees. Of the 150 grass pitches, 102 are for tourers, the remainder being occupied by seasonal units. There are some gravel pitches set aside for one night stays, plus four all-weather pitches for motorhomes. All pitches have 16A electricity and TV points.

Esch has a good range of shops, bars and restaurants, some pleasant parks and interesting churches, and the Museum of the Resistance is well worth a visit. The city of Luxembourg is a short drive to the northeast; or if you would rather leave the car behind, the site operates its own minibus to the nearby railway station for visits to the city. The border with France is just down the road, if you fancy a taste of French cuisine or a trip to a French supermarket. Alternatively, Belgium is only a few kilometres to the west.

Toilet block with washbasins in cubicles, hot showers and separate facilities for disabled visitors and babies. Laundry. Key-card entry system. Motorhome services. Gas available. Small bar, snack bar and takeaway (all year; on demand in low season). Playground. Bicycle hire. Boules. Entertainment and activity programme in high season. WiFi over site (charged).

Key Features

 Open All Year

 Pets Accepted

 Disabled Facilities

 Play Area

 Bar/Restaurant

Scan me for more information.

Capital Amsterdam
Currency Euro (€)
Language Dutch. French and German also widely spoken
Time Zone CET (GMT+1)
Telephone Code +31

Shops Hours vary throughout the year, with many shops operating on shorter hours in low and shoulder seasons. In high season 10am to 6pm Tues to Fri, 10am to 5pm Sat and Sun and noon to 5pm or 6pm on Mon (if at all). Supermarkets are open 8am to 8pm.

Money ATMs are widespread and are accessible 24hrs a day. Credit/debit cards accepted mostly. Cash is still widely used.

Travelling with children Amsterdam is one of Europe's most child-friendly cities. We recommend you stay clear of the Red Light District. Beaches are safe. Restaurants are kid-friendly, nearly all offer children's menus and colouring crayons.

Public Holidays 1 Jan New Year's Day; Mar/Apr Good Friday; Mar/Apr Easter Sunday; Mar/Apr Easter Monday; 27 Apr King's Day; 5 May Liberation Day; May Ascension Day; May/Jun Whit Sunday; May/Jun Whit Monday; 25 Dec Christmas Day; 26 Dec Boxing Day.

LEZ Low Emissions Zones in all major cities. Registration required.

● **EU Member** | ● **Schengen Area**

Tourism website holland.com

●●●●○ **Accessible Travel Score**

Generally very good, especially in cities. Public buildings and transport are well equipped. WCs in restaurants can be difficult for wheelchair users.

Driving in the Netherlands There is a comprehensive motorway system but due to the high density of population, all main roads can become very busy, particularly in the morning and evening rush hours. There are no toll roads. Trams should be overtaken on the right unless unsafe. Drink-driving and using your mobile whilst driving are illegal.

 Dashcams are legal

 Speed camera detectors are **illegal**

Netherlands

View all campsites in Netherlands
alanrogers.com/netherlands

See campsite map page 483

Climate Temperate with mild winters and warm summers.

Emergency services Call 112 for the police, ambulance and fire and rescue.

Units Netherlands uses the metric system. To convert km to miles, multiply by 0.6.

With vast areas of the Netherlands reclaimed from the sea, nearly half of the country lies at or below sea level. The result is a flat, fertile landscape crisscrossed with rivers and canals. Famous for its windmills and bulb fields, it also boasts some of the most impressive coastal dunes in Europe.

No visit to the Netherlands would be complete without experiencing its capital city, Amsterdam, with its maze of canals, bustling cafés, museums and summer festivals.

The fields of South Holland are an explosion of colour between March and May when the world's biggest flower auction takes place at Aalsmeer.

The Vecht valley and its towns of Dalfsen, Ommen and Hardenberg are best explored by bicycle, while

Giethoorn, justly dubbed the 'Venice of Holland', has to be seen from a boat. The Kinderdijk windmills on the Alblasserwaard polder are a UNESCO World Heritage Site.

The islands of Zeeland are home to beautiful old towns such as Middelburg, the provincial capital, Zierikzee, with its old harbour and the quaint old town of Veere.

Scan QR code to browse more campsites on our website

Alan Rogers Code: NL5750
140 accommodations
220 pitches
GPS: 53.21650, 5.88703
Post Code: NL-8926 XE

Leeuwarden, Friesland

Camping De Kleine Wielen

www.alanrogers.com/nl5750
info@dekleinewielen.nl
Tel: +31 511 431 660
www.dekleinewielen.nl

Open (Touring Pitches):
Start April - Start October.

Camping De Kleine Wielen is named after a small lake of the same name that lies in the nature and recreation area of De Groene Ster in central Friesland. The campsite is adjacent to the lake – possible activities include boating on the lake or cycling and walking around this beautiful area of forest, grassland and ponds. The site provides 360 pitches, of which 220 are for touring units. The remaining pitches are used for privately owned mobile homes and three for hire. All the touring pitches have 4A electricity, and many have wonderful views over the water and surrounding countryside.

The position of the site next to the water (the lake is not fenced) opens up many opportunities for sailing, rowing, canoeing or windsurfing. You can follow the river leading from the lake by boat or on shore by bicycle or car as it leads through the villages and towns such as Hindeloopen, Stavoren and Dokkum.

Four basic toilet blocks provide washbasins in cabins and preset showers (coin-operated). Maintenance is variable. Facilities for disabled visitors. Motorhome services. Shop and bar (all season). Café/restaurant and takeaway (all season). Playground. Sports pitch. Minigolf. Lake with a beach. Fishing. Rowing boats. Surfboards. Extensive recreation programme in July/Aug. WiFi throughout (charged).

Key Features

 Pets Accepted

 Disabled Facilities

 Play Area

 Bar/Restaurant

 Fishing

 Sailing

Scan me for more information.

Alan Rogers Code: NL6021
120 accommodations
79 pitches
GPS: 53.07116, 6.24274
Post Code: NL-9243 KA

Bakkeveen, Friesland

www.alanrogers.com/nl6021
info@ikeleane.nl
Tel: +31 516 541 283
www.ikeleane.nl

Open (Touring Pitches):
Start April - End October.

Camping de Ikeleane

Camping de Ikeleane (Frisian for Oak Lane) has a rural setting 14 km southeast of the pleasant town of Drachten. This is a much-loved part of Friesland, where forests alternate with dunes and heathland. De Ikeleane is a good base for exploring the Frisian countryside on foot or by bicycle and has wonderful views over the countryside. Drachten merits a visit, with an attractive centre best known for its pioneering traffic scheme. Removing almost all traffic lights and signs has led to a significant reduction in accidents.

This is a well-equipped site with 200 pitches, 79 for touring, all with 6/10A electricity, and 67 with water and drainage. Children will enjoy the football and volleyball pitches and the indoor play barn. Various activities are organised, including ballooning, cycling and volleyball matches, and there's free access to the public swimming pool at Bakkeveen.

Three toilet blocks with open-style washbasins, controllable hot showers (card operated), family showers, a baby room and facilities for disabled visitors. Bar, restaurant (simple meals) and snack bar. Washing machine. Motorhome services. Play barn. Football. Volleyball. Bicycle and go-kart hire. Entertainment and activities (High season). WiFi. New luxury chalets and caravans to rent. Twin-axle caravans are not accepted.

Key Features

 Book Online

 Pets Accepted

 Disabled Facilities

 Beach Access

 Play Area

 Bar/Restaurant

 Bike Hire

Scan me for more information.

Alan Rogers Code: NL6118
85 pitches
GPS: 53.16430, 6.22269
Post Code: NL-9865 XE

Opende, Groningen

Camping De Watermolen

www.alanrogers.com/nl6118
info@campingdewatermolen.nl
Tel: +31 594 659 144
www.campingdewatermolen.nl

Open (Touring Pitches):
Start April - Start October.

Up in the north of the country, Camping De Watermolen is located on the border of the two Dutch provinces of Friesland and Groningen. The southeast area of the Groningen region is lush, verdant countryside, ideal for walking and cycling, with miles of dedicated trails close at hand. Alternatively, you can rent a canoe to paddle along the waterways and pass through several delightful waterside villages.

This site has around 80 spacious and grassy pitches, including comfort pitches with 16A electricity, located near the well-appointed toilet block and the lake. The standard pitches are located in the older part of the site and are slightly smaller with 4/6A electricity. Some hardstanding pitches overlooking the lake and safari tents are available to rent. The site is dotted with mature trees, which adds to the peaceful charm. In the centre of the site is a recreation lake for swimming with a zip wire and a shallow area for young children with its own beach. This is a popular spot with youngsters who can happily spend hours splashing about. For anglers, there is a well-stocked fishing lake.

Two heated toilet blocks, one with a family room and facilities for babies. Launderette. Bistro/restaurant. Shop for essentials in reception. Playgrounds. Tennis. Lake with beach and zip wire. Football and volleyball. Fishing. WiFi.

Key Features

 Book Online

 Play Area

 Bike Hire

 Fishing

Scan me for more information.

Alan Rogers Code: NL6100
225 accommodations
233 pitches
GPS: 53.08611, 7.08291
Post Code: NL-9698 XV

Wedde, Groningen

www.alanrogers.com/nl6100
info@wedderbergen.nl
Tel: +31 597 561 673
www.wedderbergen.nl

Open (Touring Pitches):
Start April - Start October.

Camping Wedderbergen

Camping Wedderbergen is a well-established, modern site in the green heart of Groningen, with easy access to a large lake and good possibilities for walking and cycling tours and for boating through this part of Holland and even Germany. This area is said to have the cleanest air in Holland.

There are around 230 touring pitches, all with 10A electricity, water, wastewater and cable. A separate area provides hardstandings for larger units and motorhomes. There are some views over the Westerwoldsche river and shade in some areas from mature trees. Pitches at the front of the site have a jetty for small boats. To the back of the site is a large expanse of water with a sandy beach. A new 200 km mountain bike trail begins and ends at the site. The only disadvantage is a public road that runs through the site (some road noise).

Toilet block for touring units with toilets, washbasins in cabins and preset hot showers (hot water with key). Family shower rooms. Baby room. Facilities for disabled campers. Laundry. Motorhome services. Well stocked shop. Bar, canteen and snack bar. Swimming pool complex. Recreation lake with sandy beach. Indoor playroom/theatre and outdoor play area. Playing field. Bicycle hire. Fishing. Tennis. Bouncy cushion. Animal farm (petting zoo and deer viewing trails). WiFi on part of site (free).

Key Features

 Book Online

 Pets Accepted

 Disabled Facilities

 Play Area

 Bar/Restaurant

 Bike Hire

 Fishing

Scan me for more information.

Alan Rogers Code: NL6127
80 accommodations
100 pitches
GPS: 52.97089, 6.80762
Post Code: NL-9462 TT

Gasselte, Drenthe

Camping het Horstmannsbos

www.alanrogers.com/nl6127
info@horstmannsbos.nl
Tel: +31 559 564 270
www.horstmannsbos.nl

Open (Touring Pitches):
End March - Start October.

Het Horstmannsbos aims to attract people who want to holiday amidst nature and feel relaxed and comfortable in natural surroundings. It is an attractive, tranquil site in the woods near Gasselte. The site has some 180 pitches, of which 100 are for tourers. Arranged on level fields, taking between four and 20 units, there are 15 serviced pitches (water, electricity and drainage). To the rear of the site is a large field without electricity for tent campers, while on the far side is a separate area for mobile homes, and to the right is a bungalow park.

There is an open-air pool (10x5 m) behind reception, with sports facilities. A welcoming bar/restaurant has an open-air terrace for drinks and snacks. From the back of the site, you can walk or cycle into the woodland dunes and moorland of the Drouwenerzand nature reserve. The nearby Het Drouwenerzand theme park is a popular outing.

Several basic toilet blocks are well placed around the site, with toilets, washbasins and free hot showers. Family shower. Baby room. Facilities for disabled visitors. Basic laundry with washing machines, dryers and freezer. Motorhome service point. Bar/restaurant with terrace (high season). Outdoor swimming pool. Boules. Playground. Entertainment team for children (high season). WiFi throughout (charged).

Key Features

 Book Online

 Pets Accepted

 Disabled Facilities

 Swimming Pool

 Play Area

 Bar/Restaurant

Scan me for more information.

Alan Rogers Code: NL6868
70 accommodations
70 pitches
GPS: 52.89522, 4.71771
Post Code: NL-1787 PP

Julianadorp, Noord-Holland

Camping De Zwaluw

www.alanrogers.com/nl6868
campingdezwaluw@quicknet.nl
Tel: +31 223 641 492
www.campingdezwaluw.nl

Open (Touring Pitches):
Start April - End October.

Camping de Zwaluw is near the wide sandy beaches of the North Sea, only 7 km from Den Helder. It is a small site with 70 flat and grassy touring pitches, 10/16 amp electric hook-up point and without shade. The children's play area has an air trampoline, slides and climbing frames and there's a playhouse for the little ones next to the reception. The site has 70 bungalows, log cabins and apartments of which 10 are available to hire. It's a simple layout and the huge beach is the key attraction of course.

This is an ideal base for excursions in the area and is located on the boundary of a vast nature reserve with wide beaches. The beach is only a 5 minute walk from the campsite gates, along a path through the sand dunes. As you drive to the site you will pass the vast tulip fields and cross dunes. Driving past the multi coloured fields in spring is a glorious sight and at times the scent of hyacinths wafts across the site.

Key Features

 Pets Accepted

 Disabled Facilities

 Beach Access

 Play Area

Two toilet blocks provide showers, wash basins and WCs. Baby room. Facility for visitors who are disabled. Laundry with washing machine and dryer. Chemical toilet point. Dishwashing area. Motorhome service point. Restaurant. Snack bar. Takeaway. Defibrillator. Dogs allowed. Dog shower. WiFi. Twin-axle caravans are allowed. BBQs allowed. Freezer for ice packs. Children's play area. Bouncy castle. Multi-sports pitch.

Scan me for more information.

Alan Rogers Code: NL6870
46 accommodations
410 pitches
GPS: 52.40563, 4.58652
Post Code: NL-2051 EC

Bloemendaal aan Zee, Noord-Holland

www.alanrogers.com/nl6870
info@campingdelakens.nl
Tel: +31 235 411 570
www.campingdelakens.nl

Open (Touring Pitches):
Late March - Late October.

Camping de Lakens

Kennemer Duincamping De Lakens is beautifully located in the dunes at Bloemendaal aan Zee. This site has 900 reasonably large, flat pitches of varying sizes, whose layout makes them feel quite private - some come with a ready erected hammock! There are 410 pitches for tourers (255 with 16A electricity) separated by low hedging. Pitches are grouped according to guests, for example with activity areas, a relaxation area and a family area. A separate area is provided for groups and older teenagers to maintain the quiet atmosphere.

This friendly, welcoming site is a true oasis of peace in a part of the Netherlands usually bustling with activity. From this site it is possible to walk straight through the dunes to the North Sea and it's not far to Alkmaar and its cheese market or Amsterdam for a great day out.

The five toilet blocks for tourers include controllable showers, washbasins (open style and in cabins), facilities for disabled visitors and a baby room. Launderette. Two motorhome service points. Bar/restaurant with terrace, pizzeria and snack bar. Supermarket. Adventure playgrounds. Basketball. Bicycle hire. Entertainment programme in high season for all. WiFi over most of the site (charged). Range of glamping-style accommodations to rent. No twin-axle caravans or large motorhomes. Dogs are not accepted.

Key Features

 Disabled Facilities

 Beach Access

 Play Area

 Bar/Restaurant

 Bike Hire

Scan me for more information.

Alan Rogers Code: NL6835
60 pitches
GPS: 52.19343, 5.15521
Post Code: NL-1213 PZ

Hilversum, Noord-Holland

Camping De Zonnehoek

www.alanrogers.com/nl6835
info@campingzonnehoek.com
Tel: +31 355 771 926
www.campingzonnehoek.com

Open (Touring Pitches):
Mid March - End October.

Camping de Zonnehoek is situated in the beautiful wooded surroundings of Hilversum and the lakes of Loosdrechtse Plassen. It is a family-run site that offers its guests a quiet holiday in a natural environment and many facilities for children. There are 120 spacious pitches, with 60 for touring units. All pitches have 4A electricity, and most have plenty of shade.

A tour around the castles in the surrounding area takes you back to the 17th and 18th centuries, and the Loosdrechtse Plassen are ideal for all kinds of watersports and fishing. And for those who prefer city life, there are many possibilities with the old and new of Loosdrecht or the media city of Hilversum, where you can visit TV studios or go shopping in the covered modern shopping centre at Hilvertshof. The cathedral city of Utrecht offers cultural sights, restaurants, bars and shopping, many around the characterful old canal area.

One traditional and one modern toilet block are very clean. Washbasins in cubicles. Hot water for showers on payment (€0.50 coin). Facilities for disabled campers (key access). Laundry. Motorhome services. Bar and restaurant (all day in high season). Games area with games, books, electronic games and a screen for films. Play area. Club for children and entertainment team. WiFi throughout (charged).

Key Features

 Pets Accepted

 Disabled Facilities

 Play Area

 Bar/Restaurant

Scan me for more information.

Alan Rogers Code: NL6215
86 accommodations
540 pitches
GPS: 52.31167, 5.54356
Post Code: NL-3896 LT

Zeewolde, Flevoland

www.alanrogers.com/nl6215
reservation@rcn.eu
Tel: +31 850 400 700
www.rcn.nl

Open (Touring Pitches):
All year.

Camping Zeewolde

This site has been developed on reclaimed, wooded land in the Polderland in the province of Flevoland. There is direct lake access, and the site is split into inner and outer dykes. In the outer dyke area, there are grassy, sunny touring pitches (most with 10A electricity, water and drainage) close to the lake and its sandy beach, as well as Zeewolde's marina. The marina is a great centre for sailing, fishing and windsurfing. It also has a friendly beach bar. The inner dyke pitches are also grassy but are enclosed by hedges and have mature trees to provide more shade.

There is a jungle-style outdoor paddling pool and a covered, heated pool for more inclement days. A forest encircles the campsite, and medieval towns such as Harderwijk (with Europe's largest dolphinarium), Nijkerk and Amersfoort are all close by.

Modern sanitary block at the beach pitches with facilities for disabled visitors and children. Dog shower. Launderette. Restaurant with lake views. Bar. Beach bar. Bakery and supermarket. Beach with swimming area for toddlers. Play areas. Open air and covered pools (heated). Multisports field. Mountain bike track. Tennis courts. Bicycle hire. Go-kart hire. Jetty and beach for catamarans. 5-a-side football. Climbing wall (6.5 m). WiFi over site (free for one device). Accommodation to rent.

Key Features

 Book Online

 Open All Year

 Pets Accepted

 Disabled Facilities

 Beach Access

 Swimming Pool

 Play Area

 Bar/Restaurant

Scan me for more information.

Alan Rogers Code: NL6826
271 accommodations
90 pitches
GPS: 52.10203, 5.54076
Post Code: NL-3927 CB

Renswoude, Utrecht

www.alanrogers.com/nl6826
info@delucht.com
Tel: +31 342 412 877
www.delucht.com

Open (Touring Pitches):
Start April - End September.

Recreatiepark De Lucht

Recreatiepark De Lucht is a quality campsite located at the edge of the Utrechtse Wold between the forest and meadows. The site has 90 touring pitches (6/10A electricity) spread over six fields, each with its own climbing frame. This is a real family site, with swimming pools, riding and an animal field with deer, goats and chickens. Activities are organised for all ages, and various sports are on offer, including tennis, boules and a field for football and volleyball. Youngsters will not be bored here.

There are many easy-going cycle and walking routes, meandering through the unspoilt natural scenery. The friendly, helpful reception will always suggest routes and advise on places to visit. Renswold is a pretty local town, and Ede is great for shopping, while Arnhem is only a short drive away.

Two toilet blocks provide WCs, showers (on payment), washbasins in cabins, and baby room. En-suite facilities for disabled campers. Launderette. Small shop for essentials, bar, restaurant and takeaway (all open all season). Indoor and outdoor pools. Paddling pool. Play area and climbing frames. Riding school. Tennis. Boules. Bicycle and tricycle hire. Activity and excursion programme. Escorted walking and cycling routes. Recreation area. Film, video and TV. Electronic games. Pets' corner. Free WiFi over part of the site.

Key Features

 Book Online

 Pets Accepted

 Disabled Facilities

 Swimming Pool

 Play Area

 Bar/Restaurant

 Bike Hire

 Fishing

Scan me for more information.

Alan Rogers Code: NL6818
96 accommodations
GPS: 52.41509, 5.74526
Post Code: NL-8256 RD

Biddinghuizen, Utrecht

www.alanrogers.com/nl6818
info@aquacentrum.nl
Tel: +31 321 331 635
www.aquacentrum.nl

Open (Touring Pitches):
Mid March - Mid October.

Bremersbergse Hoek

Camping Aquacentrum Bremersbergse Hoek is the perfect campsite for those looking for adventure and relaxation, located on the widest part of the Velumemerr. There are pitches right at the water's edge and others slightly further inland where there is more shade. There's no shortage of activities for all ages to enjoy whilst staying here, such as cycling, hiking, fishing, surfing, sailing, water skiing, horse riding and golf. The adjacent beach is well-maintained and clean, and there's also a large play island for the children to enjoy.

Off-site, there's plenty to explore. The old fishing villages Harderwijk and Elburg, with their many monuments, are just a stone's throw away, while charming Amersfoort is easily reached with its elegant squares and historic waterways. Amsterdam is an iconic world city, and its museums, busy streets and canals make a great day trip. The amusement park Walibi World and the dolphinarium are also nearby. In short, Aqua Centrum Bremerbergse Hoek offers a unique combination of rest, relaxation and a chance to get out and about to explore.

Key Features

 Book Online

 Pets Accepted

 Beach Access

 Play Area

 Bar/Restaurant

 Bike Hire

 Fishing

 Sailing

Well-maintained sanitary facilities. Restaurant, Bar, Snack bar, Shop, Supermarket. Entertainment. Communal BBQ. Bouncy castle. Children's playground. Hiking, Fishing, Sailing, Water skiing, Canoeing, Boat rental. Clean beach. WiFi. Pets allowed.

Scan me for more information.

Netherlands

Alan Rogers Code: NL6822
6 accommodations
80 pitches
GPS: 52.71876, 5.75476
Post Code: NL-8302 AC

Emmeloord, Utrecht

www.alanrogers.com/nl6822
info@campinghetbosbad.nl
Tel: +31 527 616 100
www.campinghetbosbad.nl

Open (Touring Pitches):
Start April - End October.

Camping Het Bosbad

Camping Het Bosbad is tucked away among the woods in a peaceful rural setting with pleasant walking and cycling trails. There is a little 'farm' where activities are organised regularly for the children. The site has 80 large grassy pitches (30 for tourers) with electricity, mostly well-shaded by mature trees and tall hedging. There are special pitches for motorhomes and small tents, and the atmosphere is relaxed and family-friendly.

There are plenty of lovely villages around Emmeloord, for example, the old fishing village of Urk, Kampen or the former coastal villages Blokzijl, Kuinre and Vollenhove. Be sure to visit Giethoorn, also known as 'The Venice of the North', which you can explore from the water in a rented boat or on one of the canal boats. The vibrant city of Amsterdam is easily reached, and there are plenty of shops, restaurants and amenities locally: Emmeloord's city centre can be accessed on foot, just 800 metres away, with more choices at the Outletcentrum Bataviastad nearby.

Toilet block with showers (charged), washbasins and WCs. Facility for visitors who are disabled. Laundry with washing machine and dryer. Information area. WiFi. Rental of books and games. Children's play area. Table tennis. Snack bar with terrace where breakfast is served in the morning. TV room. Take away. Pets allowed.

Key Features

 Book Online

 Pets Accepted

 Disabled Facilities

 Beach Access

 Play Area

Scan me for more information.

353

Alan Rogers Code: NL5975
45 accommodations
360 pitches
GPS: 52.54462, 6.49545
Post Code: NL-7737 PK

Ommen, Overijssel

www.alanrogers.com/nl5975
info@kleinewolf.nl
Tel: +31 529 457 203
www.kleinewolf.nl

Open (Touring Pitches):
Start April - End October.

Camping De Kleine Wolf

Camp De Kleine Wolf is close to Vecht in a beautiful part of the eastern Netherlands, making it an ideal base for walking or cycling through the woods or along the River Vecht. The site has 550 pitches, including 360 for touring units, all with electricity (8A), water, drainage and a TV point. They are on large, grassy fields surrounded by mature trees that provide shade, and most have a little play area.

This site actively encourages teenage visitors, with a special clubroom and plenty of sports provisions. There is also a full activity programme in high season for younger children, and the site has its own deer park and animal farm. Children are invited to get involved at feeding times.

Two modern blocks provide toilets, washbasins (open and in cabins) and controllable hot showers (card-operated). Child-size toilets, showers and washbasins. Bathroom. Family bathroom. Attractive baby room. Facilities for disabled visitors in the main block (key access). Laundry facilities. Shop (daily in season). Bar/restaurant. Indoor (10x5m) and outdoor (20x10m) pool with paddling pools. Play areas and indoor playroom. Rowing lake. Fishing pond. Football field. Volleyball. Minigolf. Boules. Animal farm. Deer park. Entertainment programme in high season. Bicycle hire. WiFi over site (charged). No single-sex groups.

Key Features

 Book Online

 Pets Accepted

 Disabled Facilities

 Swimming Pool

 Play Area

 Bar/Restaurant

 Bike Hire

 Fishing

Scan me for more information.

Camping 't Stien'n Boer

Netherlands

Alan Rogers Code: NL6010
11 accommodations
125 pitches
GPS: 52.14007, 6.72441
Post Code: NL-7481 VP

Haaksbergen, Overijssel

www.alanrogers.com/nl6010
info@stiennboer.nl
Tel: +31 535 722 610
www.stienboer.com

Open (Touring Pitches):
Start April - Late October.

Deep in the Twente countryside, with its picturesque farms, hedgerows and forests, this is a truly rural setting between a charming village and nature reserves. There are countless trails for cyclists and hikers, with a number starting from the campsite gates. Try the 'het Ommetje' walking route of the 'Moll'npad', which takes walkers through a varied landscape full of cultural history with routes between 7.5 km and 10.5 km. Serious mountain bikers enjoy the Haaksbergen trail, which runs for 60 km.

This is a pleasant site with 125 grass pitches, some in secluded settings, others in open fields, all numbered and with 6A electricity. Much emphasis is put on facilities for children, with several play areas situated throughout the site and a large indoor play area on sand, ideally located next to the restaurant/bar. A small heated swimming pool has a separate area for children.

Four well-located toilet blocks with large, controllable hot showers on payment. A good room containing baths and showers for children. Washing machine and dryers. Shop (all season). Restaurant, bar and takeaway (variable opening). Outdoor heated pool. Entertainment programme in season. Multi-purpose all-weather sports pitch. Indoor pool complex (all year). Minigolf. Boules. Pedal go-karts. WiFi over site (charged).

Key Features

 Book Online

 Pets Accepted

 Disabled Facilities

 Swimming Pool

 Play Area

 Bar/Restaurant

 Bike Hire

Scan me for more information.

Alan Rogers Code: NL5600
42 accommodations
200 pitches
GPS: 52.01767, 4.37908
Post Code: NL-2616 LJ

Delft, Zuid-Holland

www.alanrogers.com/nl5600
info@delftsehout.nl
Tel: +31 152 130 040
www.delftsehout.nl

Open (Touring Pitches):
End March - Start November.

Vakantiepark Delftse Hout

This well-run, modern site is pleasantly situated in Delft's park and forest area on the city's eastern edge. It has 200 touring pitches quite formally arranged in groups of four to six and surrounded by attractive trees and hedges. All have sufficient space and electrical connections (10A Europlug).

Modern buildings near the entrance house the site amenities. A modern sanitary block has been developed (2021), along with a new reception and entrance. A newer, smaller restaurant is available where basic snacks are for sale. Walking and cycling tours are organised, and there is a recreation programme in the high season.

Modern, heated toilet facilities include a spacious family room and children's section. Facilities for disabled visitors. Laundry. Motorhome services. Shop for basic food and camping items (all season). Snackbar and takeaway (main season). Small heated outdoor swimming pool (mid-May - mid-Sept.) Adventure playground. Recreation room. Bicycle hire. Gas supplies. Max. 1 dog. WiFi (500 MB/day included).

Key Features

 Book Online

 Pets Accepted

 Disabled Facilities

 Beach Access

 Swimming Pool

 Play Area

 Bike Hire

Scan me for more information.

Alan Rogers Code: NL5610
56 accommodations
75 pitches
GPS: 51.83361, 4.55236
Post Code: NL-2991 SB

Barendrecht, Zuid-Holland

Camping De Oude Maas

www.alanrogers.com/nl5610
info@recreatieparkdeoudemaas.nl
Tel: +31 786 772 445
www.recreatieparkdeoudemaas.nl

Open (Touring Pitches):
All year.

This site is easily accessed from the A15 southern Rotterdam ring road and is situated right by the river, so it is well worth considering if you are visiting Rotterdam or want a peaceful stop amid rural surroundings. It also doubles as a marina, with 117 berths and a trailer ramp. The touring pitches are sited away from the residential section; all are on grass and have a 10A hook-up. Leafy trees dot the site, and there is a pleasant separate touring area for 11 motorhomes with electricity, water and wastewater connections in a hedged group near the marina and river.

The Oude Maas (Old Meuse) carries barges that make up much of the passing river traffic. The site has a section for seasonal units and mobile homes in a woodland setting, well back from the river on level grass. The small town of Heerjansdam is within 1,500 m. and has shops, bars and restaurants. The main attractions are in Rotterdam, which is within reach by bicycle and via public transport from Barendecht, which is probably best initially accessed by car or preferably by bus.

One toilet block provides all necessary facilities, including a unit for disabled visitors and a baby room. Launderette. Motorhome services. Fishing. Good play area with swings, slides and climbing frames for all ages. Bicycle hire. WiFi (charged). Max. 1 dog.

Key Features

 Open All Year

 Pets Accepted

 Disabled Facilities

 Beach Access

 Play Area

 Bike Hire

 Fishing

Scan me for more information.

Alan Rogers Code: NL5690
100 pitches
GPS: 51.93623, 4.95748
Post Code: NL-4231 VD

Meerkerk, Zuid-Holland

www.alanrogers.com/nl5690
info@campingdevictorie.nl
Tel: +31 183 352 741
www.campingdevictorie.nl

Open (Touring Pitches):
Mid March - End October.

Camping De Victorie

Within an hour's drive of the port of Rotterdam, you can be pitched on this delightful, spacious site lying south of Utrecht in the green heart of the Netherlands. De Victorie is a working organic farm, with fields all around and Limousin cattle with their calves, and offers an alternative to the bustling seaside sites. A modern building houses reception, an open plan office and a space with tables and chairs, where friendly owners may invite you to a cup of coffee. The 100 grass pitches (100-200 sq.m) are level, dotted with leafy trees and have a 6A electricity supply.

You can choose to be pitched in the apple and pear trees' shade in one of the orchards or in the more open meadow area. Children enjoy the farmland's freedom with farm animals, wildlife and tractor rides. This is an ideal site for those seeking peace and quiet whilst still being close to the main attractions of this part of Holland. Hop on a bike and explore the easy-going routes through the idyllic neighbouring countryside.

The main sanitary block is clean and fully equipped. Showers are on payment. Laundry room. Additional sanitary facilities are around the site. Farm shop and a small bar (once a week). Play area. Trampoline. Playfield. Fishing. Riding. WiFi throughout (charged).

Key Features

 Pets Accepted

 Disabled Facilities

 Play Area

 Bar/Restaurant

 Fishing

 Horse Riding

Scan me for more information.

Alan Rogers Code: NL6275
120 pitches
GPS: 51.93753, 5.54589
Post Code: NL-4041 AW

Kesteren, Gelderland

www.alanrogers.com/nl6275
info@campingbetuwe.nl
Tel: +31 488 481 477
www.campingbetuwe.nl

Open (Touring Pitches):
Mid March - Late October.

Camping Betuwe

Camping Betuwe is in the Neder-Betuwe municipality of Gelderland, an agricultural fruit-growing region. It's on the doorstep of the Utrecht Heuvelrug National Park, just 10 minutes away. You can spend days cycling and walking through the orchards and along the river banks, as well as pottering around in the sleepy little villages and exploring the medieval castles of the area.

The campsite has spacious pitches for touring units and tents, with 16A hook-up, adjacent to the new toilet facilities. There are two lakes, one with a sandy beach and play area and the other being a well-stocked fishing lake, fringed with leafy willows and tall trees. This site is suitable for all ages, those seeking peace and tranquillity in rural surroundings, and families with young children and teenagers. Age-appropriate entertainment is organised in the high season.

Sanitary facilities have washbasins in cubicles and hot showers (key operated). No facilities for disabled visitors. Well-stocked shop (fresh bread daily), takeaway, bar and restaurant (weekends only in low season). Excellent restaurant/brasserie (all year). Playgrounds. Lakeside beach and swimming. Well-stocked fishing lake. Bicycle hire. Dogs (max. 2) are allowed. Public transport is 5 min. walk away. WiFi (charged). Only gas barbecues are permitted. Riding.

Key Features

 Book Online

 Pets Accepted

 Beach Access

 Play Area

 Bar/Restaurant

 Bike Hire

 Fishing

 Horse Riding

Scan me for more information.

Alan Rogers Code: NL6350
200 accommodations
170 pitches
GPS: 52.08656, 5.76945
Post Code: NL-6731 BV

Otterlo, Gelderland

www.alanrogers.com/nl6350
wijewerelt@ardoer.com
Tel: +31 318 591 201
www.europarcs.com

Open (Touring Pitches):
Late March - Late October.

Camping De Wije Werelt

Europarks De Wije Werelt is located in the beautiful Hoge Veluwe National Park, and a special feature is the excursions with a forest ranger so you can see the deer and wild boar. The helpful reception will advise on good routes for walking and cycling, and you can even hire a GPS handset to keep you on track. The Kröller-Müller Museum is just a short drive away, and there is easy access to the major towns, including Arnhem, Apeldoorn and historic Amersfoort, a real gem with its characterful squares and great restaurants. The small local town, Otello, has shops and restaurants.

This peaceful site offers good facilities with plenty of activities for children, including a heated outdoor swimming pool with a paddling pool, a playground and an area with different play equipment for older children. The 170 grassy touring pitches all have water and drainage, 10A electricity, cable, and WiFi.

Heated toilet block with washbasins in cabins. Family wash cabins and facilities for children. Baby room. Launderette with ironing facilities. Microwave. Well-stocked shop. Bar. Restaurant. Snack bar and takeaway. TV room. Playground, bouncy castle and climbing frames. Sports field. Boules. Bicycle and tricycle hire. Entertainment in high season. Recreation area. Miniclub. Electronic games. WiFi over site (charged). Cycling and walking trails.

Key Features

 Book Online

 Pets Accepted

 Disabled Facilities

 Swimming Pool

 Play Area

 Bar/Restaurant

 Bike Hire

Scan me for more information.

Alan Rogers Code: NL6423
4 accommodations
120 pitches
GPS: 52.10284, 6.44155
Post Code: NL-7261 MR

Ruurlo, Gelderland

Camping Tamaring

www.alanrogers.com/nl6423
info@camping-tamaring.nl
Tel: +31 573 451 486
www.camping-tamaring.nl

Open (Touring Pitches):
Start April - End October.

Tamaring is a small, tranquil site, ideal for those seeking a natural setting with plenty of space. It is located close to the natural parks of Beekvliet and Grote Veld amid the rural landscape of Achterhoek. There are 120 large grassy pitches (100-150 sq.m) on 3.5 acres spread over four fields. One field has pitches separated by hedges, creating a private atmosphere. A separate field caters for tents with a covered picnic area and children's hide-out. All pitches have electricity connections (10A) and Europlugs.

Amenities include a fenced-off outdoor swimming pool, several playgrounds and organised treasure hunt cycle rides in the forest. Guided nature walks and rides are offered in high season, and the area is perfect for easy-going cycling. Nearby Ruurlo is an attractive village with some handy amenities and one of the most beautiful castles in the Netherlands, which is well worth a visit (a popular spot for weddings!). Not far from Ruurlo is a huge maze which was completely restored in 1981 and is a popular excursion.

Key Features

 Book Online

 Pets Accepted

 Disabled Facilities

 Swimming Pool

 Play Area

 Bike Hire

Modern, heated sanitary block with facilities for babies and disabled visitors. Launderette. Small shop. Fresh bread to order. Reception with terrace. Bar. Outdoor swimming pool. Bicycle hire. DVD hire. Boules. Indoor play barn. Indoor reading area. Play areas. WiFi.

Scan me for more information.

Alan Rogers Code: NL7056
10 accommodations
119 pitches
GPS: 51.72641, 3.75066
Post Code: NL-4325 DD

Renesse, Zeeland

www.alanrogers.com/nl7056
info@campingdebrem.nl
Tel: +31 111 462 626
www.campingdebrem.nl

Open (Touring Pitches):
Start April - End October.

Camping De Brem

Camping de Brem is near the seaside resort of Renesse, less than two kilometres from the huge 17 km long beach with its clean, safe sands. It's well within cycling range, taking around 10 minutes. An extensive programme is offered for all ages, such as a circus school, where children can learn to juggle, hurl a diablo high, or enjoy archery. The additional Kids & Co club provides other activities assisted by furry team members Lulu and Tiger and there are organised entertainment for everyone in high season with live music, dances, beach activities and sports.

A 25-metre pool for swimming and a kids' pool with a slide and water toys make up the pool complex, both heated and supervised. If your kids are aged ten or over, a top option is the nightly diving programme, led by an experienced instructor from the local diving school, for dips and dives under the moonlight. Catering on site is easy with a snack bar, a bar, a restaurant with a terrace and an à la carte menu offering homemade pizzas, local mussels and Zeeland oysters.

Key Features

 Book Online

 Disabled Facilities

 Swimming Pool

 Play Area

 Bar/Restaurant

 Bike Hire

Disabled facilities. Restaurant. Bar. Snack bar. Take away. Shop. Outdoor swimming pool. Entertainment. Kids club. Children's play area. Pétanque. Bicycle hire. TV. WiFi. Local buses are free in the high season. Dogs are only allowed in rental accommodations and not in the camping area.

Scan me for more information.

Alan Rogers Code: NL6645
136 pitches
GPS: 51.72698, 5.63317
Post Code: NL-5374 RK

Schaijk, Noord-Brabant

Camping Hartje Groen

www.alanrogers.com/nl6645
info@paasheuvelgroep.nl
Tel: +31 486 461 703
www.hartjegroen.com

Open (Touring Pitches):
Early April – End October.

Charme Camping Hartje Groen is situated in the middle of De Maashorst nature centre – Brabant's largest continuous nature reserve and home to European bison and wild ponies. It's a peaceful woodland area just south of the town of Schaijk. The 136 touring pitches are informally distributed, some in open meadows surrounded by trees and hedges and others in forest clearings on sandy grass or beside the lake where the children like to splash and play. Somewhat separate from the touring area are two sections specially set aside for use by youth groups.

It's a rural, tranquil setting, ideal for those looking to escape a busy lifestyle at home. The sanitary facility for the touring pitches is modern and well-maintained. A small restaurant is in keeping with the site's relaxing location, with a homely, hospitable atmosphere and plenty of outdoor seating on the terrace. The surrounding area is crisscrossed with plenty of excellent cycling, walking paths, and bridleways leading you through the unspoilt scenery of extensive woods and heathland.

Key Features

 Pets Accepted

 Disabled Facilities

 Play Area

 Bar/Restaurant

Modern toilet block with free hot showers and facilities for disabled visitors. Laundry room with washing machines and dryer. Shop. Small bar/restaurant with terrace (High season). Takeaway. Play areas, including a cable ride over a small lake. WiFi (charged).

Scan me for more information.

Alan Rogers Code: NL6650
600 accommodations
440 pitches
GPS: 51.49139, 4.89646
Post Code: NL-4861 RC

Chaam, Noord-Brabant

De Flaasbloem

www.alanrogers.com/nl6650
reservation@rcn.eu
Tel: +31 850 400 700
www.rcn.nl/flaasbloem

Open (Touring Pitches):
Late March - Early November.

RCN Vakantiepark de Flaasbloem is a large, friendly and quiet campsite set well out in the countryside. It would suit those who prefer to stay in a rural environment, on a site providing very good facilities to keep children busy and happy. The level touring pitches are set on grass among hedges and tall trees, and all have 10A electricity. They are spacious and shady, with several more open, landscaped pitches on grassy fields. The Wildenberg is a generous, vehicle-free area for tents with three Finnish huts.

The restaurant has an extensive menu and boasts an atmospheric indoor garden, creating a very pleasant dining environment. De Flaasbloem is located close to some dense forests, ideal for exploring by bicycle. With its cathedral, the city of Breda is great for those who enjoy a shopping trip, but the ancient Belgian city of Antwerp, less than an hour's drive away, is perhaps a bigger draw.

Key Features

 Book Online

 Pets Accepted

 Disabled Facilities

 Swimming Pool

 Play Area

 Bar/Restaurant

 Bike Hire

 Fishing

Good sanitary facilities, including those for disabled visitors. Launderette. Supermarket, bar, snack bar and bakery, restaurant with indoor garden (all open all season). Small covered pool, outdoor children's pool with water games, recreational lake. Games room. Library. Several play areas. Mini train around the site. Multisports terrain. Tennis. Children's farm. Bicycle and go-kart hire. WiFi (free).

Scan me for more information.

Alan Rogers Code: NL5970
65 accommodations
530 pitches
GPS: 51.33635, 5.35552
Post Code: NL-5571 TN

Bergeijk, Noord-Brabant

www.alanrogers.com/nl5970
info@campingdepaal.nl
Tel: +31 497 571 977
www.depaal.nl

Open (Touring Pitches):
Start April - End October.

Camping De Paal

A really first-class, family-run campsite, ideal for families with children up to 12 years old, with activities on a grand scale. A short distance south of Eindhoven, it's 42 hectares of woodland and has 530 touring pitches (up to 150 sq.m). The pitches are numbered and in meadows, separated by trees, with cars parked mainly in dedicated parking areas. All have 6A electricity, TV, water and drainage. There are 60 pitches with private sanitary facilities, some of which are partly underground and attractively covered with grass and flowers. Each group of pitches has a small playground.

Children are often happy to spend all day on site; such is the array of activities on offer. There are large adventure-style play areas, a kind of vast sandy dune with water and other activities, a petting zoo, a superb indoor pool complex, an outdoor aqua park and even a theatre for children's shows.

High-quality sanitary facilities are modern, including spacious washbasins in cabins, family rooms and baby baths. Facilities for disabled visitors. Launderette. Motorhome services. Underground supermarket. Restaurant (high season), bar and snack bar (all season). Indoor pool (all season, supervised in high season). Outdoor pool (May-Sept). Tennis. Play areas. Theatre. WiFi (charged). Bicycle hire. Pet zoo.

Key Features

 Book Online

 Pets Accepted

 Disabled Facilities

 Swimming Pool

 Play Area

 Bar/Restaurant

 Bike Hire

Scan me for more information.

Alan Rogers Code: NL6511
100 accommodations
150 pitches
GPS: 51.52350, 6.03562
Post Code: NL-5807 EK

Oostrum, Limburg

De Witte Vennen

www.alanrogers.com/nl6511
info@wittevennen.nl
Tel: +31 478 511 322
www.wittevennen.nl

Open (Touring Pitches):
Late March - Late August.

Parc de Witte Vennen is a family site with around 150 unusually spacious pitches for either touring units or seasonal use. Many of the pitching areas have their own playground or sports field so parents can watch the children while they go about. The quieter fields, although not on the waterside, are perfect for nature lovers and senior citizens.

Most of the pitching areas are car-free zones with parking nearby. Various activities are organised during the holiday season for children up to 12yrs, from a ride in a horse and carriage to a tour with the forest ranger. In addition, bicycles and go-karts are available for rent, or you can make free use of the pedalos.

Key Features

 Book Online

 Pets Accepted

 Disabled Facilities

 Swimming Pool

 Play Area

 Bar/Restaurant

 Bike Hire

Two toilet blocks provide showers, washbasins and WCs. Facility for guests who are disabled. Launderette. Beach volleyball. Animal Park. Draughts and chess games. Bicycle hire. Boules. Horse pastures. Recreation lake. Go-kart hire. Fishing lake. Football pitch. Volleyball pitch. Crazy golf course. Wi-Fi over the whole park. Shop. Bread to order. Pedalos. Trampoline. Children's play park. Swimming pool with children's pool. Waterslide. Sun terrace. Wellness centre. Cafeteria. Tents allowed. Bike hire. Dogs are allowed low season. Twin-axle caravans are allowed. Gas BBQ'S only allowed. TV room. Gas sales. Restaurant and bar. Takeaway.

Scan me for more information.

Alan Rogers Code: NL6575
30 accommodations
121 pitches
GPS: 50.91040, 6.07327
Post Code: NL-6374 LE

Landgraaf, Limburg

Camping De Watertoren

www.alanrogers.com/nl6575
info@campingdewatertoren.nl
Tel: +31 455 321 747
www.campingdewatertoren.nl

Open (Touring Pitches):
Late March - End October.

De Watertoren is situated near the village of Landgraaf in the rolling hills of South Limburg. Surrounded by the trees of the adjacent forest, it is peaceful, and plentiful cycle and hiking routes lead from the campsite. The helpful reception staff offer tourism information and local advice.

The site caters well for families with children under 12 years old, nature lovers and those who are seeking peace and quiet. Around 120 grassy touring pitches are neatly laid out with varying degrees of shade spread out over several small fields. The German village of Ubach Palenberg is very close, and a delightful cycle track crosses the border. The interesting cities of Aachen (20 minutes), Maastricht and Valkenburg (less than half an hour) are easily reached. Several annual music festivals are held nearby.

Comfortable, heated toilet block providing all facilities, accessed by key card (€30 deposit). Family shower room. Motorhome services. Bar and snack bar (weekends only in low season). Small shop. Daily fresh bread and the famous 'Limburgse vlaai' in high season and during holidays. Brasserie with terrace (open every day for breakfast and lunch). Two swimming pools (high season). Play area. Recreation team in high season. Bicycle hire. Sporting field. Boules. Free WiFi over part of the site.

Key Features

 Book Online

 Pets Accepted

 Disabled Facilities

 Swimming Pool

 Play Area

 Bar/Restaurant

 Bike Hire

Scan me for more information.

Capital Oslo
Currency
Norwegian Krone (NOK)
Language Norwegian
Time Zone CET (GMT+1)
Telephone Code +47

Shops Hours vary throughout the year, with many shops operating on shorter hours in low and shoulder seasons. In high season 10am to 5pm Mon to Sat and until 7pm on Thurs. Supermarkets 9am to 11pm Mon to Fri and until 10pm Sat.

Money ATMs are widespread and accessible 24hrs a day. Credit cards are universally accepted. The country is fast becoming cashless although you should always bring cash for emergencies.

Travelling with children Oslo is home to many parks and museums but not all attractions are children-friendly. Attractions are often free for under 6s and discounted for under 16s.

Public Holidays 1 Jan New Year's Day; Mar/Apr Maundy Thursday; Mar/Apr Good Friday; Mar/Apr Easter Sunday; Mar/Apr Easter Monday; 1 May Labour Day; 2 Jun Constitution Day; May Ascension; May/Jun Whit Sunday; May/Jun Whit Monday; 25 Dec Christmas Day; 26 Dec Boxing Day.

♻ **LEZ** Low Emissions Zones in most major cities. Registration required.

○ EU Member | ● Schengen Area

Tourism website visitnorway.com

●●●○○ **Accessible Travel Score**

Generally well equipped, especially in cities. Public transport and street crossings are good but planning ahead is always a smart idea.

Driving in Norway Be prepared for long tunnels and hairpin bends. Some roads are closed to caravans (check tourist website). Vehicles must have sufficient road grip, and it may be necessary to use winter tyres with or without chains. Use dipped headlights during the day. Vehicles entering major cities must pay a toll, and other tolls are levied on certain roads. Drink-driving and using a mobile whilst driving are illegal.

 Dashcams are legal

 Speed camera detectors are **illegal**

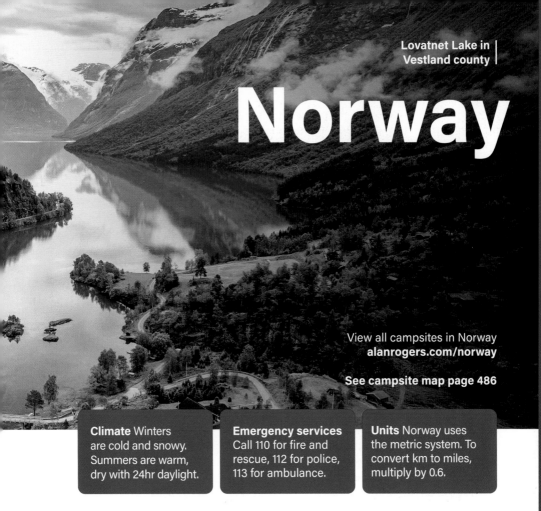

Norway

View all campsites in Norway
alanrogers.com/norway

See campsite map page 486

Climate Winters
are cold and snowy.
Summers are warm,
dry with 24hr daylight.

Emergency services
Call 110 for fire and
rescue, 112 for police,
113 for ambulance.

Units Norway uses
the metric system. To
convert km to miles,
multiply by 0.6.

A land full of contrasts, from magnificent snow-capped mountains, dramatic fjords, vast plateaux with wild, untamed tracts to huge lakes and rich green countryside. With nearly one-quarter of the land above the Arctic Circle, Norway has the lowest population density in Europe.

Norway is made up of five regions. In the heart of the eastern region, Oslo has everything one would expect from a major city and is the oldest of the Scandinavian capitals. The west coast boasts some of the world's most beautiful fjords, with plunging waterfalls and mountains.

In the heart of central Norway, Trondheim is a busy university town with many attractions, notably the Nidarosdomen Cathedral. The sunniest region is the south; its rugged coastline

with white wooden cottages is popular with Norwegians and ideal for swimming, sailing and scuba diving.

The north is the Land of the Midnight Sun and the Northern Lights. It is home to the Sami, the indigenous people of Norway, whose traditions include fishing, hunting and reindeer herding. The scenery varies from forested valleys and narrow fjords to icy tundra. There are several cities worth visiting, including Tromsø, with the Fjelheisen cable car, Polaria aquarium with bearded seals, and the Arctic Cathedral.

Scan QR code
to browse more
campsites on
our website

Alan Rogers Code: NO2475
23 accommodations
80 pitches
GPS: 67.23550, 14.62091
Post Code: N-8056

Saltstraumen, Nordland

www.alanrogers.com/no2475
post@salcampi.no
Tel: +47 75 58 75 60
saltstraumen-camping.no

Open (Touring Pitches):
All year.

Saltstraumen Camping

PlusCamp Saltstraumen is a popular site is in a very scenic location. It has a magnificent backdrop and is close to one of the strongest maelstroms in the world. It is an easy short walk to this outstanding natural phenomenon. As well as 23 cabins, the site has 80 simple touring pitches, mostly on level, gravel hardstandings, with water, wastewater and electricity (10A). Twenty 'softer' pitches are available for tents. The nearby fjord is renowned for the prolific numbers of coalfish and cod caught from the shore. Many try their hand at catching the evening meal. You are advised to arrive by late afternoon.

At the Saltstraumen Maelstrom, 400 million cubic metres of water are pressed through a 150m wide strait at a rate of about 20 knots in the course of six hours. The effect is greatest at new or full moons and tide tables to find the optimum time to visit are available from reception.

Excellent heated sanitary facilities are clean and fully equipped. Unisex with four large individual cubicles containing a WC, shower and washbasin. Other cubicles have a toilet and washbasin, and one family room provides both adult and child-size WC, washbasin and shower. Full wet room with access for disabled visitors. Motorhome services. Kitchen with two full cookers. Fish cleaning area and free use of fish freezer. Laundry facilities. Playground. Fishing. WiFi (free).

Key Features

 Open All Year

 Pets Accepted

 Disabled Facilities

 Play Area

 Fishing

Scan me for more information.

Alan Rogers Code: NO2489
10 accommodations
120 pitches
GPS: 64.29916, 10.49674
Post Code: N-7740

Osen, Nord-Trøndelag

www.alanrogers.com/no2489
booking@osen-fjordcamping.no
Tel: +47 41 14 68 02
osen-fjordcamping.no

Open (Touring Pitches):
All year.

Osen Fjordcamping

Ideally located next to the picturesque Osen Fjord, this campsite boasts a small marina as well as around 120 level grassy pitches, 90 of which have electricity. Fishing is an everyday part of life in this area, and you can hire boats from the site to fish in both salt and freshwater.

The site's sanitary facilities are well kept, and a camper's kitchen is available. Three communal BBQ/fire pits are found around the site; these have benefited from recent improvements. Around 10 cabins are available to hire and have been undergoing a period of gradual improvement over recent years. A small shop with a coffee corner offers a small selection of goods.

The small community of Osen can be found about 1km away where groceries and a petrol station can be found.

Children's playground. Minigolf. WiFi available. Camper's kitchen, with fish-freezing facilities available. Boat launch and a small marina. Showers are included in your pitch fee. Washing machine and dryer. Shop and cafe nearby.

Key Features

 Open All Year

 Disabled Facilities

 Play Area

 Fishing

Scan me for more information.

Alan Rogers Code: NO2500
19 accommodations
30 pitches
GPS: 63.34686, 9.96234
Post Code: N-7354

Viggja, Sør Trøndelag

www.alanrogers.com/no2500
post@trasavika.no
Tel: +47 72 86 78 22
www.trasavika.no

Open (Touring Pitches):
All year.

Tråsåvika Camping

On a headland jutting into the Trondheimfjord, some 40 km. from Trondheim, Tråsåvika commands an attractive position. For many, this compensates for the extra distance into town.

The 30 touring pitches with fjord views (some slightly sloping), all with electricity connections (10/16A), are on an open grassy field at the top of the site or on a series of terraces below. These run down to the small sandy beach, easily accessed via a well-designed gravel service road. To one side, on a wooded bluff at the top of the site, are 19 cabins (open all year), many in the traditional style. The smart reception complex also houses a small shop, a licensed café, a lounge area, and a terrace overlooking the entire panorama.

There are opportunities for boating and fishing from the beach on the site. The local River Orkla is also one of Norway's most famous salmon rivers.

The fully equipped sanitary unit feels a little dated with warm showers available (on payment). Water for touring pitches is also accessed from this block. Hot water (on payment) in kitchen and laundry. Shop. Café (sells beer, wine and food (seasonal) TV/ sitting room. Small children's play ara. Jetty and boat hire. Free fjord fishing with catches of good-sized cod from the shore. Free WiFi on touring pitches.

Key Features

 Open All Year

 Pets Accepted

 Play Area

 Fishing

 Sailing

Scan me for more information.

Alan Rogers Code: NO2505
10 accommodations
50 pitches
GPS: 62.49703, 9.58535
Post Code: N-7340

Oppdal, Sør Trøndelag

Magalaupe Camping

www.alanrogers.com/no2505
anja.moene@gmail.com
Tel: +47 99 25 99 93
en.magalaupe.no

Open (Touring Pitches):
All year.

This friendly, good value, riverside site in a sheltered position in the mountains is easily accessed from the E6. The 50 unmarked and grassy touring pitches (34 with 10-16A electricity) are in natural surroundings amongst birch trees and rocks and served by gravel access roads. There are also several attractive and fully equipped site-owned cabins. As the site rarely fills up, the facilities should be adequate at most times.

There are a host of unusual activities in the surrounding area. These include caving, canyoning, rafting, gold panning, mineral hunting and musk oxen, reindeer and elk safaris. In winter, the more adventurous can try various winter sports in the high Dovrefjell National Park. The nearby centre of Oppdal gives access to one of Norway's largest alpine complexes with 16 ski lifts and 80 km. of prepared ski trails. In summer, fishing and hunting are possible.

The small, clean, heated sanitary unit is fully equipped and has showers on payment. Extra WC/washbasin units in the reception building. A small kitchen with sinks, hot plate, fridge and freezer, and a combined washing/drying machine. Motorhome services. Kiosk for ices, soft drinks, etc. (seasonal). Bar (mid-June - Aug). TV lounge. Fishing. Bicycle hire. WiFi (free).

Key Features

 Open All Year

 Pets Accepted

 Disabled Facilities

 Bar/Restaurant

 Bike Hire

 Fishing

Scan me for more information.

Alan Rogers Code: NO2515
13 accommodations
45 pitches
GPS: 62.13113, 10.56915
Post Code: N-2560

Alvdal, Hedmark

Gjelten Bru Camping

www.alanrogers.com/no2515
post@gjeltenbrucamping.no
Tel: +47 97 32 35 88
www.gjeltenbrucamping.no

Open (Touring Pitches):
Late May - Start October.

Located a few kilometres west of Alvdal, this peaceful little site with its traditional turf-roofed buildings, makes an excellent base from which to explore the area. The 45 touring pitches are on level, neatly trimmed grass, served by gravel access roads and with electricity (10A) available to all.

Some pitches are in the open, others under tall pine trees spread along the river bank. There are also 13 cabins to rent all year round. Across the bridge on the other side of the river and main road, the site owners also operate the local, well-stocked supermarket and post office.

The site has its own small play area but also has use of a large play area in the school grounds. This is accessed by steps at the rear of the central sanitary block. There is skiing near the site in winter.

Heated toilet facilities are clean and housed in two buildings. One unit has been refurbished and is well appointed, the other is of newer construction. There is a mix of conventional washbasins and stainless steel washing troughs, and hot showers (on payment). Separate unit with WC, basin, shower and handrails for disabled visitors. Two small kitchens provide sinks, hot plates and an oven, all free of charge. Laundry facilities. Motorhome services. TV room. Swings. Fishing.

Key Features

 Pets Accepted

 Disabled Facilities

 Play Area

 Fishing

Scan me for more information.

Alan Rogers Code: NO2578
34 accommodations
200 pitches
GPS: 60.86703, 11.55600
Post Code: N-2407

Elverum, Oppland

www.alanrogers.com/no2578
booking@elverumcamping.no
Tel: +47 62 41 67 16
elverumcamping.no

Open (Touring Pitches):
All year.

Elverum Camping

Elverum Camping offers around 200 flat grassy pitches located on the banks of the Glomma River. Reservations are not possible, but overbooking is unlikely due to the size of the site. Shops including a bakery can be found a short walk away from the site. With its waterfront setting canoeing and fishing are popular activities with guests. A children's playground features a sandpit and climbing equipment.

Several bungalows and cabins are also available to hire accommodating from 2 to 4 people per cabin. The Valhalla function room accommodates up to 30 people and BBQs can be provided for larger groups.

The town of Elverum has quite a history and served as the temporary capital of Norway during the Second World War. Much of the town was destroyed by German troops, as reflected in the modern architecture of the town centre. Whilst in the area a couple of museums are worth a visit; the Norwegian Forest Museum and Glomdal Museum focus on the role of forestry and the outdoors in the character and life of the Norwegians.

Children's playground. Washing machine and dryer (chargeable) Free WiFi throughout. Camper's kitchen with a microwave, oven and dishwashing facilities. Wastewater disposal point. Small shop at reception.

Key Features

 Open All Year

 Pets Accepted

 Disabled Facilities

 Play Area

 Bike Hire

Scan me for
more information.

Alan Rogers Code: NO2317
40 accommodations
100 pitches
GPS: 60.42536, 7.12341
Post Code: N-5784

Øvre Eidfjord, Hordaland

www.alanrogers.com/no2317
post@saebocamping.com
Tel: +47 94 98 28 62
www.saebocamping.com

Open (Touring Pitches):
Start May - Mid September.

Sæbø Camping

Enclosed by high mountains, in a peaceful location close to woodland, Sæbo Camping sits on the shore of Lake Eidfjord and adjacent to a salmon and trout river. Its 100 touring pitches are on level grass, and about 60 have 10A electricity hook-ups. Some 40 pitches are occupied by wood cabins, and 14 of these can be rented.

Its position by road 7, the main route between Oslo and Bergen, makes Sæbø a convenient stopover while travelling through Norway. However, if you have time to linger, there is much of interest in the local area including the Vøringfossen, Norway's most famous waterfall at 182 metres. Reservations are not usually required outside of the high season.

The refurbished and extended heated sanitary block is adequate, with washbasins in cubicles, hot showers (coin-operated), a family room, baby changing and facilities for disabled visitors. Laundry room. Campers' kitchen. Fresh bread delivered. Playground. Fishing. Boat and canoe hire. WiFi.

Key Features

 Pets Accepted

 Disabled Facilities

 Beach Access

 Play Area

 Fishing

Scan me for
more information.

Alan Rogers Code: NO2628
13 accommodations
50 pitches
GPS: 58.04325, 7.49554
Post Code: N-4516

Mandal, Vest-Agder

Sandnes Camping

www.alanrogers.com/no2628
sandnescamping@online.no
Tel: +47 98 88 73 66
www.sandnescamping.no

Open (Touring Pitches):
All year.

Sandnes Camping is located in the extreme south of Norway and makes a convenient stop-off point when arriving or departing for Denmark via Kristiansand. Just off the E39 road next to the Mandalselva or Marna River the site has an open aspect and around 50 firm grass pitches serviced by gravel roads. Two BBQ/fire pits provide a communal focus, as does the camper's kitchen. Five pitches are made available for reservation per day, though extended stays can be negotiated upon arrival.

The river is important for salmon breading, and a licence is required for fishing with a limited catch allowed and restrictions on bait types, more information and licences can be bought at reception. There is a small beach with a floating jetty available for swimming and boat rental is an option.

Several hiking trails can be found close to the site, and basic bicycles can be hired. The site has no playground, but a couple of push-along toys are available for smaller children. Older children are encouraged to make use of the forest.

Tables and benches are scattered throughout the site, with 2 more formal firepits available. 4 showers and 6 toilets along with a changing room for families and adapted facilities are available. The kitchen comprises a stove, fridge, freezer and dishwasher. A motorhome service point is available.

Key Features

 Open All Year

 Pets Accepted

 Disabled Facilities

 Bike Hire

 Fishing

Scan me for more information.

Capital Lisbon
Currency Euro (€)
Language Portuguese
Time Zone GMT
Telephone Code +351

Shops Hours vary throughout the year, with many shops operating on shorter hours in low and shoulder seasons. In high season 9.30am to noon and 2pm to 7pm Mon to Fri. 10am to 1pm Sat.

Money ATMs can be found in towns and cities, are accessible 24hrs a day and most have multilingual instructions. Less common in rural areas. Not everywhere accepts credit/debit cards so take cash just in case.

Travelling with children
Portugal has a lot to offer children. Lisbon has a good choice of attractions. The Algarve is one of the best destinations for kids with its long sandy beaches, zoos, water parks and boat trips.

Public Holidays 1 Jan New Year's Day; Mar/Apr Good Friday; Mar/Apr Easter Sunday; 25 Apr Liberation Day; 1 May Labour Day; 10 Jun National Day; May/Jun Corpus Christi; 15 Aug Assumption; 5 Oct Republic Day; 1 Nov All Saints; 1 Dec Independence Restoration Day; 8 Dec Imaculate Conception; 25 Dec Christmas Day.

♻ **LEZ** Low Emissions Zone in Lisbon. Registration required.

● EU Member | ● Schengen Area

Tourism website visitportugal.com

●●○○○ **Accessible Travel Score**

Access is limited but improving. Newer public buildings are required to cater for wheelchair users. Accessible parking spaces are available but are often occupied.

Driving in Portugal The standard of roads is very variable; even some of the main roads can be very uneven. Tolls are levied on some auto-estradas. An electronic tag called Via Verde can be purchased for repeat trips. Drink-driving and using a mobile whilst driving are illegal. Parked vehicles must face the same direction as moving traffic.

 Dashcams are **illegal**

 Speed camera detectors are **illegal**

Portugal

View all campsites in Portugal
alanrogers.com/portugal

See campsite map page 484

Climate Hot summers and mild winters with varied rainfall in north/south.

Emergency services Call 112 for the police, ambulance and fire and rescue.

Units Portugal uses the metric system. To convert km to miles, multiply by 0.6.

Portugal is the westernmost country of Europe, situated on the Iberian peninsula, bordered by Spain in the north and east, with the Atlantic coast in the south and west. Despite its relatively small size, the country offers a tremendous variety, both in its way of life and its history and traditions.

Every year the Algarve is the destination for some ten million sunseekers and watersports enthusiasts who love its sheltered sandy beaches and clear Atlantic sea. In contrast, the lush hills and forests of central Portugal are home to historic buildings and monuments, particularly the capital city of Lisbon, adjacent to the estuary of the River Tagus. Lisbon's history can still be seen in the Alfama quarter, which survived the devastating earthquake of 1755;

at night, the city comes alive with vibrant cafés, restaurants and discos.

The land becomes rather impoverished to the southeast of Lisbon, consisting of stretches of vast undulating plains dominated by cork plantations. Most people head for Evora, a medieval walled town and UNESCO World Heritage Site. The Minho area in the north is said to be the most beautiful part of Portugal, home to the country's only National Park and vineyards producing the famous Port wine.

Scan QR code to browse more campsites on our website

Alan Rogers Code: PO8370
16 accommodations
200 pitches
GPS: 41.76310, -8.19050
Post Code: P-4840 030

Campo do Gerês, Braga

Parque Cerdeira

www.alanrogers.com/po8370
info@parquecerdeira.com
Tel: +351 253 351 005
www.parquecerdeira.com

Open (Touring Pitches):
All year.

Located in the Peneda-Gerês National Park amidst spectacular mountain scenery, this excellent, well-run site offers modern facilities in a truly natural area. The national park is home to all manner of flora, fauna and wildlife, including the roebuck, wolf and wild boar. There's plenty of scope in the immediate area for fishing, riding, canoeing, mountain biking and climbing, so outdoorsy types take advantage of the quality mountain hospitality and enjoy the clear, fresh air and activities amidst the dramatic scenery.

The well-fenced, peaceful site offers 200 good-sized, unmarked, mostly level, grassy pitches in a shady woodland setting. Electricity (5/10A) is available for the touring pitches, though some long leads may be required. A very large timber complex, tastefully designed with the use of noble materials – granite and wood - provides a superb restaurant with a comprehensive menu.

Three clean, sanitary blocks provide mixed-style WCs, controllable showers and hot water. Good facilities for disabled visitors. Laundry. Gas supplies. Shop. Restaurant/bar. Outdoor pool (high season). Playground. TV room (satellite). Medical post. Good tennis courts. Minigolf. Adventure park. Car wash. Barbecue areas. Torches useful. English spoken. Attractive bungalows to rent. WiFi in reception/bar area.

Key Features

 Book Online

 Open All Year

 Pets Accepted

 Disabled Facilities

 Swimming Pool

 Play Area

 Bar/Restaurant

 Bike Hire

Scan me for
more information.

Alan Rogers Code: PO8040
35 accommodations
360 pitches
GPS: 40.55810, -8.74528
Post Code: 3840-254

Gafanha da Boa-Hora, Vagueira

www.alanrogers.com/po8040
infovagueira@orbitur.pt
Tel: +351 234 797 526
www.orbitur.com

Open (Touring Pitches):
All year.

Camping Vagueira

Within easy reach of an extensive beach, Orbitur Camping Vagueira is a large site shaded under tall pine trees behind the dunes. Pitches are on sandy soil with sparse grass, and the central area is fairly level. Elsewhere pitches are on sloping ground between the trees. Electrical connections (6A) are available throughout, although long leads may be needed.

The campsite lies in a pine forest 500 m from the Ria de Costa Nova, a delightful little village with traditional brightly painted houses and a colourful fish market. It's 1 km from Vagueira, 8 km from Vagos and 16 km from Aveiro and Ílhavo, with the nearest beaches being those of Vagueira and Areão, 1.5 km away and popular with surfers. Be sure to visit Vagos and its Sanctuary of Nossa Senhora de Vagos, the beautiful chapels of Senhora da Misericórdia, Santo António and the Torre Militar. The area's excellent gastronomy is another highlight.

Seven modern sanitary buildings, clean but fairly basic, mainly British-style WCs, open washbasins (some with warm water) and free showers. Facilities for disabled campers. Washing machines and dryer. Shop, bar/snacks and restaurant (March-Sept). Basic supplies from reception at other times. Outdoor disco (high season). Games room. Playground. Tennis (charged). Satellite TV. WiFi throughout (free). Torches useful.

Key Features

 Book Online

 Open All Year

 Pets Accepted

 Disabled Facilities

 Beach Access

 Swimming Pool

 Play Area

 Bar/Restaurant

Scan me for more information.

Alan Rogers Code: PO8077
750 pitches
GPS: 40.18802, -8.39890
Post Code: P-3030-011

Coimbra, Coimbra

www.alanrogers.com/po8077
coimbra@cacampings.com
Tel: +351 239 086 902
www.coimbracamping.com

Open (Touring Pitches):
All year.

Coimbra Camping

Situated just at the southern edge of the city, this all-year site is an excellent base for exploring Coimbra, an important university city and former capital of Portugal. Pitches are terraced, generally unshaded, reasonably sized, and most have electrical connections. Leisure facilities are impressive and include an attractive swimming pool with a sun terrace, paddling pool, beach volleyball, gym and an all-weather sports terrain. There is also a good restaurant here. The city centre can be easily accessed, thanks to the bus stop close to the site entrance, and excursions and guided walks are organised.

Coimbra enjoys a spectacular hilltop setting on a bend in the Mondego River and has a vibrant history dating back to Roman times. Its heyday was during the 12th and 13th centuries when it was Portugal's capital. The entire town centre features on UNESCO's world heritage list and boasts a remarkable array of civic buildings and elegant monuments, many linked with its ancient university. There are also many delightful shady parks, including one of the world's oldest botanical gardens, founded in 1772.

Swimming pool (additional cost). Paddling pool. Beach volleyball. Gym. Children's play area. All-weather sports terrain. Restaurant. Tourist information. Chalets and mobile homes to rent.

Key Features

 Book Online

 Open All Year

Scan me for more information.

Alan Rogers Code: PO8450
10 accommodations
320 pitches
GPS: 39.52283, -9.12300
Post Code: P-2460-697

São Martinho do Porto, Leiria

www.alanrogers.com/po8450
geral@colinadosol.net
Tel: +351 262 989 764
www.colinadosol.org

Open (Touring Pitches):
All year (excl. 25 December).

Colina do Sol

Parque de Campismo Colina do Sol is a spacious and well-appointed site situated close to a beach, and the village of São Martinho do Porto. It has around 320 touring pitches on grassy terraces, some marked by fruit and ornamental trees. Electricity (6A) is available, and there are numerous seasonal caravans. The attractive entrance, with its beds of bright flowers, is wide enough for even the largest of units.

The nearest beach is reached via a gate at the side of the site; it is a stiff walk and is described as 'wild and dangerous for swimming.' In the village, the beach is very safe, and there are some good shops, bars, restaurants and a market on Sundays. This is a convenient base for exploring the Costa de Prata and excursions to Leiria's charming old town. A short drive to the north is the fishing village of Nazaré, which has a long stretch of sandy beach with opportunities for watersports. To the south, the saltwater Lagoa de Óbidos also offers water sports, riding, and golf.

Two large, clean toilet blocks with showers, open-style washbasins (some with hot water) and British-style WCs (some with bidets). A third block is opened in the high season. Motorhome services. Supermarket. Small café (limited opening in low season). Bar and restaurant. Satellite TV. Swimming pool (high season). WiFi in some parts (free).

Key Features

 Pets Accepted

 Disabled Facilities

 Beach Access

 Swimming Pool

 Play Area

 Bar/Restaurant

Scan me for more information.

Alan Rogers Code: PO8120
100 accommodations
75 pitches
GPS: 38.97706, -9.41627
Post Code: P-2655-319

Ericeira, Lisbon

Ericeira Camping

www.alanrogers.com/po8120
info@ericeiracamping.com
Tel: +351 261 862 706
www.ericeiracamping.com

Open (Touring Pitches):
All year.

This site can be found to the north of the pretty fishing village of Ericeira, just 40 minutes north of Lisbon and 200 m. from the beach. The local beaches are magnificent, with sandy stretches and rugged outcrops, and are world-renowned for serious surfing. Pitches are of a good size, terraced and laid out on hard surfaces among the trees, though many have limited shade from the tall pines. Most have electrical connections (6A), and a range of mobile homes and cabins are available to rent. There is also a bar/restaurant with a terrace and a well-stocked shop.

Ericeira lies close to Mafra National Park, created by King João V for hunting and recreation, which extends over 2,000 acres of tree-clad hills, shallow rivers and forested walking trails. The park is home to wild boar, deer and various birds of prey. Nearby, Mafra's vast National Palace dwarfs the surrounding city and is one of Europe's largest 18th-century Baroque buildings and a Portuguese national monument. Ericeira is a pleasant resort with four beaches and a fine musical heritage with its Filarmónica Cultural dating back to 1849.

Key Features

 Open All Year

 Beach Access

 Swimming Pool

 Bar/Restaurant

The usual sanitary facilities are provided. Laundry. Motorhome services. Shop. Bar. Restaurant with terrace. Play area. Mobile homes, chalets and tents to rent.

Scan me for more information.

Alan Rogers Code: PO8355
2 accommodations
15 pitches
GPS: 39.41001, -7.34074
Post Code: 7330-204

Marvão, Portalegre

Camping Asseiceira

www.alanrogers.com/po8355
gary-campingasseiceira@hotmail.com
Tel: +351 245 992 940
www.campingasseiceira.com

Open (Touring Pitches):
Start January - End October.

Set amongst unspoilt mountain scenery in the spectacular Serra de São Mamede National Park, Camping Asseiceira is a British-owned site where visitors receive a warm welcome. The Spanish border is just eight kilometres away, and there's a historic frontier feel about this rugged, untamed region that was once strategically important. Arranged in a small olive grove are 15 touring pitches with 10A electricity available and five tent pitches. Views rise up to the spectacular medieval castle and the ancient town of Marvão, a real eagle's nest. This is a small, pleasant, well-cared-for site with few facilities, although the Santo António das Areias village is only a few minutes walk with shops, restaurants and a bank. There is plenty of cultural and historical sightseeing in the surrounding area.

Apart from the fascinating hilltop town of Marvão, the nearby village of Portagem has a Roman bridge, and there are also the remains of a Roman city at Ammaia. Nearby Beirã has an impressive railway station, a frontier post designed to impress arrivals on the now defunct line from Madrid to Lisbon; the ceramic murals depict typical scenes from the Alentejo region.

Key Features

 Pets Accepted

 Swimming Pool

 Bar/Restaurant

The shower block is equipped to a high standard. Hot water throughout. Baker calls daily. Swimming pool and terrace (May-Oct).

Scan me for more information.

Alan Rogers Code: PO8341
30 pitches
GPS: 38.60645, -7.34674
Post Code: P-7250-999

Rosário/Alandroal, Evora

www.alanrogers.com/po8341
info@campingrosario.com
Tel: +351 268 459 566
www.campingrosario.com

Open (Touring Pitches):
Early January - Start October.

Camping Rosário

This is a small, adult-only campsite tucked away in the charming Alentejo, about 60 km due east of ancient Evora. This is the jewel in the region's crown, with fabulous sightseeing, including the cathedral, elegant squares, Roman temple and Chapel of Bones for starters. There's so much cultural richness that the whole town is recognised as a UNESCO World Heritage site. The nearest village is Rosário, just 2 km away.

The campsite setting is rural and peaceful, surrounded by countless olive trees on the rolling hillsides. Pitches (all 6A) are of a good size, and level and benefit from the shade provided by the olive trees dotted about. There's plenty to do, including fishing, bird watching, wine tasting, star gazing (this is an internationally recognised Dark Sky Reserve), canoeing and wonderful hiking around the vast Lake Alqueva. A simple but pleasant swimming pool is most welcome for cooling off on hot days.

Centrally positioned sanitary block equipped with separate hot showers, lavatories, chemical disposal and the option of doing laundry and washing up. Charcoal barbecue for communal use. Drinks and snacks are served in the shade of the veranda or underneath the orange trees of the farmhouse terrace. Comfortable lounge with TV, books, games and a charging station for your portable devices.

Key Features

 Adults Only

 Pets Accepted

 Swimming Pool

 Bar/Restaurant

 Fishing

Scan me for more information.

Alan Rogers Code: PO8180
221 accommodations
740 pitches
GPS: 37.73190, -8.78301
Post Code: P-7645-300

Vila Nova de Milfontes, Beja

www.alanrogers.com/po8180
geral@campingmilfontes.com
Tel: +351 283 996 140
www.campingmilfontes.com

Open (Touring Pitches):
All year.

Camping Milfontes

This popular site is within walking distance of the beach and the town, with a covered market, shops, bars and restaurants. There are opportunities for watersports, fishing, canoeing and swimming from the resort beaches. Well-lit and fenced, the site has around 900 shady pitches (740 for touring units) on sandy terrain, many marked out and divided by hedges. There is an area, mainly for motorhomes, where you park under the trees. Some pitches are small, and cars may have to be parked in an internal car park. Electricity (6A) is available throughout.

Milfontes is located in the Parque Natural do Sudoeste Alentejano, and there are wonderful opportunities for walking and cycling along the numerous marked paths. The park extends away to the south for over 80 km. and flora and fauna are magnificent. Even at the height of the season, it is possible to find almost deserted beaches along the Costa Vicentina.

Four well-maintained toilet blocks, two with en-suite units for disabled visitors with ramped entrances. Mainly British-style WCs, bidets, washbasins (some with hot water), controllable showers and limited facilities for children. Laundry. Motorhome services. Supermarket, bar, snacks and takeaway (all seasonal). Outdoor pool (High season). TV room. Playground. Car wash. Gas supplies. WiFi throughout (free).

Key Features

 Open All Year

 Pets Accepted

 Disabled Facilities

 Beach Access

 Swimming Pool

 Play Area

 Bar/Restaurant

Scan me for more information.

Alan Rogers Code: PO8202
132 accommodations
240 pitches
GPS: 37.10111, -8.73278
Post Code: P-8600-109

Lagos, Faro

Turiscampo Algarve

www.alanrogers.com/po8202
info@turiscampo.com
Tel: +351 282 789 265
www.turiscampo.com

Open (Touring Pitches):
All year.

Yelloh! Village Turiscampo is an outstanding site run by the friendly Coll family. It's wonderful for children, with very good activities, but also 'snow birds' over winter. The site provides 240 pitches for touring units, mainly in rows of terraces, 197 of which have 6/10A electricity, some with shade. There are 43 deluxe pitches with water and drain. 132 bungalows for rent occupy the upper terraces.

Just down the road is the fashionable resort of Praia de Luz, with a beach, shops, bars and restaurants. Head west, and the road takes you to Sagres and the western tip of the Algarve. Portugal's 'Land's End' remains unspoilt, with numerous rocky coves and little sandy beaches to explore. A member of Leading Campings and Yelloh! Village groups.

Two excellent heated toilet blocks with a third facility beneath the pool. Spacious controllable showers, hot water throughout. Children & baby room. Facilities for disabled visitors. Dog shower. Laundry facilities. Shop. Gas supplies. Modern restaurant/bar with buffet & some theme party dinners. Pizza bar & takeaway. Swimming pools (All year) with extensive terrace & Jacuzzi. Aquagym. Wellness facility. Bicycle hire. Entertainment on the bar terrace. Miniclub. Two playgrounds. Boules. Archery. Multisports court, WiFi (Partial coverage) on payment.

Key Features

 Book Online

 Open All Year

 Pets Accepted

 Disabled Facilities

 Beach Access

 Swimming Pool

 Play Area

 Bar/Restaurant

Scan me for more information.

388

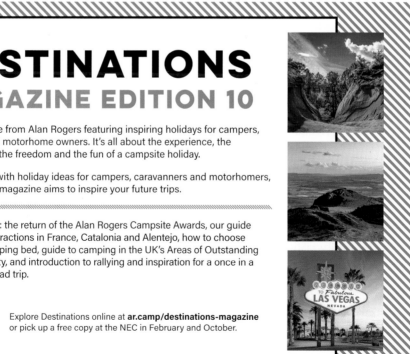

Alan Rogers Code: PO8210
28 accommodations
1400 pitches
GPS: 37.10639, -8.25361
Post Code: P-8200-555

Albufeira, Faro

Camping Albufeira

www.alanrogers.com/po8210
geral@campingalbufeira.net
Tel: +351 289 587 629
www.campingalbufeira.pt/en

Open (Touring Pitches):
All year.

Here's a very pleasant, well-run site, close to bustling Faro and with a bus service to the resort of Albufeira from the gate. There's space for 1400 touring units on generally flat ground with some terracing on the upper area: trees and shrubs giving reasonable shade in most parts. Pitches are not marked or numbered; you can take as much space as you wish. Electrical connections (10A) are available throughout. Winter stays are encouraged, with the main facilities remaining open, including a pool.

An attractively designed complex of traditional Portuguese-style buildings on the hill houses an impressive range of restaurants and bars with the popular pool complex adjacent. It has large sunbathing terraces with pleasant views and is surrounded by a variety of flowers, shrubs and well-watered lawns, complete with a fountain.

Very clean and spacious toilet blocks include hot showers and open-style washbasins (hot water to some). Launderette. Motorhome services. Very large supermarket. Kiosk (English papers). Waiter and self-service restaurants. Pizzeria. Bars. The main facilities are open all year. Swimming pools. Satellite TV. Soundproofed disco. Tennis. Playground. Bicycle hire. WiFi over part of the site (charged). First aid post with a doctor nearby. Car wash. ATM. Car hire.

Key Features

 Open All Year

 Pets Accepted

 Disabled Facilities

 Beach Access

 Swimming Pool

 Play Area

 Bar/Restaurant

Bike Hire

Scan me for more information.

Alan Rogers Code: PO8231
55 accommodations
240 pitches
GPS: 37.14332, -7.60392
Post Code: P-8800-058

Cabanas de Tavira, Algarve

Camping Ria Formosa

www.alanrogers.com/po8231
info@campingriaformosa.com
Tel: +351 281 328 887
www.campingriaformosa.com

Open (Touring Pitches):
All year.

Not far east of Faro, Camping Ria Formosa is situated very close to a true natural paradise, the Parque Natural da Ria Formosa. This is one of the few in Europe to be so well-preserved, and the beaches here are magnificent. The campsite is just a 20-minute walk from the local village of Cabanas with its shops, bars and restaurants. Here you can take a ferry across to the island, which is essentially a long spit of stunning soft, white sand.

The site has 295 pitches (240 for tourers) all with an electrical connection and modest shade from the small trees and shrubs that delimit the hard-standing pitches. Bus services provide regular access to many of the Algarve highlights, such as the regional capital of Faro and colourful Olhao - much more convenient than driving yourself. The site is open all year and is a popular choice over winter for those wishing to enjoy an extended stay in the winter sunshine.

Key Features

 Open All Year

 Pets Accepted

 Disabled Facilities

 Beach Access

 Swimming Pool

 Play Area

 Bar/Restaurant

Two toilet blocks with hot and cold water, shower cubicles, toilets and washbasins. Facilities for guests who are disabled. Laundry. Mini Market. Restaurant. Takeaway. Mini Gym. Reading Room. Swimming pools for adults and children. Children's play area. Boules pitch. Barbecues allowed. Artificial lake. Motorhome service point. Late-night arrivals area. Beach 1km. Dogs allowed. WiFi free.

Scan me for more information.

Capital Ljubljana
Currency Euro (€)
Language Slovene
Time Zone CET (GMT+1)
Telephone Code +386

Shops Hours vary throughout the year, with many shops operating on shorter hours in low and shoulder seasons. In high season 8am to 7pm Mon to Fri, and until 1pm Sat.

Money ATMs are widespread and accessible 24hrs a day. Most places will accept credit/debit cards. If you're paying in cash, many businesses won't accept large denominations (over €50) for smaller purchases.

Travelling with children Great during the summer months. Most regions have castles that children will love exploring. Some attractions offer free entry for minors. Most restaurants cater for children.

Public Holidays 1 Jan New Year's Day; 8 Feb Prešeren Day; Mar/Apr Easter Sunday; Mar/Apr Easter Monday; 27 Apr Resistence Day; 1 May May Day; May/Jun Whit Sunday; 25 Jun National Day; 15 Aug Assumption; 31 Oct Reformation Day; 1 Nov All Saints; 25 Dec Christmas Day; 26 Dec Independence & Unity Day.

There are no Low Emission Zones currently in place.

● EU Member | ● Schengen Area

Tourism website slovenia.info

●●●●● **Accessible Travel Score**

Generally well-equipped with Ljubljana leading in most areas. Public transport and buildings are fully accessible and car parks have reserved spaces.

Driving in Slovenia A small but expanding network of motorways. You will need to display a vignette as proof of payment to use motorways. You shouldn't indicate when entering a roundabout but must do so when leaving one. Winter driving equipment is mandatory between November and March. Headlights must be on at all times. Speed camera detection equipment isn't banned but is advised against. Drink-driving and using a mobile whilst driving are illegal.

 Dashcams are legal

 Speed camera detectors are legal

Slovenia

View all campsites in Slovenia
alanrogers.com/slovenia

See campsite map page 474

Climate Cold, sometimes snowy winters and warm summers.

Emergency services Call 112 for the police, ambulance and fire and rescue.

Units Slovenia uses the metric system. To convert km to miles, multiply by 0.6.

What Slovenia lacks in size, it makes up for in exceptional beauty. Situated between Italy, Austria, Hungary and Croatia, it has a diverse landscape; mountains, rivers, forests and the warm Adriatic coast.

Mount Triglav is at the heart of the snow-capped Julian Alps, a paradise for lovers of the great outdoors, with hiking, rafting, and mountaineering opportunities. From the Alps down to the Adriatic coast, the Karst region is home to the famous Lipizzaner horses, vineyards and myriad underground caves, including the Postojna and Skocjan Caves.

The tiny Adriatic coast has several bustling beach towns, including Koper, Slovenia's only commercial port, whose 500 years of Venetian rule is evident in its Italianate style. Ljubljana, one of Europe's smallest capitals with beautiful baroque buildings, lies on the Ljubljanica river, spanned by numerous bridges, including Jože Plečnik's triple bridge.

Heading eastwards, the hilly landscape is dotted with monasteries, churches and castles, including the 13th century Zuzemberk castle, one of Slovenia's most picturesque. The old city and castle sit alongside a thriving commercial centre. The Posavje region produces cviček, a famous blend of white and red wines.

Scan QR code to browse more campsites on our website

Alan Rogers Code: SV4200
8 accommodations
244 pitches
GPS: 46.36155, 14.08075
Post Code: SLO-4260

Bled, Slovenia

www.alanrogers.com/sv4200
info@camping-bled.com
Tel: +386 4575 2000
www.camping-bled.com

Open (Touring Pitches):
Start April - Mid October.

Camping Bled

Camping Bled is situated on the western tip of Lake Bled and is an excellent example of how a site should be run, check-in is quick and efficient, and English is spoken. The site is large but well-spaced, with 244 touring pitches, all with electric, 40 fully serviced pitches and six with private sanitary facilities; most pitches benefit from shade. Pitches at the front are used mainly for overnighters. There are lovely views across the lake toward its famous island. This site is well-organised, and the facilities are modern and spotless.

You have direct access to Lake Bled, which does not disappoint if you wish to enjoy the view. The waterfront here has a small public beach immediately behind, which runs a gently sloping narrow wooded valley. A bar/Restaurant/Coffee & Cake shop on site overlooks the lake. If you are feeling more active, walking or cycling around the lake is a good option, or rent a picnic basket, hire a rowing boat and enjoy a relaxing afternoon.

Key Features

 Book Online

 Pets Accepted

 Disabled Facilities

 Play Area

 Bar/Restaurant

 Bike Hire

 Fishing

Toilet facilities in five blocks are of a high standard (with free hot showers). Three blocks are heated. Private bathrooms for rent. Solar energy is used. Washing machines and dryers. Motorhome services. Gas supplies. Fridge hire. Supermarket. Restaurant. Play area and children's zoo. Games area. Trampolines. Organised activities in July/Aug, including children's club, excursions and sporting activities. Mountain bike tours. Live entertainment. Fishing. Bicycle hire. Free WiFi.

Scan me for
more information.

Alan Rogers Code: SV4370
50 pitches
GPS: 46.23332, 14.56664
Post Code: SLO-1240

Kamnik, Slovenia

www.alanrogers.com/sv4370
info@kampresnik.com
Tel: +386 4143 5380
www.kampresnik.com

Open (Touring Pitches):
Early May - Late September.

Camp Resnik

Just an hour's drive north of Ljubljana, this is a simple campsite with pleasant grassy pitches scattered among tall trees, which help create a restful ambience. Although the actual camping area is not large, it is on the edge of a much larger meadow, with a sports centre adjoining. Opposite the site is a friendly bar/café. The site may be rather unprepossessing, comprising a small open field with two very basic prefabricated toilet units, but these are spectacular surroundings.

The Kamnik Alps form an epic backdrop, grandiose and dramatic, with summits of 2,000 metres. There are wonderful hiking and cycling trails in the area, taking you through sublime scenery, and many routes start at the campsite. Just ask for advice at the reception. Nobody should visit central Slovenia without stopping off to wander around the medieval, rural town of Kamnik, which was once Ljubljana's main trade rival. It's delightful and is only five minutes walk from the campsite. A popular excursion is to Velika Planina, one of Europe's oldest highland pastures, with its traditional mountain houses and grazing cattle in the summer.

Two very basic prefabricated toilet units. Shop. The site is part of the Kamnik sports centre, which boasts a large swimming pool and many tennis, badminton and squash courts. Free WiFi throughout.

Key Features

 Swimming Pool

 Play Area

Scan me for
more information.

Alan Rogers Code: SV4410
150 accommodations
300 pitches
GPS: 46.67888, 16.22165
Post Code: SLO-9226

Moravske Toplice, Slovenia

Camping Terme 3000

www.alanrogers.com/sv4410
recepcija.camp2@terme3000.si
Tel: +386 2512 1200
www.terme3000.si

Open (Touring Pitches):
All year.

Camping Terme 3000 lies next to the renowned thermal springs of Prekmurje. It's a large site with over 400 pitches. Three hundred are for touring units (all with 16A electricity, 30 with hardstanding), the remaining pitches being taken by seasonal campers. On a grass and gravel surface (hard tent pegs may be needed), the level, numbered pitches are of 50-100 sq.m. The site is part of an enormous thermal spa and fun pool complex (free entry to campers) under the same name. There are over 5,000 sq.m. of water activities – swimming, jet streams, waterfalls, water massages, four water slides (the longest is 170 m.) and thermal baths.

The complex prides itself on its gastronomic offerings, with a range of bars, restaurants, and even a large golf course. Once you have had enough of the 14 indoor and outdoor pools, you could go walking or cycling through the surrounding woods and fields or try the delicious wines of the Goricko region. The site is open all year, so perhaps a great choice for some winter R&R and spa treatments in comfortable surroundings.

Modern and clean toilet facilities provide British style toilets, open washbasins and controllable, free hot showers. Laundry facilities. Football field. Tennis. Water gymnastics. Daily activity programme for children. Golf. WiFi (charged).

Key Features

 Book Online

 Open All Year

 Pets Accepted

 Swimming Pool

 Play Area

 Bar/Restaurant

 Bike Hire

 Golf

Scan me for more information.

Camping Terme Catez

Alan Rogers Code: SV4415
472 accommodations
250 pitches
GPS: 45.89137, 15.62598
Post Code: SLO-8251

Catez ob Savi, Slovenia

www.alanrogers.com/sv4415
info@terme-catez.si
Tel: +386 7493 6700
www.terme-catez.si

Open (Touring Pitches):
All year.

Terme Catez is part of the modern Catez thermal spa, which includes very large and attractive indoor (31°C) and outdoor swimming complexes, among the largest waterparks in Europe, with large slides and waves. The campsite has 700 pitches, with 250 places for tourers, arranged on one large, open field with some young trees – a real sun trap – and provides level, grass pitches numbered by markings on the tarmac access roads. All have 10A electricity connections.

Although the site is ideally placed for an overnight stop, it is well worth spending some time here and indulging in the excellent facilities that are included in the overnight camping charges. Off-site, go hiking in the Gorjanci Mountains and explore this delightful region's castles, vineyards and unspoilt nature.

Two modern toilet blocks with British-style toilets, washbasins in cabins, and large, controllable hot showers. Washbasins for children. Facilities for disabled visitors. Laundry facilities. Motorhome services. Supermarket. Kiosks for fruit, newspapers, souvenirs and tobacco. Attractive restaurant with a buffet. Bar with terrace. Large indoor and outdoor (high season) swimming complexes. Sauna. Solarium. Rowing boats. Jogging track. Fishing. Golf. Riding. Organised activities. Video games. Bicycle hire. WiFi throughout (free).

Key Features

 Open All Year

 Pets Accepted

 Disabled Facilities

 Swimming Pool

 Play Area

 Bar/Restaurant

 Bike Hire

 Fishing

Scan me for more information.

Alan Rogers Code: SV4330
24 accommodations
300 pitches
GPS: 45.79068, 14.19092
Post Code: SLO-6230

Postojna, Slovenia

www.alanrogers.com/sv4330
avtokamp.pivka.jama@siol.net
Tel: +386 5720 3993
www.camping-postojna.com

Open (Touring Pitches):
Mid April - Late October.

Camping Pivka Jama

Postojna, in the Notranjska region of southwest Slovenia, is renowned for its extraordinary limestone caves, forming one of the country's prime tourist attractions. Staff at reception can arrange day trip excursions to the Postojna Caves for a fascinating insight into their formation. The Pivka Cave is just adjacent to the campsite restaurant, with 317 steps leading down to an underground river and a 65m gorge. The visitors' trail leads up the river before opening out into the magnificent Depression Hall with exquisite stalagmites and stalactites.

This is a peaceful, wooded spot and a great base for exploring the beautiful scenery of this region and historic places like the Predjama Castle (9 km), one of the world's largest cave-based fortresses. The campsite's 300 pitches are well dispersed amongst the trees and in small clearings, all connected by a neat network of paths and slip roads. Some level, gravel hardstandings are provided.

Key Features

 Book Online

 Pets Accepted

 Swimming Pool

 Play Area

 Bar/Restaurant

 Bike Hire

Two toilet blocks with very good facilities. Washing machines. Motorhome services. Campers' kitchen with hobs. Supermarket (High season). Bar/restaurant. Swimming and paddling pools (High season). Tennis. Table tennis. Volleyball. Bicycle hire. Fishing. Riding. Bird watching. Day trips to Postojna Caves and other excursions can be organised. WiFi.

Scan me for more information.

Alan Rogers Code: SV4310
150 accommodations
300 pitches
GPS: 45.57797, 13.73633
Post Code: SLO-6280

Ankaran, Slovenia

www.alanrogers.com/sv4310
booking@adria-ankaran.si
Tel: +386 056 637 350
www.adria-ankaran.si

Open (Touring Pitches):
Mid April - Mid October.

Camping Adria

Camping Adria is on the south side of the Milje/Muggia peninsula, right on the shore of the Adriatic Sea and just beyond the port. It has a concrete promenade with access to the sea, complemented by an Olympic size pool (June-September) with a children's pool, both filled with seawater. The site has 450 pitches (300 for tourers), all with 10A electricity, set up on one side of the site close to the sea. Pitches are off tarmac access roads running down to the sea; most are between 80 and 90 sq.m, and six are fully serviced.

This part of the Slovenian Riviera has much to offer architecturally and culturally, and you can visit the Adria hotel (once the Benedictine monastery of St Nicholas). Although the port facilities are visible from part of the site, this does not detract from its overall attractiveness.

Five modern toilet blocks with British and Turkish-style toilets, and open-style washbasins. Free hot and cold water, controllable showers. Facilities for disabled visitors. Laundry room. Fridge box hire. Supermarket. Beach shop. Newspaper kiosk. Bar/restaurant with terrace. Swimming pool (40x15 m) with large slide. Wellness centre. Riding (July/Aug). A playground on gravel. Playing field. Tennis. Beach ball. Volleyball. Basketball. Minigolf. Fishing. Jetty for mooring boats. Boat launching. Bowling club. WiFi (charged).

Key Features

 Book Online

 Pets Accepted

 Disabled Facilities

 Beach Access

 Swimming Pool

 Play Area

 Bar/Restaurant

 Bike Hire

Scan me for more information.

Capital Madrid
Currency Euro (€)
Language Spanish and six co-official regional variants
Time Zone CET (GMT+1)
Telephone Code +34

Shops Hours vary throughout the year, Many shops operating shorter hours in low season. In high season 10am to 2pm and 5pm to 9pm Mon to Fri, 10am to 2pm Sat. Supermarkets 9am to 9pm Mon to Sat.

Money ATMs are widespread, accessible 24hrs a day and most have multilingual instructions. You should bring cash for emergencies. When paying with a credit/debit card, you will often be asked to show ID.

Travelling with children Spain is family-friendly and has a good range of attractions. Many restaurants cater well for kids and beaches are safe. Extremely hot during the summer, weather remains warm well into October.

Public Holidays 1 Jan New Year's Day; 6 Jan Epiphany; Mar/Apr Maundy Thursday; Mar/Apr Good Friday; Mar/Apr Easter Sunday; 1 May Labour Day; 16 Jun Corpus Christi; 15 Aug Assumption; 12 Oct Fiesta Nacional de España; 1 Nov All Saints; 6 Dec Constitution Day; 8 Dec Imaculate Conception; 25 Dec Christmas Day.

♻ **LEZ** Low Emissions Zones in all major cities. Registration required.

● EU Member | ● Schengen Area

Tourism website spain.info

●●●○○ **Accessible Travel Score**

There is a push to improve accessibility, with Barcelona leading the way. Buildings and transport in other major cities are adapting.

Driving in Spain The surface of main roads is generally good. Certain roads use tolls. You can buy an electronic tag called Via T for repeat trips. If your caravan or motorhome exceeds 12m, you must display one long or two short reflectors at the rear. Drink-driving, using a mobile whilst driving and using the horn in urban areas are illegal.

 Dashcams are legal

 Speed camera detectors are legal

Spain

View all campsites in Spain
alanrogers.com/spain

See campsite map pages 478, 484, 485

Climate Temperate in the north, dry and hot in the centre, hot along the Med coast.

Emergency services Call 112 for the police, ambulance and fire and rescue.

Units Spain uses the metric system. To convert km to miles, multiply by 0.6.

One of the largest countries in Europe with glorious beaches, a fantastic sunshine record, vibrant towns and laid back sleepy villages, plus a diversity of landscape, culture and artistic traditions, Spain has all the ingredients for a great holiday.

Spain's vast and diverse coastline is a magnet for visitors; glitzy, hedonistic resorts packed with bars and clubs are a foil to secluded coves backed by wooded cliffs.

Yet Spain has much more to offer – the verdant north with its ancient pilgrimage routes where the Picos de Europa sweep down to the Atlantic gems of Santander and Bilbao. Vibrant Madrid in the heart of the country boasts the Prado with works by Velázquez and Goya, the beautiful cobbled Plaza Major, plus all the attractions of a capital city.

Passionate Andalucía in the sun-soaked south dazzles with the symbolic art of flamenco. It offers the cosmopolitan cities of Córdoba, Cádiz and Málaga, alongside magnificent examples of the past such as the Alhambra at Granada and the awe-inspiring Alcázar, a magical Moorish palace with scents of orange and Jasmine wafting through the air, a must-see in dreamy Seville. On the Mediterranean east coast, Valencia has a wealth of monuments and cultural sites, including the magnificent City of Arts and Science.

Scan QR code to browse more campsites on our website

Alan Rogers Code: ES80360
100 accommodations
140 pitches
GPS: 42.18166, 2.79499
Post Code: E-17832

Girona, Cataluña-Catalunya

www.alanrogers.com/es80360
informa@campingesponella.com
Tel: +34 972 59 70 74
www.campingesponella.com

Open (Touring Pitches):
All year.

Camping Esponellà

This large campsite has a lovely setting alongside a slow-flowing river against a backdrop of stunning cliffs and tree-covered slopes. 240 small to medium-sized pitches are scattered amongst the trees, 140 for touring, all with 5A electricity. Many are fully serviced (water, drainage and electricity).

The older part of the campsite houses a well-stocked shop and a bar/restaurant adjacent to the swimming pools. A small stream runs along the lower side, which can be seen from the pool and restaurant area, which faces the swimming pool complex, which acts as the main hub. This is a peaceful, rural area north of Girona, with excellent walking and cycling opportunities and just 30 km from the wonderful beaches of the Costa Brava.

Two old toilet blocks, a smaller one with only toilets and washbasins near the rental accommodation and a newer one at the front part of the site. Some washbasins with only cold water. Small shop (Easter-Sept). An attractive restaurant with a terrace, serving traditional Mediterranean cuisine, adjacent bar and takeaway (all year). Three heated swimming pools (all year). Play area. Boules. Minigolf. Tennis. Children's activities. Small disco. Fishing, swimming and kayaking in the river. Bicycle and kayak hire. Free WiFi in the bar area. Communal barbecue area (not allowed on pitches).

Key Features

 Book Online

 Open All Year

 Pets Accepted

 Beach Access

 Swimming Pool

 Play Area

 Bar/Restaurant

 Bike Hire

Scan me for more information.

Alan Rogers Code: ES80330
30 accommodations
230 pitches
GPS: 42.18805, 3.10270
Post Code: E-17470

Girona, Cataluña-Catalunya

www.alanrogers.com/es80330
info@campinglaspalmeras.com
Tel: +34 972 52 05 06
www.campinglaspalmeras.com

Open (Touring Pitches):
Start April - End October.

Camping Las Palmeras

A very welcoming, open site that is attractive and well-maintained. The 230 grass pitches are flat and well maintained, with some shade and 10A electricity. Ten pitches also have water and drainage. Thirty smart mobile homes are placed unobtrusively at one end of the site. A pleasant pool complex, fringed by attractive palm trees, has a lifeguard, and the brightly coloured play areas are clean and safe.

It's just 200 metres walk from a great beach, noted for watersports, which is part of the arc of magnificent sand known as the Platja Sant Pere Pescador, which runs along this sunny coastline. The area is generally flat and makes it ideal for gentle cycling and walking excursions through the surrounding countryside of the adjacent Natural Park of Aiguamolls de l'Empordà and the sleepy little villages.

Two excellent, spotless, solar-powered toilet blocks include first-class facilities for disabled campers. Baby rooms. Facilities may become a little busy at peak periods. Washing machines. Motorhome services. Supermarket, restaurant/bar/takeaway open all season (children's menu). Swimming pools (heated). Play areas. Tennis. Five-a-side. Fronton. Boules. Gym. Barbecue. Bicycle hire. Miniclub. Entertainment. Satellite TV. Internet. WiFi over site (charged). ATM. Torches useful.

Key Features

 Book Online

 Pets Accepted

 Disabled Facilities

 Beach Access

 Swimming Pool

 Play Area

 Bar/Restaurant

 Bike Hire

Scan me for more information.

Alan Rogers Code: ES80350
152 accommodations
720 pitches
GPS: 42.18147, 3.10405
Post Code: E-17470

Girona, Cataluña-Catalunya

www.alanrogers.com/es80350
info@campingamfora.com
Tel: +34 972 52 05 40
www.en.campingamfora.com

Open (Touring Pitches):
Mid April - Late September.

Camping l'Amfora

This spacious, friendly site is run by Michelle, Josep and their daughter and is always a popular destination. It is spotlessly clean and well-maintained, and the owners operate the site in an environmentally friendly way. There are 872 level grass pitches (720 for touring units) laid out in a grid system, all with 10A electricity.

Attractive trees and shrubs have been planted around each pitch. There is good shade in the more mature areas, which include 64 large pitches (180 sq.m), each with an individual sanitary unit (toilet, shower and washbasin). The newer area is more open with less shade; you can choose which you prefer.

Three excellent sanitary blocks, one heated, provide washbasins in cabins and roomy, free showers. Baby rooms. Laundry facilities and service. Motorhome services. Supermarket. Terraced bar, self-service and waiter-service restaurants. Pizzeria/takeaway. Restaurant and bar on the beach with a limited menu (high season). Disco bar. Swimming pools with two long waterslides (seasonal) as also a spa area. Pétanque. Tennis. Minigolf. Play area. Miniclub. Entertainment and activities. Windsurfing. Kite surfing (low season). Sailing, kayaking, fishing. Games rooms. Bicycle hire. Internet room and WiFi over site (charged). Car wash. Torches are required in most areas.

Key Features

 Book Online

 Pets Accepted

 Disabled Facilities

 Beach Access

 Swimming Pool

 Play Area

 Bar/Restaurant

 Bike Hire

Scan me for more information.

Av. Josep Tarradellas, 2, 17470 Sant Pere Pescador, Girona
972 52 05 40 | info@campingamfora.com | www.campingamfora.com

Alan Rogers Code: ES80400
175 accommodations
1500 pitches
GPS: 42.16098, 3.10777
Post Code: E-17470

Girona, Cataluña-Catalunya

www.alanrogers.com/es80400
info@campinglasdunas.com
Tel: +34 972 52 17 17
www.campinglasdunas.com

Open (Touring Pitches):
Mid May - Mid September.

Camping Las Dunas

Las Dunas is an extremely large, impressive and well-organised resort-style site with many on-site activities and an ongoing programme of improvements. The site has direct access to a superb sandy beach that stretches along the site for nearly a kilometre, with a windsurfing school and beach bar. There is also a much-used, huge swimming pool, plus a large double pool for children.

Las Dunas has around 1,700 individual hedged pitches (1,500 for touring units) of around 100 sq.m. laid out on flat ground in long, regular parallel rows. All have electricity (6/10A), and 400 have water and drainage.

Five excellent large toilet blocks with electronic sliding glass doors. Toilets without seats, controllable hot showers and washbasins in cabins. Excellent facilities for children, babies and disabled campers. Laundry facilities. Motorhome services. Supermarket, boutique and other shops. Large bar with terrace. Large restaurant & takeaway. Ice cream parlour. Beach bar (seasonal). Disco club. Swimming pools. Adventure crazy golf. Playgrounds. Tennis. Minigolf. Sailing/windsurfing school and other watersports. Programme of sports, games, excursions and entertainment, partly in English. Exchange facilities. ATM. Safety deposit. Internet café. WiFi over site (charged). Dogs accepted in one section. Torches are required in some areas.

Key Features

 Pets Accepted

 Disabled Facilities

 Beach Access

 Swimming Pool

 Play Area

 Bar/Restaurant

 Bike Hire

Fishing

Scan me for
more information.

CAMPING LAS DUNAS
CAMPING BUNGALOWPARK
www.campinglasdunas.com

COSTA BRAVA
SPAIN

SEASIDE HOLIDAY PARADISE FOR THE WHOLE FAMILY!

Camping & Bungalow Park located right at one of the most beautiful beaches in the Bay of Rosas. Offers a large variety of entertainment and activities for all ages, state-of-the-art sanitary facilities and a large shopping centre. AQUAPARK with slides guarantees fun and relax for the whole family.

Camping Las Dunas
17130 L'Escala (Girona)
Tel. +34 972 521 717
info@campinglasdunas.com
www.campinglasdunas.com

Alan Rogers Code: ES81400
165 accommodations
371 pitches
GPS: 41.83631, 3.08711
Post Code: E-17250

Girona, Cataluña-Catalunya

www.alanrogers.com/es81400
info@campingtreumal.com
Tel: +34 972 65 10 95
www.campingtreumal.com

Open (Touring Pitches):
Mid March - End September.

Camping Treumal

This beautiful terraced site has been developed on a hillside around the beautiful gardens of a large, spectacular estate house which is close to the sea. The floral displays in summer are quite something. The house is the focus of the site's excellent facilities, including a superb restaurant with terraces overlooking two tranquil beaches protected in pretty coves. Several excellent walking and cycling trails lead from the campsite entrance and invite guests to explore this rural hinterland.

The site has 536 pitches on well-shaded terraces. Of these, 371 are accessible to touring units, and there are some 50 pitches on flat ground alongside the sea – the views are stunning, and you wake to the sound of the waves. Electricity (6/10/16A) is available in all parts. Cars must be left in car parks or the site roads.

Four well-maintained sanitary blocks have free hot water in the washbasins (with some private cabins), controllable showers, and a tap to draw from for the sinks. No facilities for disabled visitors. Beachside sanitary block. Washing machines. Motorhome services. Gas supplies. Supermarket, bar and takeaway (all season). Restaurant (seasonal). Beach bar. Fishing. Play area. Sports area. Games room. Bicycle hire. Satellite TV. Internet access and WiFi (charged). ATM. Safes. Dogs are not accepted.

Key Features

Beach Access

Swimming Pool

Play Area

Bar/Restaurant

Bike Hire

Fishing

Sailing

Scan me for more information.

Alan Rogers Code: ES80220
280 accommodations
200 pitches
GPS: 41.66202, 2.78043
Post Code: E-17300

Girona, Cataluña-Catalunya

Camping Solmar

www.alanrogers.com/es80220
campingsolmar@campingsolmar.com
Tel: +34 972 34 80 34
www.campingsolmar.com

Open (Touring Pitches):
Mid March - Mid October.

The Ribas family has run Camping Solmar for over 40 years, and a warm welcome awaits you. The well-equipped site is located 150 metres from a sandy beach in the busy resort of Blanes and is sprinkled with palm trees. The accessible, shaded pitches are 65-85 sq.m., and all have 6A electricity connections. On-site amenities include an attractive restaurant, bar and terrace area, and a central swimming pool complex with islands and bridges.

A children's club operates in the peak season (4-12 years), and an outdoor complex of sports facilities is available. A range of fully equipped mobile homes and wooden chalets are available for rent. Regular excursions are available in the town to all the area's main attractions, including Barcelona (65 km) and the Dalí museum in Figueres. The town has a wide range of attractions, including some memorable fireworks displays.

Key Features

 Pets Accepted

 Beach Access

 Swimming Pool

 Play Area

Y Bar/Restaurant

Four toilet blocks are clean and have open-style washbasins, controllable showers in cabins and baby baths. Facilities for disabled visitors. Washing machines. Motorhome services. Supermarket. Restaurant. Bar. Swimming pool and terrace complex. Outdoor sports complex. Play areas. Miniclub (June onwards). Evening entertainment (high season). Tourist information and excursions. WiFi over site (charged). Mobile homes and chalets for rent.

Scan me for more information.

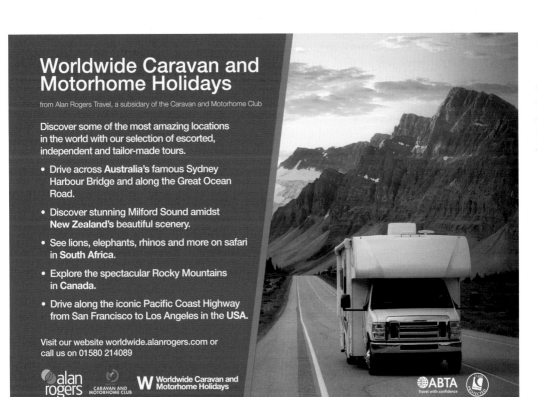

Alan Rogers Code: ES82100
130 accommodations
209 pitches
GPS: 41.69720, 2.82170
Post Code: E-17310

Girona, Cataluña-Catalunya

Camping Tucan

www.alanrogers.com/es82100
info@campingtucan.com
Tel: +34 972 36 99 65
www.campingtucan.com

Open (Touring Pitches):
Start April - Late September.

Situated on the busy Costa Brava at Lloret de Mar, north of Barcelona, Camping Tucan is well-placed to access all the attractions of the area and the town itself. The site has a friendly, family-orientated approach, with a children's multisports pitch, water slides and various water features in the attractive pool area and an all-season children's activity programme that complements a wide range of sports activities for all ages. It is set back slightly from the wonderful coastline, with sandy beaches and rocky little coves that will delight youngsters.

The campsite is well laid out in a herringbone pattern, with 209 accessible, level touring pitches in three different sizes. They are terraced and separated by hedges, all with electricity (3/6/10A) and good shade to many.

Two modern toilet blocks include washbasins with hot water and facilities for children and disabled visitors, although access can be difficult. Washing machines. Gas supplies. Shop. Busy bar and good restaurant. Takeaway. Swimming pool, paddling pool, water slides and jacuzzi. Playground and fenced play area for toddlers. Multisports pitch. TV in bar. Bicycle hire. Entertainment all season. Miniclub. Internet and WiFi (charged). Only charcoal and gas barbecues are permitted. Large motorhomes and twin-axle caravans are accepted.

Key Features

 Book Online

 Pets Accepted

 Disabled Facilities

 Beach Access

 Swimming Pool

 Play Area

 Bar/Restaurant

 Bike Hire

Scan me for more information.

Alan Rogers Code: ES83900
940 accommodations
343 pitches
GPS: 41.23237, 1.69092
Post Code: E-08800

Barcelona, Cataluña-Catalunya

www.alanrogers.com/es83900
info@vilanovapark.com
Tel: +34 938 93 34 02
www.vilanovapark.com

Open (Touring Pitches):
All year.

Vilanova Park

Sitting on the terrace in front of the restaurant – a beautifully converted Catalan farmhouse dating from 1908 – it is difficult to believe that in 1982 this was still a farm with few trees and known as Mas Roque (literally, Rock Farm). Since then, the imaginative planting of thousands of trees and gloriously colourful shrubs have made this large campsite most attractive. It has an impressive range of high-quality amenities and facilities open all year.

There are 343 marked pitches for touring units in separate areas, all with 6/10A electricity, while 168 larger pitches also have water and, in some cases, drainage. They are on hard surfaces, on gently sloping ground and with plenty of shade. Chalets mostly occupy a further 1,000 or so pitches to rent and by tour operators.

Excellent, heated toilet blocks with controllable showers and many washbasins in cabins. Baby rooms. Units for disabled visitors. Serviced and self-service laundry. Motorhome services. Supermarket. Souvenir shop. Restaurants. Bar with simple meals and tapas. Outdoor pools (seasonal), indoor pool (all year, charged). Wellness centre including sauna, jacuzzi and gym. Play areas. Sports field. Games room. Excursions. Activity and entertainment programme for all ages. Bicycle hire. Tennis. ATM and exchange facilities. WiFi throughout (charged). Caravan storage.

Key Features

 Book Online

 Open All Year

 Pets Accepted

 Disabled Facilities

 Beach Access

 Swimming Pool

 Play Area

 Bar/Restaurant

Scan me for more information.

Alan Rogers Code: ES84100
177 accommodations
800 pitches
GPS: 41.16945, 1.47075
Post Code: E-43883

Tarragona, Cataluña-Catalunya

Camping Park Playa Barà

www.alanrogers.com/es84100
info@barapark.es
Tel: +34 977 80 27 01
www.barapark.es

Open (Touring Pitches):
Late March - End September.

Camping Park Playa Barà is a family-friendly campsite located in the town of Roda de Barà, approximately 20 km from Tarragona. The beach is just a short walk away and is a long stretch of fine golden sand with various water sports on offer. This is a well-equipped site with high-quality facilities, well demarcated and well-shaded pitches and loads of activities for children, such as volleyball tournaments, handball, basketball, tennis, paddle tennis, mini-golf and table tennis. The pool complex is superb, and you can also relax in the hot tub or go to the solarium to top up your tan. The campsite's restaurant is ideal for sharing time with the family and enjoying local culinary specialities.

Roda de Barà, the main tourist centre of the Costa Daurada, is endlessly appealing for its successful blend of wonderful beaches and rich cultural heritage. It's a town rich in history, with numerous ancient monuments, notably the Arc de Barà, a 2,000-year-old Roman arch and something of a local icon.

Key Features

 Pets Accepted

 Disabled Facilities

 Beach Access

 Swimming Pool

 Play Area

 Bar/Restaurant

 Bike Hire

Four sanitary blocks are equipped with showers, private washing cubicles and facilities for babies. Washing machines and dryers. Supermarket & souvenir shop. Bar, Pool Bar, Restaurant, Beach Restaurant and takeaway. Outdoor pools. Spa Area. Daily entertainment program with nightly shows. Tennis & paddle courts. Minigolf. Bicycle hire.

Scan me for more information.

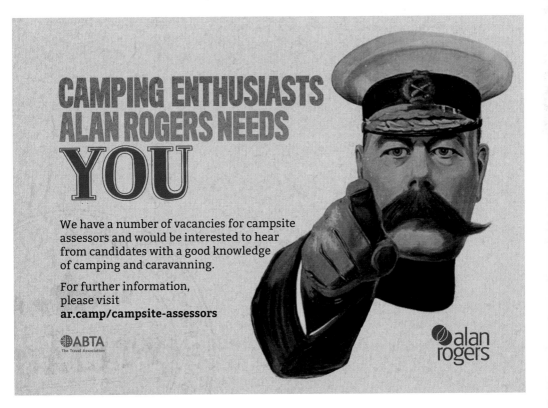

Alan Rogers Code: ES84830
156 accommodations
425 pitches
GPS: 41.13160, 1.36100
Post Code: E-43008

Tarragona, Cataluña-Catalunya

www.alanrogers.com/es84830
resort@tamarit.com
Tel: +34 977 65 01 28
www.tamarit.com

Open (Touring Pitches):
Mid March - Mid October.

Tamarit Beach Resort

This is a marvellous, beach-side site, attractively situated at the foot of the imposing Tamarit Castle at one end of a superb one-kilometre-long beach of fine sand. It is landscaped with lush Mediterranean shrubs, studded with pines and palms, and home to mischievous red squirrels. There are 425 good-sized pitches for touring, all with electricity (16A), 340 of which are fully serviced with water, drainage, TV connection and 16A electricity. Fifty very popular pitches are virtually on the beach. On hard sand and grass, some are attractively separated by hedging and shaded by trees.

This delightful site is an oasis - a great base for a beach holiday and exploring the local area. The management and staff here are keen to please, and the standards are very high. The charming restaurant and snack bar serve typical Spanish dishes whilst offering superb views of the sandy beach and castle.

The high-quality sanitary blocks (two heated) are modern and tiled. Private bathrooms to rent. Laundry facilities. Motorhome services. Fridge hire. Gas supplies. Supermarket, boutique, bars, restaurant and takeaway. Bakery. Wellness area. Swimming pool. Tennis. Pétanque. Bicycle hire. Minigolf. Playground. Sports zone. Club room with bar. Miniclub. Entertainment programme. Fishing. WiFi throughout (code).

Key Features

 Book Online

 Pets Accepted

 Disabled Facilities

 Beach Access

 Swimming Pool

 Play Area

 Bar/Restaurant

 Bike Hire

Scan me for more information.

Alan Rogers Code: ES85330
283 accommodations
229 pitches
GPS: 41.04136, 0.98139
Post Code: E-43892

Tarragona, Cataluña-Catalunya

Alannia Els Prats

www.alanrogers.com/es85330
reservas@alannia.com
Tel: +34 965 48 49 45
www.alanniaresorts.com

Open (Touring Pitches):
All year.

This Costa Daurada beach resort is in a prime location right on the beach, close to the Ebro Valley, not far from Tarragona and around 15 minutes drive from Port Aventura theme park. The site is popular with young people searching for watersports and a lively atmosphere and families looking for a varied programme of high-quality activities for children and adults alike.

There are over 200 pitches, most with some shade, ranging from 60m2 to 110m2, with a number close to the beach, all with drainage, TV connection, water connection, 220v electrical and internet connection.

Key Features

 Open All Year

 Pets Accepted

 Disabled Facilities

 Beach Access

 Swimming Pool

 Play Area

 Bar/Restaurant

 Bike Hire

Three blocks provide with controllable showers and some washbasins in cubicles. A fourth, modern unit has WCs and open style washbasins. En-suite unit for disabled visitors. Baby rooms with bath. Washing machines. Motorhome services. Supermarket. Restaurant, takeaway and three bars. Gym and Spa. Three pools (seasonal) one with water jets (aged 16+) a family pool with a waterslide and a shallow children's pool. Children's play area. Minigolf, padel tennis, football and basketball pitch, pétanque and table tennis. Bicycle hire (organised trips). Sailing, windsurfing, canoeing and diving. Activities, excursions and some evening entertainment all season (more in high season). Dogs are accepted in one area. WiFi. Some road/rail possible.

Scan me for
more information.

Alan Rogers Code: ES85300
263 accommodations
990 pitches
GPS: 41.03345, 0.96921
Post Code: E-43300

Tarragona, Cataluña-Catalunya

www.alanrogers.com/es85300
info@playamontroig.com
Tel: +34 977 81 06 37
www.playamontroig.com

Open (Touring Pitches):
Late March - Mid October.

Camping Playa Montroig

Playa Montroig is about 30 kilometres from Tarragona, set in its own tropical gardens with direct access to a very long, narrow, soft sand beach. The main part of the site lies between the sea, road and railway (as at other sites on this coast, with occasional train noise on some pitches) with a huge underpass. Aside from a wide range of superlative facilities, notably an impressive aqua park and dining options, Port Aventura theme park is 20 km or so away, making this a highly desirable location for many families.

The site is divided into spacious, marked pitches with excellent shade provided by a variety of lush vegetation, including impressive palms set in wide avenues. There are 990 pitches with electricity (10A) and 661 with water and drainage. Some 47 pitches are directly alongside the beach. A member of Leading Campings group.

Sanitary buildings with washbasins in private cabins and separate WCs. Facilities for babies and disabled campers. Several launderettes. Motorhome services. Gas. Good shopping centre. Restaurants and bars. Pool complex. Fitness suite. Hairdresser. TV lounges. Beach bar. Playground. Jogging track. Sports area. Tennis. Minigolf. Organised activities, including pottery. Open-air theatre. Pedalo hire. Boat mooring. Bicycle hire. WiFi over site. Dogs are not accepted.

Key Features

 Book Online

 Disabled Facilities

 Beach Access

 Swimming Pool

 Play Area

 Bar/Restaurant

 Bike Hire

 Fishing

Scan me for more information.

Alan Rogers Code: ES85610
41 accommodations
66 pitches
GPS: 40.27028, 0.30673
Post Code: E-12579

Castellón, Comunidad
Valenciana

www.alanrogers.com/es85610
info@campingribamar.com
Tel: +34 964 76 16 01
www.campingribamar.com

Open (Touring Pitches):
All year.

Camping Ribamar

Camping Ribamar lies to the north of Alcossebre, tucked away within the National Park of the Sierra de Irta, a magnificent landscape of intense colours. Alcossebre is a delightful resort town which has retained its Spanish identity, unlike some of the larger resorts to the north, and offers three Blue Flag beaches and a wealth of cafés and restaurants. Although a little over two hours drive south of Barcelona, this is a very underpopulated region with excellent long-distance footpaths and cycle paths.

The site has direct access to a rugged beach and little coves, and the generous swimming pool, fringed by leafy palms, is a natural focal point with plenty of sun loungers. Twice per week, a free shuttle service whisks guests into the town, available during the winter. The gravel pitches are neat and orderly, with plenty of well-maintained hedging and leafy trees, and all are classified as Premium (90-100sqm) with electricity (6A/10A) and a water supply.

Toilet block with facilities for babies and campers with disabilities. Laundry facilities. Bar. Restaurant. Shop. Swimming pool. Paddling pool. Multisports terrain. Tennis. Five-a-side football. Basketball. Boules. Padel tennis. Bicycle hire. Play area. Library/social room. Chalets to rent. Direct access to the rocky beach. Fishing. WiFi (charged). Charcoal barbecues are not allowed.

Key Features

 Book Online

 Open All Year

 Pets Accepted

 Disabled Facilities

 Beach Access

 Swimming Pool

 Play Area

 Bar/Restaurant

Scan me for more information.

Alan Rogers Code: ES85800
56 accommodations
320 pitches
GPS: 40.05708, 0.07432
Post Code: E-12560

Castellón, Comunidad
Valenciana

Bonterra Resort

www.alanrogers.com/es85800
info@bonterraresort.com
Tel: +34 964 30 00 07
bonterraresort.com

Open (Touring Pitches):
All year.

A well-organised site with extensive facilities that is popular all year. It is a 300 m. walk to a good beach, and parking is not too difficult. The site has 320 pitches (60-90 sq.m), all with electricity (6/10A), and a variety of bungalows, some attractively built in brick. There are dedicated 'green' pitches for tents.

Bonterra has a clean and neat appearance with tarmac roads, gravel-covered pitches, palms, grass and trees that give good shade. Overhead sunshades are provided for the more open pitches in summer. There is a little road and rail noise. The site has an attractive pool complex, including a covered pool for the winter months.

Four attractive, well-maintained sanitary blocks provide some private cabins, some washbasins with hot water, and others with cold. Baby and dog showers. Facilities for disabled campers. Laundry. Motorhome services. Restaurant/bar with takeaway. Shop. Swimming pool (heated Sept-June) and paddling pool. Playground (some concrete bases). Tennis. Boules. Multisports court. Small gym (charged). Disco. Bicycle hire. Miniclub. Satellite TV. WiFi over site (charged). Dogs are not accepted in July/Aug.

Key Features

 Book Online

 Open All Year

 Pets Accepted

 Disabled Facilities

 Beach Access

 Swimming Pool

 Play Area

 Bar/Restaurant

Scan me for
more information.

Alan Rogers Code: ES85700
512 accommodations
517 pitches
GPS: 40.12781, 0.15894
Post Code: E-12595

Castellón, Comunidad
Valenciana

www.alanrogers.com/es85700
camping@bravoplaya.com
Tel: +34 964 31 97 44
www.bravoplaya.com

Open (Touring Pitches):
All year.

Camping Bravoplaya

Camping Bravoplaya is a very large site divided into two by a quiet road, with a reception on each side with friendly, helpful staff. There are three pool complexes (one can be covered in cooler weather and is heated), all of which are on the west side, whilst the beach (of shingle and sand) is on the east. Both sides have a restaurant – the one on the beach side has two air-conditioned wooden buildings and a terrace.

The flat pitches vary in size, some have their own sinks, and most have decent shade. All have 10A electricity, and a few have a partial view of the sea. This high-quality site offers a huge range of excellent facilities, perennially popular with active families over the summer months. The site was previously known as Camping Torre la Sal 2.

Toilet facilities in both sections, with British-style WCs, hot water to some sinks, and facilities for disabled campers. Baby rooms. Washing machines (laundry service if required). Motorhome services. Shop, bars, restaurants and takeaway. Swimming pool complex with flumes (one pool has a bar in the centre). Jacuzzi and sauna (winter). Play park. Large disco. Sports centre. Tennis. Squash. Two football pitches. Pétanque. Outdoor gym. Games room. Bullring. Hairdresser. A varied programme of activities and entertainment. WiFi (charged). Torches are useful.

Key Features

 Book Online

 Open All Year

 Pets Accepted

 Disabled Facilities

 Beach Access

 Swimming Pool

 Play Area

 Bar/Restaurant

Scan me for more information.

ABTA
Travel with confidence

Need a campsite for tonight?

Need inspiration at short notice?
Been let down or disappointed by your
original choice of campsite?

Find out more at
ar.camp/near-me

We can help you find campsites near you
and get you on your way. In most corners of
Europe, there are campsites situated close by.

We'll show you the campsites closest to your
current location based on the shortest distance
as the crow flies. Use the filters to narrow your
campsite choice further.

Alan Rogers Code: ES86150
31 accommodations
170 pitches
GPS: 38.93160, -0.09680
Post Code: E-46780

Valencia, Comunidad Valenciana

www.alanrogers.com/es86150
info@kikopark.com
Tel: +34 962 85 09 05
www.kikopark.com

Open (Touring Pitches):
All year.

Kiko Park Oliva

Kiko Park is a smart site nestling behind protective sand dunes alongside a Blue Flag beach. There are sets of attractively tiled steps over the dunes or a long boardwalk near the beach bar (good for prams and wheelchairs) to take you to the fine white sandy beach and the sea.

From the central reception point (where good English is spoken), flat, fine gravel pitches and access roads are divided to the left and right. Backing onto one another, the 170 large pitches all have electricity, and the aim is to upgrade all these with full services progressively. There are plenty of flowers, hedging and trees, adding shade, privacy and colour.

A pleasant outdoor swimming pool with adjacent children's pool has a paved area with a bar in summer. The restaurant (lunchtimes only out of season) overlooks the marina, beautiful beach and sea. A wide variety of entertainment is provided all year, and Spanish lessons are taught along with dance classes and aerobics during the winter.

Four heated shower and toilet blocks, including facilities for babies and for disabled visitors (who will find this site flat and convenient). Outdoor swimming pools. ATM. Laundry. Restaurant, bar and beach-side bar. Supermarket. Motorhome services. Gas supplies. Playground. Watersports facilities. Diving school in high season. Paddle SUP. Entertainment for children. Pétanque. WiFi. Car rental. Bicycle hire. Pets are allowed on the pitch.

Key Features

 Book Online

 Open All Year

 Pets Accepted

 Disabled Facilities

 Beach Access

 Swimming Pool

 Play Area

 Bar/Restaurant

Scan me for
more information.

Alan Rogers Code: ES87420
91 accommodations
450 pitches
GPS: 38.12965, -0.64958
Post Code: E-03194

Alicante, Comunidad Valenciana

www.alanrogers.com/es87420
info@lamarinaresort.com
Tel: +34 965 41 92 00
www.lamarinaresort.com

Open (Touring Pitches):
All year.

Camping La Marina

Very efficiently run by a friendly family, Camping Internacional La Marina has 450 touring pitches of three different types and sizes ranging from 50 sq.m. to 150 sq.m. with electricity (10/16A), TV, water and drainage. Artificial shade is provided, and the pitches are well maintained on level, well-drained ground with a special area allocated for tents in a small orchard.

A walk through the pines and dunes takes you to the long sandy beach. Back on site, the vast lagoon swimming pool complex is fabulous and has something for everyone (with lifeguards). William Le Metayer, the owner, is passionate about La Marina and is constantly innovating. A magnificent, modern building which uses the latest architectural technology houses many superb extra amenities. A member of Leading Campings group.

Sanitary blocks with private cabins and facilities for disabled visitors & babies. Laundry facilities. Motorhome services. Gas. Supermarket. Bars. Restaurant and café. Ice cream kiosk. Swimming pools (seasonal). Indoor pool. Superb fitness centre. Sauna. Solarium. Jacuzzi. Playrooms. Extensive activity and entertainment programme including barbecues, soundproof disco and swimming nights. Sports area. Tennis. Huge playgrounds. Hairdresser. Bicycle hire. Road train to the beach. Exclusive area for dogs. Internet café (charged) and free WiFi.

Key Features

 Open All Year

 Pets Accepted

 Disabled Facilities

 Beach Access

 Swimming Pool

 Play Area

 Bar/Restaurant

 Bike Hire

Scan me for more information.

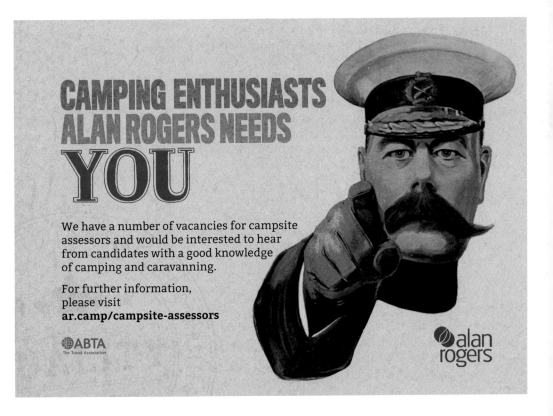

Alan Rogers Code: ES87435
540 accommodations
594 pitches
GPS: 38.17790, -0.80950
Post Code: E-03330

Alicante, Comunidad Valenciana

www.alanrogers.com/es87435
reservas@alannia.com
Tel: +34 965 48 49 45
www.alanniaresorts.com

Open (Touring Pitches):
All year.

Alannia Costa Blanca

Alannia Costa Blanca (formerly Marjal) is a fully equipped site situated 15 km. inland on the southern Alicante coast, close to the towns of Crevillente and Catral, and the Parque Natural de El Hondo. Around 1,200 hardstanding pitches range in size from 90-95 sq.m, and all have electricity (16A), water, drainage, TV and high-speed internet connections (charged).

On-site amenities include a tropical-themed swimming pool complex and a state-of-the-art wellness centre. There is full disabled access, including at the swimming pool and staffed gym. There is accommodation to rent, including 46 Balinese-style bungalows adapted for disabled visitors. The site is ideal for family holidays in summer and winter sun-seekers.

Six modern, spotlessly clean toilet blocks have washbasins and free showers in cabins. Facilities for children, babies & disabled visitors. Well-equipped shop. Bar, restaurant and takeaway (all year). Swimming pool complex with outdoor pool (Mar-Sept), heated indoor pool (all year), sauna and Hammam. Fully equipped gym. Wellness centre. Hairdresser. Play areas. Games rooms. Library. Multisports courts. Minigolf. Tennis. Football. Entertainment and activity programme (inc Spanish lessons). Kids club. Bicycle hire. Car hire service. Doctor and vet. Free WiFi areas. Mobile homes and chalets to rent.

Key Features

 Book Online

 Open All Year

 Pets Accepted

 Disabled Facilities

 Beach Access

 Swimming Pool

 Play Area

 Bar/Restaurant

Scan me for more information.

Alan Rogers Code: ES90970
29 accommodations
272 pitches
GPS: 38.93717, -2.84744
Post Code: E-02611

Albacete, Castilla-La-Mancha

www.alanrogers.com/es90970
camping@losbatanes.com
Tel: +34 926 69 90 76
www.losbatanes.com

Open (Touring Pitches):
All year.

Camping Los Batanes

This large campsite is in a lovely setting at the side of one of the many lakes in this area. The route to get here is beautiful, and it is well worth the trip, but careful driving was necessary in parts with our large motorhome.

A smaller, older part of the campsite houses reception, a small shop and a bar/restaurant. Here are medium-sized pitches shaded by pine trees with a small river running through them. By the entrance are 18 new, fully serviced, hardstanding pitches. Over a wooden bridge is the main, newer part of the site with over 200 level, gravel and sand pitches of mixed sizes, shaded again by pine trees. Electricity is 6A on most pitches.

Three modern toilet blocks have hot showers, washbasins in cabins and facilities for disabled visitors. Small shop. Simple restaurant, snacks and bar. Swimming and paddling pools (high season). Play area. Children's activities (4-12 yrs, July/Aug).

Key Features

 Open All Year

 Pets Accepted

 Disabled Facilities

 Swimming Pool

 Bar/Restaurant

Scan me for more information.

Alan Rogers Code: ES90890
6 accommodations
80 pitches
GPS: 38.34307, -3.53528
Post Code: E-23213

Jaén, Andalucia

www.alanrogers.com/es90890
info@campingdespenaperros.com
Tel: +34 953 66 41 92
www.campingdespenaperros.com

Open (Touring Pitches):
All year.

Camping Despeñaperros

This site is on the edge of Santa Elena in a natural park with shade from mature pine trees. This is a good place to stay en route from Madrid to the Costa del Sol or to explore the surrounding countryside.

The pitches are fully serviced, including a satellite TV/Internet link. All rubbish must be taken to large bins outside the site gates (a long walk from the other end of the site). The site is run in a very friendly manner where nothing is too much trouble. Reception has a monitor link with tourist information and access to the region's sites of interest.

Two traditional, central sanitary blocks have Turkish-style WCs and well-equipped showers. Facilities for disabled visitors. One washing machine (launderette in town). Shop. Excellent bar (all year) and charming restaurant (May-Oct). Swimming pools (high season). Tennis. Caravan storage. Night security. Communal barbecue area. WiFi over part of the site.

Key Features

 Book Online

 Open All Year

 Pets Accepted

 Disabled Facilities

 Swimming Pool

 Play Area

 Bar/Restaurant

Scan me for more information.

Alan Rogers Code: ES87510
2 accommodations
179 pitches
GPS: 37.23700, -1.79800
Post Code: E-04617

Almería, Andalucia

www.alanrogers.com/es87510
reservas@cuevasmar.com
Tel: +34 950 46 73 82
www.campingcuevasmar.com

Open (Touring Pitches):
All year.

Camping Cuevas Mar

This popular, well-established campsite is busy during the warm winter months with 179 pleasant pitches with shrubs and trees providing pitch dividers and shade. A few pitches are quite close to the road, but it is not busy with traffic.

All the pitches are flat and are of an acceptable 80-100 sq.m. with a clean stone chip surface and 6/10A electricity supply. Overhead shade canopies are erected on several pitches during the hot summer months. This is a pleasant, uncomplicated site with a peaceful atmosphere and spa.

The well-designed sanitary blocks provide sufficient showers and toilets for all. Washing machines and dryer. Water to the taps is to European standard; however, a single tap near reception provides high-quality water from a nearby mountain spring source. Daily fresh bread, emergency provisions and gas from reception. Open-air unheated swimming pool and jacuzzi (May-Sept). Caravan storage. WiFi throughout (weekly charge).

Key Features

 Open All Year

 Pets Accepted

 Disabled Facilities

 Beach Access

 Swimming Pool

 Bar/Restaurant

Scan me for more information.

Alan Rogers Code: ES87680
29 accommodations
731 pitches
GPS: 36.79781, -2.59099
Post Code: E-04740

Almería, Andalucia

www.alanrogers.com/es87680
info@campingroquetas.com
Tel: +34 950 34 38 09
www.campingroquetas.com

Open (Touring Pitches):
All year.

Camping Roquetas

This site is well-maintained on the sunny gulf coast of Almeria, just 400m from a pebble beach. It's conveniently situated 9 km from the A7 motorway within easy reach of the shops and amenities of Roquetas de Mar, an old fishing village. This is a relaxed family-run site, with English spoken, and there's a willingness to help guests - ask at reception for suggestions for local walking and cycling routes, perhaps into Roquetas and Aguadulce. The site is within easy reach of the popular resort of Almeria and the Cabo de Gata nature park. At the same time, the stunning beach of Playa de Los Muertos Carboneras and the desert terrain of Desierto de Tabernas are popular excursions.

There are 731 quite small touring pitches (60 sq.m), although, during the winter months, two pitches are allocated for the price of one. Most are hard standing and have electricity (5-15A), and 65 also have water and drainage (18 of these are for longer units). Tall palm trees provide a welcome shade to many.

Key Features

 Open All Year

 Pets Accepted

 Disabled Facilities

 Beach Access

 Swimming Pool

 Play Area

 Bar/Restaurant

Five well-equipped toilet blocks are spread throughout the site. Two units for disabled visitors are close to the pools, as is a baby room. Launderette. Shop. Spanish restaurant with an excellent menu and reasonable prices. Two swimming pools, one with a paddling pool. Tennis. Pétanque. Outdoor fitness. Play area. Bike hire. Golf nearby. WiFi (free by reception).

Scan me for more information.

Alan Rogers Code: ES92890
8 accommodations
94 pitches
GPS: 36.99181, -3.27753
Post Code: E-18417

Granada, Andalucia

www.alanrogers.com/es92890
info@campingtrevelez.net
Tel: +34 958 85 87 35
www.campingtrevelez.com

Open (Touring Pitches):
All year.

Camping Trevélez

Set high up in the Alpujarras region of the Sierra Nevada, Camping Trevélez is a super site that was bought in 2005 by the resident owners, Richard and Alexandra. Since taking over, they have worked tirelessly to improve the site and, each year, have made significant progress.

The site, which is open all year, is reached via a narrow, winding road and is ideally suited to tents and smaller motorhomes which are sited on terraced plots, each with spectacular mountain views. Twenty of the 94 touring pitches have 4-6A electricity. Sit outside at night and wonder at the stars above but make sure you have a torch; it gets very dark at night.

One sanitary block, recently redecorated, provides toilets, washbasins and shower cubicles. Facilities for disabled visitors. Washing machine and dryer. Shop. Bar and restaurant. Play area. Swimming pool (high season). Barbecues are only allowed in designated areas and not at all from mid-June to mid-October. Free WiFi over part of the site.

Key Features

 Book Online

 Open All Year

 Pets Accepted

 Beach Access

 Swimming Pool

 Bar/Restaurant

 Bike Hire

Scan me for more information.

Alan Rogers Code: ES92930
11 accommodations
20 pitches
GPS: 36.88708, -3.41754
Post Code: E-18400

Granada, Andalucia

www.alanrogers.com/es92930
info@campingorgiva.com
Tel: +34 958 78 43 07
www.campingorgiva.com

Open (Touring Pitches):
All year.

Camping Orgiva

Set on the high slopes of the Sierra Nevada and only 2 km. from Orgiva, this is a small and well-managed site that offers the opportunity to escape into rural Spain. It is open all year and is an ideal place to relax. For those who feel more energetic, there are facilities for climbing, horse riding and canoeing, all within close proximity of the site.

The touring pitches are well-defined and separated by shrubs and small trees, and all have views of the surrounding countryside. Access to the site is good, but being high in the mountains, it is not suitable for large units.

One centrally placed sanitary block provides toilets, washbasins and shower cubicles. Facilities for disabled visitors. Washing machine and dryer. Very good swimming pool with adjacent small pool for children (June-Sept). Shop. Terrace bar. No barbecues allowed on the site.

Key Features

 Book Online

 Open All Year

 Pets Accepted

 Swimming Pool

 Bar/Restaurant

 Skiing

 Bike Hire

Scan me for
more information.

Alan Rogers Code: ES90840
5 accommodations
35 pitches
GPS: 37.62300, -4.85870
Post Code: E-14547

Córdoba, Andalucia

Camping la Campiña

www.alanrogers.com/es90840
info@campinglacampina.es
Tel: +34 957 31 53 03
www.campinglacampina.es

Open (Touring Pitches):
All year.

A charming site amongst the olive trees, set high on a hill to catch cool summer breezes. Matilde, the daughter of the Martin-Rodriguez family, and her husband run this site with enthusiasm and hard work, making a visit here a delightful experience. Everything is immaculately kept with excellent amenities and standards.

The 35 pitches are level with a gravel surface, and most have shade. There is a large pool in a garden setting and the restaurant, with its traditional rustic charm, has a delightful menu of homemade food. Breakfast is included in pitch prices. Fresh bread and croissants are cooked to order, or you can have an inclusive breakfast on the terrace with the piquant smell of olive trees drifting from the fields. The area is famous for its natural beauty, wine and olives (excursions can be arranged to see olive oil made and to a local 'bodega' for the winemaking). Reservation is essential for the high season and November-February.

Key Features

 Book Online

 Open All Year

 Pets Accepted

 Disabled Facilities

 Swimming Pool

 Play Area

 Bar/Restaurant

 Bike Hire

Two small traditional sanitary blocks (heated in winter) have clean services, including separate facilities for disabled campers (key at reception). Washing machines. Restaurant. Snack bar. Shop. Outdoor swimming pool (Apr-Oct). Bicycle hire. Play area. TV room. Yoga lessons. Torches useful. Walks and excursions arranged. WiFi throughout.

Scan me for more information.

Alan Rogers Code: ES87870
17 accommodations
71 pitches
GPS: 36.45404, -5.08071
Post Code: E-29680

Málaga, Andalucia

Camping Parque Tropical

www.alanrogers.com/es87870
info@campingparquetropical.com
Tel: +34 952 79 36 18
www.campingparquetropical.com

Open (Touring Pitches):
All Year.

Situated between Estepona and Marbella, Parque Tropical is a small, family-run site and is well-placed for those wishing to explore the Costa del Sol. Set with attractive tropical plants, the overall atmosphere is peaceful and quiet, and the friendly staff will help arrange day trips on request. A 5-minute walk takes you to the nearest beach across the road, where there are opportunities for water sports such as windsurfing and snorkelling.

The colourful town of Estepona is a short drive or bus ride away and offers a lovely beach, promenade and old town bedecked with flowers, as well as some excellent cafés and tapas bars. Glamorous Marbella has an attractive old town and busy harbour and is accessible via a handy bus service (ask reception for details). Gibraltar is less than an hour's drive, home to its native Barbary apes and boasting wonderful scenic views. The site has 88 pitches, of which 71 gravel pitches are for tourers, each with a 10A hook-up (note: some pitches have a curb at the edge).

Toilet block with showers, washbasins & WCs. Facility for visitors who are disabled. Laundry. Fitness facility. Partially covered swimming pool. Children's pool. Play area. Restaurant. Bar. Shop. WiFi free, Security barrier. Golf 8 km. Beach adjacent. Pets welcome. Dogs allowed. Some road noise is possible.

Key Features

 Book Online

 Open All Year

 Pets Accepted

 Disabled Facilities

 Beach Access

 Swimming Pool

 Play Area

 Bar/Restaurant

Scan me for more information.

Alan Rogers Code: ES88580
70 accommodations
335 pitches
GPS: 36.29317, -6.09547
Post Code: E-11140

Cádiz, Andalucia

Camping la Rosaleda

www.alanrogers.com/es88580
info@campinglarosaleda.com
Tel: +34 956 44 33 27
www.campinglarosaleda.com

Open (Touring Pitches):
All year.

Lying 40 km south of the charming old port of Cadiz and set back slightly from the busy coast, this is a great base from where to explore and enjoy everything this Costa de la Luz coastline offers. Head to Cadiz for its winding streets and ancient monuments, then visit Jerez, famous for its sherry and the Royal Andalusian Horse School. Back at the base, various excursions and activities are offered, such as Flamenco, music nights and cookery lessons. Alternatively, enjoy the wonderful surroundings of Conil and its white sandy beaches or venture along the local cycle trails.

The site is friendly, with English-speaking staff, and there are 335 well-kept pitches of three different sizes (70-120 sq.m), the smallest just for tents, the largest with electricity (10A) and water. All are well laid out in orderly avenues with neat hedging and shady trees.

Key Features

 Book Online

 Open All Year

 Pets Accepted

 Disabled Facilities

 Beach Access

 Swimming Pool

 Play Area

 Bar/Restaurant

Four modern, fully equipped sanitary blocks include facilities for campers with disabilities. Motorhome services. Gas supplies. Excellent supermarket (all year). Bar/restaurant (all year). Swimming pool complex. Large play area. Bicycle hire. Massage, sauna, gym, yoga room, hairdressing. Golf, Mini golf, Horse riding, Surfing, Kayaking, Sailing, Fishing nearby. Free WiFi over the site. No barbecues on pitches in high season. Fridge hire. Dogs are not accepted in high season.

Scan me for more information.

Alan Rogers Code: ES88730
64 accommodations
246 pitches
GPS: 37.14280, -6.49116
Post Code: E-21750

Huelva, Andalucia

www.alanrogers.com/es88730
info@campinglaaldea.com
Tel: +34 959 44 26 77
www.campinglaaldea.com

Open (Touring Pitches):
All year.

Camping la Aldea

Camping La Aldea lies on the edge of the famous Parque Nacional de Doñana, southwest of Seville. This important park is a UNESCO World Heritage Site and the largest eco-reserve in Europe, home to the Iberian lynx, unique ecosystems and rare birds. The campsite is family-run and friendly, offering excursions to Almonte, Matalascanas beach and even the Algarve. For something a little different, ask at reception about expeditions into the national park on horseback or by 4x4 - it's a great way to experience this unique landscape.

Closer to home, the campsite is set on the outskirts of El Rocio village, the site of one of Spain's largest religious pilgrimages every May. Not far away is vibrant Seville, a thousand-year-old city and the capital of Andalusia. Don't miss the stunning Alcázar palace complex, the ancient cathedral and other fascinating monuments. This modern site is well run with 246 pitches laid out along neatly arranged avenues, each with at least some natural shade from the trees that are liberally dotted across the site. All have 10A electricity, and 52 are serviced pitches with water and drainage.

Two sanitary blocks with provision for disabled visitors. Washing machines and dryers. Motorhome services. Shop. Bar/snack bar and restaurant. Sports pitch. Swimming pool (May-Oct). Playground. Riding. WiFi.

Key Features

 Book Online

 Open All Year

 Pets Accepted

 Disabled Facilities

 Beach Access

 Swimming Pool

 Play Area

 Bar/Restaurant

Scan me for more information.

Alan Rogers Code: ES90280
50 pitches
GPS: 39.44123, -5.32200
Post Code: E-10140

Cáceres, Extremadura

www.alanrogers.com/es90280
Tel: +34 927 36 71 39
campinglasvilluercasguadalupe.es

Open (Touring Pitches):
Start April - Late Ocober.

Camping Las Villuercas

This rural, wooded site nestles in an attractive valley northwest of Guadalupe, in the Extremadura region deep in central Spain. It's a simple, good value, friendly site surrounded by dramatic countryside threaded with countless walking and hiking trails (ask at reception for tips), and with imposing hills rising up on all sides. It's possible to walk into Guadalupe, an attractive historic tourist town with plenty of bars and restaurants.

The 50 pitches (25 with 10A electricity) are mostly long and narrow, informally set out among the abundant shady poplars and plane trees. Large units will experience difficulty. The site is co-located with hostel accommodation, and the bar/restaurant is in an adjacent building. This is a peaceful, relaxed spot, ideal for visiting the imposing but ornate 14th-century Monastery of St Mary (4 km) in Guadalupe, one of the country's most important religious monuments and a UNESCO World Heritage site since 1993.

The single toilet block is old but clean, with one area for women and one for men, providing WCs, washbasins and showers (hot water is from a 40-litre immersion heater which could be overwhelmed in busy periods). Facilities for disabled visitors. Laundry facilities. Shop. Restaurant. Bar. Swimming pools (high season). Tennis. Small playground. Barbecue area. No English is spoken.

Key Features

 Pets Accepted

 Disabled Facilities

 Swimming Pool

 Play Area

 Bar/Restaurant

Scan me for more information.

Alan Rogers Code: ES90260
30 pitches
GPS: 40.47480, -5.99885
Post Code: E-37660

Salamanca, Castilla y León

www.alanrogers.com/es90260
camping.elburroblanco@gmail.com
Tel: +34 626 22 76 46
www.elburroblanco.net

Open (Touring Pitches):
Start April - Mid October / Closed
5-14 Sept.

Camping El Burro Blanco

Set on a hillside, within the Sierra Peña de Francia and with views of the romantic walled village of Miranda del Castañar and its charming, crumbling castle, this site is run by a Dutch couple, Eddy and Vera.

In total, there are just 30 level touring pitches, all between 80-120 sq.m. and all have 6/10A electricity. The pitches are beautifully set in 2.5 hectares of the most attractive natural woodland. Owners of large caravans and motorhomes (max. 7m.) should contact the site first due to the minimal number of suitable pitches. There are rough tables and chairs made from local stone, a fountain fed by a well and a small stream which traces a route through the site.

One central, modern sanitary facility. Launderette. Library and bar with terrace. WiFi in some areas (free).

Key Features

 Pets Accepted

 Bar/Restaurant

Scan me for more information.

Alan Rogers Code: ES92120
10 accommodations
125 pitches
GPS: 40.94992, -3.72927
Post Code: E-28739

Gargantilla del Lozoya, Madrid

www.alanrogers.com/es92120
monteholiday@monteholiday.com
Tel: +34 918 69 52 78
www.monteholiday.com

Open (Touring Pitches):
All year.

Camping Monte Holiday

This picturesque and conservation-minded site is situated in an open, sunny lower valley in Madrid's only beech forest in the Parque Natural Sierre de Guadarrama. The area is ideal for walkers and nature lovers and offers many opportunities for outdoor sports enthusiasts.

The site is mainly terraced and has 450 pitches, with 125 for touring units. These include a new area of 30 larger comfort pitches. All the pitches are mainly flat with grass or gravel surfaces and shade from mature trees. Permanent units take the upper area. An extensive new activity area includes a zip wire accessed via climbing walls.

The modern, heated and well-equipped toilet block is well-maintained. Facilities for disabled visitors and babies. Laundry facilities. Motorhome services. Shop (basic provisions in low season). Bar and restaurant (15/6-15/9, B.Hs and weekends). TV in the bar. Library. Swimming pool with lifeguard (mid-June - mid-Sept). Multisports court. Tennis. Beach volleyball. Play area. Gas supplies. Barbecues are not permitted from mid-May to the end of August. Bicycle hire. Excursions and activities (high season). WiFi in the bar (free).

Key Features

 Book Online

 Open All Year

 Pets Accepted

 Disabled Facilities

 Swimming Pool

 Play Area

 Bar/Restaurant

 Bike Hire

Scan me for more information.

Alan Rogers Code: ES89355
113 accommodations
75 pitches
GPS: 42.06379, -8.89142
Post Code: E-36309

Pontevedra, Galicia

www.alanrogers.com/es89355
info@camping-muino.com
Tel: +34 986 73 16 91
campingmuino.com

Open (Touring Pitches):
Start April - End September.

Camping O Muiño

Situated right on the water, offering beautiful views of the cliff coast and the Atlantic Ocean, Camping O Muiño has around 70 mainly level touring pitches with Water and electricity hookups. The numbered sites are spacious and well looked after.

You will find a sizeable sanitary building with enough showers and toilets for the number of pitches. There is also a small toilet building at the beach, which can be reached via stairs from the camping site. The complex includes a bar, a restaurant, a mini-market, and an outdoor swimming pool. It also has a games room, children's play area, and entertainment activities for both children and adults.

Camping O Muiño is located in an incomparable setting in Galicia, surrounded by the sea and the mountains. Situated in the town of Oia and the heart of the Rías Baixas, it offers you everything you need to have an unforgettable holiday. Nature, Leisure, Fun and Quality Services are at your fingertips.

One modern heated sanitary block provides washbasins and well-equipped showers. Disabled facilities, Laundry facilities, Children's Facilities, Children's playground, Multisport pitch, Tennis court, Entertainment (high season only), Restaurant, Shop, WiFi, Outdoor pool, Pets allowed, Petanque area. Bicycle hire on site.

Key Features

 Book Online

 Pets Accepted

 Disabled Facilities

 Beach Access

 Swimming Pool

 Play Area

 Bar/Restaurant

 Bike Hire

Scan me for more information.

Alan Rogers Code: ES89480
150 accommodations
40 pitches
GPS: 43.55439, -6.14458
Post Code: E-33150

Cudillero, Asturias

Camping l'Amuravela

www.alanrogers.com/es89480
info@lamuravela.com
Tel: +34 985 59 09 95
www.lamuravela.com

Open (Touring Pitches):
Early April - Mid September.

This well-maintained, family-run site, west of Santander, is walking distance from the quaint little fishing port of Cudillero with wonderful fish restaurants and jauntily painted houses. This is a great base for exploring the verdant 'green Spain'. Nearby is some of the most attractive mountain scenery in the region, with plenty of gorgeous cycling and walking routes that lead you through stunning, lush countryside.

There are around 192 pitches, with 40 good-sized touring pitches on level or gently sloping grass with easy access. Some pitches can accommodate large units. Mature trees give some shade, and all pitches have 6A electricity. This site is relatively quiet but can be busy and noisy at weekends when the seasonal units tend to be occupied. The spectacular Costa Verde, and its myriad sandy beaches and little coves, has many places to explore, and the towns of Gigon and Oviedo are fascinating places that are not to be missed.

One modern and very well maintained toilet block is close to all pitches and includes washbasins and shower cubicles. Facilities for disabled visitors. Washing machines and dryers. Well stocked shop. Café/bar area. Swimming pool (June-Sept). Play area. Very little English is spoken. Gas and charcoal barbecues permitted. Free WiFi in bar area. 19 bungalows for hire.

Key Features

 Pets Accepted

 Beach Access

 Swimming Pool

 Play Area

 Bar/Restaurant

Scan me for
more information.

Alan Rogers Code: ES90288
7 accommodations
190 pitches
GPS: 41.80520, -4.58688
Post Code: E-47290

Valladolid, Castilla Y Leon

www.alanrogers.com/es90288
info@campingcubillas.com
Tel: +34 983 58 50 02
www.campingcubillas.com

Open (Touring Pitches):
Mid January - End December.

Camping Cubillas

Go walking, fishing or sightseeing with a stay at Camping Cubillas Valladolid in Castilla y León. A walkers paradise near the Canal de Castilla hiking route, 10 minutes walk from the superb casting off of the Pisuerga river, and 10 minutes drive from the cities of Palencia and Valladolid.

Camping Cubillas has an outdoor pool and a vast surrounding area to lounge and soak up some sun. Cooking your food is covered at the barbecue facilities of the site's extensive garden, or stroll along to the on-site restaurant to eat traditional dishes made with fresh local produce.

Disabled facilities, Bar, Snack bar, Restaurant, shop (small) BBQ' allowed, Children's play area, Outdoor swimming pool, Entertainment (high season) Pétanque, Volleyball, TV room, Take away, Fishing on-site, Pets allowed, WiFi.

Key Features

 Book Online

 Pets Accepted

 Swimming Pool

 Play Area

 Bar/Restaurant

 Fishing

Scan me for more information.

Alan Rogers Code: ES89710
50 accommodations
120 pitches
GPS: 43.38527, -4.33814
Post Code: E-39547

San Vicente de la Barquera,
Cantabria

www.alanrogers.com/es89710
camping@oyambre.com
Tel: +34 942 71 14 61
www.oyambre.com

Open (Touring Pitches):
Early March - End October.

Camping Oyambre

This exceptionally well-managed site is ideally positioned to use as a base to visit the spectacular Picos de Europa or one of the many sandy beaches along this northern coast. Despite its name, it is a kilometre from the beach on foot.

The 120 touring pitches have 10A electricity (long leads needed in places), and ten are fully serviced. The fairly flat central area is allocated to tents, while caravans are mainly sited on wide terraces (access to some could be a little tight for larger units), and there is some shade. There may be some traffic noise on the lower terraces.

Good, clean, sanitary facilities are in one well-kept block. Facilities for babies and disabled visitors. Washing machines. Motorhome services. Shop in the bar. Restaurant. Takeaway. Swimming pools with a lifeguard. Playground. Bicycle hire. Free WiFi over the site.

Key Features

 Book Online

 Pets Accepted

 Disabled Facilities

 Beach Access

 Swimming Pool

 Play Area

 Bar/Restaurant

 Bike Hire

Scan me for more information.

Alan Rogers Code: ES90000
315 accommodations
800 pitches
GPS: 43.48948, -3.53700
Post Code: E-39180

Noja, Cantabria

Playa Joyel

www.alanrogers.com/es90000
info@playajoyel.com
Tel: +34 942 63 00 81
www.playajoyel.com

Open (Touring Pitches):
Late March - Late September.

This very attractive holiday and touring site is some 40 kilometres from Santander and 80 kilometres from Bilbao. It is a busy, high-quality, comprehensively equipped site with a superb beach providing 800 well-shaded, marked and numbered pitches with 6A electricity available. These include 80 large pitches of 100 sq.m. Tour operators and seasonal units occupy some 250 pitches. This well-managed site has a lot to offer for family holidays, with much going on in the high season when it gets crowded. The swimming pool complex (with a lifeguard) is free to campers, and the superb beaches are cleaned daily from mid-June to mid-September.

Two beach exits lead to the main beach, where there are some undertows, or if you turn left, you will find a reasonably placid estuary. An unusual feature here is the nature park within the site boundary, with a selection of animals to see. This overlooks a protected area of marsh where European birds spend the winter.

Six excellent, spacious and fully equipped toilet blocks include baby baths. Large laundry. Motorhome services. Gas supplies. Freezer service. Supermarket. General shop. Kiosk. Restaurant and bar. Takeaway (July/Aug). Swimming pools, and bathing caps are compulsory (high season). Entertainment organised with a soundproofed pub/disco (July/Aug). Gym park. Tennis. Playground. Riding. Fishing. Nature animal park. Hairdresser (July/Aug). Medical centre. Torches are necessary in some areas. Animals are not accepted. WiFi on part of the site (charged).

Key Features

 Book Online

 Disabled Facilities

 Beach Access

 Swimming Pool

 Play Area

 Bar/Restaurant

 Bike Hire

 Fishing

Scan me for more information.

Alan Rogers Code: ES90400
20 accommodations
125 pitches
GPS: 42.57894, -2.85157
Post Code: E-26200

Haro, La Rioja

www.alanrogers.com/es90400
campingdeharo@fer.es
Tel: +34 941 31 27 37
www.campingdeharo.com

Open (Touring Pitches):
Mid January - Early December.

Camping de Haro

This quiet riverside site is on the outskirts of the old town of Haro, the commercial centre for the renowned Rioja wines. It is a family-run site with pleasant pools (open high season). The staff in the modern reception are helpful, and you may get a cheery welcome from Carlos, the owner's son, who speaks excellent English.

All pitches are on level ground and of reasonable size, including some open pitches. Around 50% are occupied on a seasonal and weekend basis. Most of the touring pitches have some shade; a few have a great deal. Electricity connections (6A, Europlug) are provided throughout the site.

Two toilet blocks, one heated in winter, the other with facilities for disabled campers and children. Laundry. Bar/restaurant and snack bar with small counter selling basic provisions (high seasons and w/ends). Swimming pool (high season). Multisports area. Play area. Bicycle hire. Entertainment for children in high season. WiFi throughout (charged). Charcoal barbecues are not permitted.

Key Features

 Book Online

 Pets Accepted

 Disabled Facilities

 Swimming Pool

 Play Area

 Bar/Restaurant

 Bike Hire

 Fishing

Scan me for more information.

447

Alan Rogers Code: ES90370
29 accommodations
109 pitches
GPS: 43.28909, -2.24750
Post Code: E-20750

Gipuzkoa, Pais Vasco-Euskadi

www.alanrogers.com/es90370
info@campingzumaia.com
Tel: +34 943 86 04 75
www.campingzumaia.com

Open (Touring Pitches):
Mid January - Mid December.

Camping Zumaia

Set on a hillside above the interesting little port of Zumaia, this campsite was opened in June 2015 and offers 109 level hardstanding and grass touring pitches, plus a further ten pitches for tents.

Pitches are numbered and separated by small hedges and are located on one of four terraces cut into the hillside. Some have good views of the surrounding hills. All have 10A electricity, and most have water at the pitch. There is a good-sized swimming pool with a sun terrace and a small pool for children. The site is family owned and run, and although there is still work to be completed, the standard so far is excellent.

One modern sanitary block in the centre of the site provides controllable hot showers and open-style washbasins. Facilities for disabled visitors. Laundry facilities. Motorhome service point. No shop, but essentials are available from reception. Good bar/restaurant and takeaway. Solar-heated swimming pool and paddling pool (July/Aug). Play area. WiFi throughout (charged). Bungalows are available to rent. Only small dogs are accepted.

Key Features

 Book Online

 Pets Accepted

 Disabled Facilities

 Beach Access

 Swimming Pool

 Play Area

 Bar/Restaurant

Scan me for more information.

Alan Rogers Code: ES90430
125 accommodations
90 pitches
GPS: 42.62423, -1.84259
Post Code: E-31150

Mendigorria, Navarra

www.alanrogers.com/es90430
info@campingelmolino.com
Tel: +34 948 34 06 04
www.campingelmolino.com

Open (Touring Pitches):
Mid January - Mid December.

El Molino de Mendigorria

This is an extensive site set by an attractive weir near the town of Mendigorria alongside the River Arga. It takes its name from an old water mill close by and features a sophisticated dock and boat launching facility and an ambitious watersports competition programme in the season with a safety boat present at all times. A Roman aqueduct (4km) is well worth a visit, perhaps by bike. July is very busy due to the bull running festival in Pamplona (28 km).

Run by the friendly owner, Anna Beriain, the site is split into separate permanent and touring sections. The touring area has 90 good-sized flat pitches with electricity and water for touring units and a separate area for tents. All are grassy, and though many trees have been planted around the site, shade can still be at a premium.

Clean, well-equipped toilet block with cold water to washbasins. Facilities for children and disabled visitors. Washing machine. Large restaurant pleasant bar. Supermarket. 2 swimming pools for adults and children (June-mid Sept), including an indoor pool with spa and another outside with slide. Bicycle hire. Canoe/pedalo hire. Riverside bar. Weekly entertainment programme (July/Aug) and many sporting activities. Squash courts. Riverwalk. Torches useful. Wine-tasting tours arranged. Gas barbecues only. WiFi on part of site (charged).

Key Features

 Book Online

 Pets Accepted

 Disabled Facilities

 Swimming Pool

 Play Area

 Bar/Restaurant

 Bike Hire

 Fishing

Scan me for more information.

Alan Rogers Code: ES91040
70 accommodations
105 pitches
GPS: 41.63766, -0.94273
Post Code: E-50012

Zaragoza, Aragon

www.alanrogers.com/es91040
info@campingzaragoza.com
Tel: +34 876 24 14 95
www.campingzaragoza.com

Open (Touring Pitches):
All year.

Camping de Zaragoza

This large, busy municipal site 4 km. from Zaragoza, is primarily for short-stay, transit visitors, being well placed halfway between the ports of Santander and Bilbao and the beaches of the Costa Brava. The city, however, has much more to offer as the former capital of Aragon and now Spain's fifth-largest city.

There are 105 touring pitches with electricity and water, mostly on gravel and with a little shade. There are good facilities for children and the very pleasant swimming and paddling pools are welcome as it gets very hot here. Staff and facilities can be stretched at busy times.

Modern toilet blocks include good facilities for disabled visitors. Washing machine and dryer. Motorhome services. Shop, bar and restaurant (high season plus w/ends). Swimming and paddling pools (high season). Tennis. Pétanque. Multisports pitch. Play areas. Bungalows for rent. Hostel. Club and TV room. Communal barbecue area. Internet access. WiFi throughout (free).

Key Features

 Open All Year

 Pets Accepted

 Disabled Facilities

 Swimming Pool

 Play Area

 Bar/Restaurant

Scan me for more information.

Alan Rogers Code: ES90580
21 accommodations
143 pitches
GPS: 42.43958, 0.69918
Post Code: E-22486

Huesca, Aragon

Camping Baliera

www.alanrogers.com/es90580
info@baliera.com
Tel: +34 974 55 40 16
www.baliera.com

Open (Touring Pitches):
Start December - End October.

With its wonderful location in a quiet river valley with views of the surrounding mountains, Camping Baliera is an excellent site for enjoying this beautiful area which offers a wide range of active and less strenuous outdoor pursuits.

Combining camping with timber chalets and apartments, the site, under the energetic ownership of Sergi, has 143 well-kept grass touring pitches (80-120 sq.m) which are open and spacious. All have electricity (5/7/10A). The approach to this site is by narrow and winding mountain roads, and it is 5 km. from the nearest village. However, the trip is well worth making.

Key Features

 Book Online

 Pets Accepted

 Disabled Facilities

 Swimming Pool

 Play Area

 Fishing

Two heated toilet blocks, one part of the apartment block near the entrance, the other in the reception building (closed in low season). They are good with well-equipped showers and vanity-style washbasins. Laundry room and drying room. Motorhome services. Shop (July/Aug). Bar (automatic). Takeaway (July/Aug). Swimming pool (high season). Fitness equipment. Play area. Entertainment in high season. Communal barbecue. WiFi.

Scan me for more information.

Capital Stockholm
Currency Swedish Krona (SEK)
Language Swedish
Time Zone CET (GMT+1)
Telephone Code +46

Shops Hours vary throughout the year, with many shops operating on shorter hours in low and shoulder seasons. In high season 9am to 6pm Mon to Fri, and until 1pm Sat.

Money ATMs are widespread, accessible 24hrs a day and have multilingual instructions. Most places accept credit cards, Visa and Mastercard widely accepted, Amex less so. Electronic and mobile payments are common and there is a trend towards cashless payments.

Travelling with children
Sweden is great for all ages with good transport links and accommodating, friendly locals. Most museums are free for minors. Restaurants often offer a kids menu.

Public Holidays 1 Jan New Year's Day; 6 Jan Epiphany; Mar/Apr Good Friday; Mar/Apr Easter Sunday; Mar/Apr Easter Monday; 1 May Labour Day; May Ascension; May/Jun Whit Sunday; 6 Jun National Day; Jun Midsummer Day; 5 Nov All Saints; 25 Dec Christmas Da; 26 Dec Boxing Day.

 LEZ Low Emissions Zones in all major cities. Registration required.

All major cities have implemented LEZs but only Stockholm's scheme affects passenger cars.

● **EU Member** | ● **Schengen Area**

Tourism website visitsweden.com

●●●●● **Accessible Travel Score**

One of the best equipped European countries for disabled visitors. Most transport, public spaces/buildings offer adapted facilities.

Driving in Sweden Dipped headlights are obligatory year-round. Away from large towns, petrol stations are rarely open 24hrs, but most have self-serve pumps. There are no services or emergency phones on motorways. Come prepared if driving in winter months. Beware of large animals in the road. Drink-driving and using a mobile whilst driving are illegal.

 Dashcams are legal

 Speed camera detectors are **illegal**

Sweden

View all campsites in Sweden
alanrogers.com/sweden

See campsite map page 486

Climate Temperate in the north, dry and hot in the centre, hot along the Med coast.

Emergency services Call 112 for the police, ambulance and fire and rescue.

Units Sweden uses the metric system. To convert km to miles, multiply by 0.6.

With giant lakes and waterways, rich forests, majestic mountains and glaciers, and vast, wide-open countryside, Sweden is almost twice the size of the UK but with a fraction of the population.

Southern Sweden's unspoiled islands with their beautiful sandy beaches offer endless opportunities for boating and island hopping. The coastal cities of Gothenburg and Malmö, once centres of industry, now have an abundance of restaurants, cultural venues and attractions.

With the Oresund Bridge, Malmö is just a short ride from Copenhagen. Stockholm, the capital, is a delightful place built on fourteen small islands on the eastern coast. It is a vibrant city with magnificent architecture, fine museums and historic squares.

Sparsely populated northern Sweden is a land of forests, rivers and wilderness inhabited by moose and reindeer.

Östersund, located at the shores of a lake in the heart of the country, is well known for winter sports, while Frösö Zoo is a popular attraction. Today Sweden is one of the world's most developed societies and enjoys an enviable standard of living.

Scan QR code to browse more campsites on our website

Alan Rogers Code: SW2870
58 accommodations
170 pitches
GPS: 66.59497, 19.89270
Post Code: S-962 22

Jokkmokk, Norrbottens Län

www.alanrogers.com/sw2870
arcticcamp@jokkmokk.com
Tel: +46 971 123 70
www.arcticcampjokkmokk.se

Open (Touring Pitches):
Mid May - Mid September.

Jokkmokks Camping Center

This attractive site is just 8 km from the Arctic Circle. Large and well organised, it is bordered on one side by the river and by woodland on the other and is just 3 km from the town centre. It has 170 level, grassy touring pitches, an area for tents, and 58 cabins to rent. Electricity (10A) is available to 159 pitches. The site has a heated, open-air pool complex open in summer (no lifeguard).

There are opportunities for snowmobiling, cross-country skiing in spring and ice fishing in winter. Try visiting the famous Jokkmokk Winter Market (first Thursday to Saturday in February) or the less chilly Autumn Market (end of August).

Heated sanitary buildings provide mostly open washbasins and controllable showers – some are curtained with a communal changing area, and a few are in cubicles with dividers and seats. A unit by reception has a baby bathroom, a fully equipped suite for disabled visitors, a games room, plus a very well-appointed kitchen and launderette. A further unit with WCs, washbasins, showers, plus a steam sauna, is by the pool. Shop, restaurant and bar (in summer). Takeaway (High season). Swimming pools (25x10 m. main pool with water slide, two smaller pools and paddling pool, high season). Sauna. Bicycle hire. Playground and adventure playground. Minigolf. Football field. Games machines. Free fishing.

Key Features

 Pets Accepted

 Disabled Facilities

 Swimming Pool

 Play Area

 Bar/Restaurant

 Bike Hire

 Fishing

Scan me for more information.

Alan Rogers Code: SW2857
31 accommodations
150 pitches
GPS: 63.84652, 15.53441
Post Code: S-833 24

Strömsund, Jämtlands Län

Strömsunds Camping

www.alanrogers.com/sw2857
turism@stromsund.se
Tel: +46 670 164 10
www.stromsund.se/
stromsundscamping

Open (Touring Pitches):
All year.

A quiet waterside town on the north-south route 45, known as the Inlandsvägen, Strömsund is a good place to begin a journey on the Wilderness Way. This is route 342, which heads northwest towards the mountains at Gäddede and the Norwegian border. Being on the confluence of many waterways, there is a wonderful feeling of space and freedom in Strömsund. There are 150 touring pitches (94 with 10A electricity) set on a gentle grassy slope backed by forest. Another part of the site, across the road, overlooks the lake. Cabins are set in circular groups of either six or seven. The town council owns the site.

Besides the main bridge is an excellent open-air museum with a collection of buildings dating back several centuries; there are well-marked trails in the forests. Walk here alone at midnight on Midsummer's Eve in an intense blue light – nothing moves as the path ahead leads deeper into the dense forest – it is a memorable experience.

Excellent facilities include two toilet blocks. Both contain showers, toilets, washbasins with dividers and underfloor heating. Facilities for disabled visitors. Laundry. Large campers' kitchen with cooking rings, microwave and sinks. Motorhome services. Café (seasonal). Fishing. Golf. Bicycle, canoe, pedalo and boat hire. Play area. WiFi throughout (charged).

Key Features

 Open All Year

 Pets Accepted

 Disabled Facilities

 Swimming Pool

 Play Area

 Bike Hire

 Fishing

 Golf

Scan me for
more information.

Alan Rogers Code: SW2845
25 accommodations
91 pitches
GPS: 62.03367, 14.37250
Post Code: S-842 32

Sveg, Jämtlands Län

Svegs Camping

www.alanrogers.com/sw2845
info@svegscamping.se
Tel: +46 680 130 25
www.svegscamping.se

Open (Touring Pitches):
All year.

On the 'Inlandsvägen' route through Sweden, the town centre is only a short walk from this neat, friendly site. Two supermarkets, a café and a tourist information office, are adjacent. The 91 pitches are in rows, on level grass, divided into bays by tall hedges, and with electricity (10/16A) available to 70. The site has boats, canoes and bicycles for hire, and the river frontage has a barbecue area with covered seating and fishing platforms. Alongside the river with its fountain and running through the site is a pleasant well-lit riverside walk.

This is a pleasantly rural spot, with serene countryside to explore on the doorstep. Places to visit include the local town with its lovely church and adjacent gardens, some interesting old churches in the surrounding villages, and 16th-century Remsgården, 14 km. to the west.

Key Features

 Open All Year

 Pets Accepted

 Disabled Facilities

 Bike Hire

 Fishing

In the older style, sanitary facilities are functional rather than luxurious, providing stainless steel washing troughs, controllable hot showers with communal changing areas, and a unit for disabled visitors. Although a little short on numbers, facilities will probably suffice at most times as the site is rarely full. Kitchen and dining room with TV, four full cookers and sinks. Laundry facilities. River beach. TV room. Minigolf. Canoe, boat and bicycle hire. Fishing. Reduced services in low season.

Scan me for
more information.

Alan Rogers Code: SW2715
63 accommodations
180 pitches
GPS: 58.89942, 11.93487
Post Code: S-668 32

Ed, Västra Götalands Län

www.alanrogers.com/sw2715
gronebackecamping@telia.com
Tel: +46 534 101 44
www.gbcamp.nu

Open (Touring Pitches):
All year.

Gröne Backe Camping

In the heart of the beautiful Dalsland region, this pleasant, well-shaded (mostly pine) site is open all year. It is well laid out, mostly overlooking the Lilla Le lake, and there is easy access from road no. 164. There are 180 grass pitches for caravans and motorhomes, most with electricity (10/16A) and special areas for tents. Although the pitches are a little on the small side and slightly uneven, the site has a really good feel and is certainly friendly and easy to find. Also on the site are 23 cabins to rent and 40 seasonal pitches. An unusual feature is a floating sauna on the lake.

A path from the site follows the edge of the lake into town, and it is possible to complete a circular route of 4 km. around it. In this region of forests and lakes, there are great opportunities for walking, cycling, canoeing, swimming and fishing and, in winter, cross-country and downhill skiing.

Three heated toilet blocks, two in the centre and one at reception, provide washbasins, both vanity type and in cubicles. Showers (on payment). Baby rooms. Facilities for disabled visitors. Laundry. Cooking facilities. Motorhome services. Small shop. Café and restaurant. Internet and WiFi. Playground. Minigolf. Sports field. Canoes, rowing boats, bicycles and pedal cars for hire. Beach. Sauna raft on the lake (charged).

Key Features

 Open All Year

 Pets Accepted

 Disabled Facilities

 Play Area

 Bar/Restaurant

 Bike Hire

 Fishing

Scan me for more information.

Alan Rogers Code: SW2730
26 accommodations
260 pitches
GPS: 58.71557, 13.79490
Post Code: S-542 45

Mariestad, Västra Götalands Län

www.alanrogers.com/sw2730
ekudden@firstcamp.se
Tel: +46 501 106 37
www.firstcamp.se

Open (Touring Pitches):
Start May - Mid September.

Ekudden Camping

First Camp Ekudden Camping occupies a long stretch of the eastern shore of Lake Vanern, to the northwest of the town, in a mixed woodland setting, and next door to the municipal complex of heated outdoor pools and sauna. The lake, of course, is also available for swimming and boating, and there are bicycles, tandems and canoes for hire at the tourist information office in town. Using the site as a base, you can visit the nearby Old Town of Mariestad, take a trip on a passenger boat out on Lake Vänern or visit the Göta Canal with its locks at Sjötorp. During the high season, the site can become very busy.

The spacious site can take 260 units on numbered pitches, and most have electrical hook-ups (16A). Most pitches are on level ground, either on grass or honeycomb grass paving blocks. Most are under the trees, but some at the far end of the site are on more open ground with good views over the lake.

Key Features

 Pets Accepted

 Disabled Facilities

 Swimming Pool

 Play Area

 Bar/Restaurant

 Bike Hire

 Fishing

 Sailing

Four sanitary blocks, all clean and well-maintained. Free hot showers in cubicles. Facilities for disabled visitors with good access ramps. Baby rooms. Excellent kitchen with cooking and dining facilities. Laundry. Shop. Licensed bar. Takeaway (high season). Playground. Minigolf. TV room. Lake swimming, boating and fishing. Entertainment in high season. WiFi (free). Note that some services are seasonal.

Scan me for more information.

Alan Rogers Code: SW2675
142 accommodations
900 pitches
GPS: 57.73821, 16.66846
Post Code: S-593 53

Västervik, Kalmar Län

www.alanrogers.com/sw2675
lysingsbadet@vastervik.se
Tel: +46 490 889 20
www.vastervikresort.se

Open (Touring Pitches):
All year.

Västervik Resort

One of the largest sites in Scandinavia, Västervik Resort has unrivalled views of the 'Pearl of the East Coast' – Västervik and its fjords and islands. There are around 1,000 large, mostly marked and numbered pitches, spread over a vast area of the rocky promontory and set on different plateaux, terraces, valleys and woodland or beside the water. It is a very attractive site that never looks or feels crowded, even when busy.

There are 143 fully serviced pitches with TV, water, drainage and electrical connections, 87 with TV and electricity and 490 with electricity only, the remainder for tents. Shade is generally plentiful. This is an 'all singing, all dancing' site with something to suit all tastes and ages.

Ten modern toilet blocks house a comprehensive mix of showers, washbasins and WCs. All are kept very clean. Several kitchens with sinks and cookers. Four laundry rooms. All facilities and hot water are free. Key cards operate the barriers and gain access to sanitary blocks, pool complex and other facilities. Motorhome services. Supermarket (High season). Restaurant and café/takeaway (High season). Swimming pool complex (High season). Playgrounds. Golf. Minigolf. Bicycle and boat hire. Fishing. Entertainment and dances in high season. Quick stop service. Bus service. Free WiFi throughout.

Key Features

 Open All Year

 Pets Accepted

 Disabled Facilities

 Swimming Pool

 Play Area

 Bike Hire

 Fishing

 Golf

Scan me for more information.

Alan Rogers Code: SW2645
44 accommodations
235 pitches
GPS: 56.27088, 12.52952
Post Code: S-260 42

Mölle, Skåne Län

Camping Mölle - Höganäs

www.alanrogers.com/sw2645
molle@firstcamp.se
Tel: +46 423 473 84
www.firstcamp.se/molle-hoganas

Open (Touring Pitches):
All year.

FirstCamp Mölle - Höganäs is a family campsite with a fine location at the foot of the Kullaberg, which marks the point where the Atlantic divides into the Kattegatt and Öresund. The site is open all year with around 240 mostly grassy pitches, generally of a good size and 220 with electrical connections. There's plenty of mature hedging to demarcate pitches and provide some shade. On-site amenities include a heated paddling pool and water games complex, well laid out and a natural focal point for the campsite. There are plentiful activities for children, including an area where they can play games and run around. The nearest beach is just 1.5 km distant and is popular for kayaking and fishing.

This is a peaceful, rural area with fertile fields and dense forests. The nearby Kullaberg Nature Park is dramatic and well worth a visit. The region is also well known for its ceramics; many potters and artists have settled there.

Two modern sanitary blocks with free hot water and facilities for disabled visitors. Family shower rooms. Laundry with washing machines and dryers. Kitchen with cooking rings and microwave. Motorhome services. Restaurant with bar and café. Shop. Minigolf. Sports pitch. Heated paddling pool. Entertainment and children's activity programme (high season). Bicycle hire. TV room. WiFi. Cabins to rent.

Key Features

 Open All Year

 Pets Accepted

 Swimming Pool

 Play Area

 Bar/Restaurant

 Bike Hire

Scan me for more information.

Alan Rogers Code: SW2280
41 accommodations
220 pitches
GPS: 55.94120, 14.31301
Post Code: S-29633

Åhus, Skåne Län

www.alanrogers.com/sw2280
ahus@regenbogen.ag
Tel: +46 442 489 69
www.firstcamp.se/ahus-kristianstad

Open (Touring Pitches):
Start April - End December.

Camping Åhus – Kristianstad

First Camp Åhus – Kristianstad is in the Skåne province on the South Baltic coast, set in a natural environment amongst mature pine trees which provide shade to all pitches. There are 420 large, level pitches on grass and hardstanding, 220 of which are for touring. They are informally laid out and have 10A electricity connections. A large, white sandy beach is only 500 m. from the campsite and the fishing village of Åhus, with its castle, museum and many festivals, can easily be reached by bike or on foot. A wellness centre near the beach offers the usual spa facilities plus an adjoining restaurant.

Places to visit include the Åhus museum, the Absolut Vodka exhibition, the Ales Stenar stone circle, the Forsakar waterfalls, Simrishamn medieval castle, Sandhammaren nature reserve and Tosselilla adventure park, all in a serene landscape. A stronghold of the Viking era, there is an abundance of medieval churches and picture-perfect villages.

Modern sanitary facilities, including for disabled visitors and children. Washing machines. Motorhome services. Shop. Large wellness area with spas, sauna, massage and beauty treatment. Licensed restaurant with a wide-ranging menu with a terrace overlooking the play area. Bicycle and kayak hire. Minigolf. Tennis. WiFi at reception and restaurant (charged).

Key Features

 Pets Accepted

 Disabled Facilities

 Beach Access

 Play Area

 Bike Hire

Scan me for more information.

Capital Bern
Currency Swiss Franc (CHf)
Language German, French, Italian and regional variants
Time Zone CET (GMT+1)
Telephone Code +41

Shops Hours vary throughout the year, with many shops operating on shorter hours in low and shoulder seasons. In high season 10am to 6pm Mon to Fri, and until 4pm Sat.

Money ATMs are widespread, accessible 24hrs a day and have multilingual instructions. Most restaurants and shops accept Euros, change given in Swiss Francs at daily exchange rate.

Travelling with children Switzerland is a great destination for families. Most restaurants offer a kids menu. Children aged 6 or under travel free on trains.

Public Holidays 1 Jan New Year's Day; Mar/Apr Good Friday; Mar/Apr Easter Monday; May Ascension; May/Jun Whit Monday; May/Jun Corpus Christi; 1 Aug National Day; 1 Nov All Saints; 25 Dec Christmas Day; 26 Dec Boxing Day.

There are no Low Emission Zones currently in place.

○ EU Member | ● Schengen Area

Tourism website myswitzerland.com

●●●●● **Accessible Travel Score**

Switzerland ranks highly when it comes to ease of access for the less abled. Transport and public spaces offer adapted facilities and most walking trails are wheelchair-friendly.

Driving in Switzerland An annual road tax is levied on all cars using Swiss motorways, and the 'Vignette' windscreen sticker must be purchased at the border or in advance, plus a separate one for a towed caravan or trailer. Many mountain resorts are vehicle-free. You are encouraged to use Park 'n' Ride schemes and cable cars. Drink-driving and using a mobile whilst driving illegal.

 Dashcams are **illegal**

 Speed camera detectors are **illegal**

Switzerland
& Liechtenstein

View all campsites in Switzerland
alanrogers.com/switzerland

View all campsites in Liechtenstein
alanrogers.com/liechtenstein

See campsite map page 487

Climate Mild and refreshing in the north. South of the Alps it is warmer.

Emergency services Call 112 for the police, ambulance and fire and rescue.

Units Switzerland uses the metric system. To convert km to miles, multiply by 0.6.

A small, wealthy country best known for its outstanding mountainous scenery, fine cheeses and delicious chocolates. Centrally situated in Europe, it shares its borders with France, Austria, Germany and Italy, each one having its own cultural influence on the country.

With its snowy peaks and rolling hills, the Bernese Oberland is the most popular area; Gstaad is a favourite haunt of wealthy skiers, while the mild climate and breezy conditions around Lake Thun are perfect for watersports.

German-speaking Zurich is a multicultural metropolis with over 50 museums, sophisticated shops and colourful festivals set against a breathtaking backdrop of lakes and mountains. The southeast of Switzerland has densely forested mountain slopes and the glamorous resort of Saint Moritz.

Geneva, Montreux and Lausanne make up the bulk of French Switzerland, with vineyards that border the lakes and medieval towns. The southernmost canton, Ticino, is home to the Italian-speaking Swiss, with the Mediterranean style lakeside resorts of Lugano and Locarno.

Scan QR code to browse more campsites in Switzerland

Scan QR code to find out more about Liechtenstein

Alan Rogers Code: CH9032
148 accommodations
60 pitches
GPS: 46.85721, 6.84796
Post Code: CH-1470

Estavayer-le-Lac, Fribourg

www.alanrogers.com/ch9032
info@nouvelle-plage.ch
Tel: + 41 26 663 16 93
www.nouvelle-plage.ch

Open (Touring Pitches):
End March - Mid October.

La Nouvelle Plage

Situated right beside Lake Neuchâtel in Switzerland, Camping La Nouvelle Plage is the perfect site for active holidaymakers as it offers families a chance to enjoy all kinds of water-based activities. The campground is located on an attractive sandy beach with direct access to the lake. You'll find plenty of water sports to try out, including water skiing, paddle boarding and pedalos. Beach volleyball and ping pong are also available for active families.

The campsite has 60 touring pitches, with electric hookups available and the option to be positioned near the lake's beach or closer to the nature reserve. For those who aren't into water sports, there are many facilities to keep the whole family occupied, including volleyball, a multi-sport pitch, a water slide and a children's playground, or there are plenty of spaces to lounge around by the lake and watch the activities in comfort. Alternatively, tour the local vineyards or visit the region's dramatic castles and picturesque villages.

Key Features

 Pets Accepted

 Disabled Facilities

 Play Area

 Bar/Restaurant

 Fishing

 Sailing

Disabled sanitary facilities. Fresh bread. Bar. Snack Bar. Restaurant. Shop. Pizzeria. Takeaway meals. Children's playground. Bicycle hire. Kayaking. Volleyball. Multisport field. Sailing. Pedal boats. Table tennis table. Multi-sports field. Fishing on-site. Open water swimming. Pets allowed. WiFi.

Scan me for more information.

Alan Rogers Code: CH9045
5 accommodations
69 pitches
GPS: 47.05000, 7.11000
Post Code: CH-3235

Erlach, Bern

www.alanrogers.com/ch9045
info@camping-erlach.ch
Tel: +41 32 513 01 00
www.camping-erlach.ch

Open (Touring Pitches):
Easter - Mid October.

Camping Erlach

Gemeinde Camping Erlach is a lakeside site within walking distance of the small town of Erlach, west of Bern. There's a small beach backed by a grassy expanse offering wonderful views across the lake to the wooded hills opposite. With only 69 touring pitches of small to medium size, it can fill up quickly during the high season, especially at weekends. Some pitches have hardstandings suitable for motorhomes, and several tent-only pitches are available. Many pitches have lovely views over the Bielersee, and the marina, with numerous lake cruise options, is only a few minutes walk away.

Although technically in the Bern canton, it is close to Neuchâtel, which can be reached courtesy of the many excellent ferries that stop near the site. The trip takes an hour each way, and the charming sandstone elegance of the old town of Neuchâtel has much to offer visitors, from the 16th-century fountains by Laurent Perroud to the museums of art and history.

The modern, heated sanitary block is of a high standard, with free showers. Facilities for disabled campers. An older block is unisex and has limited facilities. Washing machine and dryer. Motorhome services. Shop. Restaurant/bar with a shaded terrace overlooking the lake. Fishing. Boules area. Play area. Pedalo hire. WiFi (free). Pods are available for hire.

Key Features

Pets Accepted

Disabled Facilities

Play Area

Bike Hire

Fishing

Scan me for
more information.

Alan Rogers Code: CH9430
12 accommodations
90 pitches
GPS: 46.68605, 7.83063
Post Code: CH-3800

Unterseen-Interlaken, Bern

www.alanrogers.com/ch9430
info@lazyrancho.ch
Tel: +41 33 822 87 16
www.lazyrancho.ch

Open (Touring Pitches):
Start May - Start October.

Camping Lazy Rancho

This popular site is in a quiet location with fantastic views of the dramatic mountains of Eiger, Monch and Jungfrau. Neat, orderly and well-maintained, the site is situated in a wide valley just 1 km. from Lake Thun and 1.5 km. from the centre of Interlaken. The English-speaking owners lovingly care for the site and will endeavour to make you feel very welcome.

Connected by gravel roads, the 155 pitches, of which 90 are for touring units, are on well-tended level grass (seven with hardstanding, all with 10A electricity). There are also 30 pitches with water and wastewater drainage. This is a quiet, friendly site, popular with British visitors who return year after year.

Two good sanitary blocks are both heated with free hot showers, good facilities for disabled campers and a baby room. Laundry. Campers' kitchen with microwave, cooker, fridge and utensils. Motorhome services. Well-stocked shop. TV and games room. Play area. Small swimming pool, sauna and hot tub (all season). Wooden igloo pods, XL-igloos, Love-igloo and bungalows for rent. Internet/laptop room. WiFi throughout (free).

Key Features

 Book Online

 Pets Accepted

 Disabled Facilities

 Beach Access

 Swimming Pool

 Play Area

Scan me for more information.

Alan Rogers Code: CH9845
80 pitches
GPS: 46.64000, 10.02000
Post Code: CH-7526

Cinuos-chel, Graubünden

www.alanrogers.com/ch9845
info@campingchapella.ch
Tel: +41 81 854 12 06
www.campingchapella.ch

Open (Touring Pitches):
Start May - End October.

Camping Chapella

If you're looking for a simple campsite set amidst glorious scenery and well-placed for exploring the area's possibilities for outdoor activities, then here it is. Camping Chapella doesn't even boast a reception, but it has glorious views of the valley with its pine-covered slopes and snow-capped mountains. There's canoeing on the cascading river, mountain meadows, and densely forested slopes to hike and cycle through. There's a family-friendly feel, and everyone can enjoy the serenity of the natural surroundings.

There are 100 modestly sized pitches, 80 for touring, set amongst the pines, perhaps in a clearing or overlooking the tumbling river. Some are level, and all have 16A electricity. However, they are unmarked and are clearly allocated on a 'first come, first served' basis, so not all have access to electricity when it is busy. There are warning signs about entering the river, which is about 50 feet below the level of the site because the water level can be suddenly affected by hydroelectric power activity further upstream.

The modern heated toilet block is of a good standard and well maintained, with free hot showers and some washbasins in cabins. Washing machine and dryer. Motorhome services. Groceries and fresh bread (early May - mid Sept). Playground. River swimming. WiFi (charged). Limited railway noise is possible.

Key Features

 Pets Accepted

 Play Area

 Fishing

Scan me for more information.

Alan Rogers Code: CH9890
91 accommodations
712 pitches
GPS: 46.16895, 8.85592
Post Code: CH-6598

Tenero, Ticino

Campofelice Camping

www.alanrogers.com/ch9890
camping@campofelice.ch
Tel: +41 91 745 14 17
www.campofelice.ch

Open (Touring Pitches):
Late March - End October.

Considered by many to be the best family campsite in Switzerland, Campofelice Camping Village borders Lake Maggiore and the Verzasca estuary, where the site has its own marina. There are 712 generously sized touring pitches on flat grass on either side of hard access roads. Mostly well-shaded, all pitches have electricity connections (13A, 360 Europlug), and 376 also have water, drainage and TV connections. A special area is reserved for small tents. Pitches near the lake cost more (these are not available for motorhomes until September).

It's a little more expensive than other sites in the area, but excellent value for the range and quality of the facilities. The surrounding scenery is sublime, with sensational views from the gently shelving beach and the cycle trails into Locarno.

Key Features

 Book Online

 Disabled Facilities

 Swimming Pool

 Play Area

 Bar/Restaurant

 Bike Hire

Modern heated sanitary facilities. Laundry. Sandy beach (400m). Pool and Wellness Area. Aquapark. Charging station for Tesla and electric cars. Two playgrounds. Tennis courts. Minigolf. Bike track. Beach volleyball. Bicycle hire. Canoe. SUP and pedalo hire. Car hire. Car wash. Free WiFi. Boat launch. Football field. Pizzeria. Restaurant. Snack bar. Camping accessories and various shops. Lifeguards. Pavilion with a LEDWall. Doctor on call. Entertainment program with shows. Games and sports competitions. Pets are not accepted. Accommodation is available.

Scan me for more information.

Alan Rogers Code: CH9460
250 pitches
GPS: 46.58807, 7.91077
Post Code: CH-3822

Lauterbrunnen, Bern

Camping Jungfrau

www.alanrogers.com/ch9460
info@camping-jungfrau.ch
Tel: +41 33 856 20 10
www.campingjungfrau.swiss

Open (Touring Pitches):
All year.

This friendly and ever-popular site has a very imposing and dramatic situation in a steep valley with a fine view of the Jungfrau at the end. Mountain meltwater cascades hundreds of feet down the sheer rock walls of the valley. Many active pursuits are available in the area, as well as trips on the Jungfrau railway and mountain lifts. In winter, the site runs a free shuttle bus to the local ski lifts, and large community lounges are available for après-ski enjoyment.

A large area is made up of grass pitches and hardcore access roads. All 391 pitches (250 for touring) have shade in parts, and electrical connections (13A), and 50 have water and drainage too. This family-owned, friendly site offers a warm welcome and English is spoken. A perfect spot for relaxing amid epic scenery.

Three fully equipped modern sanitary blocks (heated in winter), one providing facilities for disabled visitors. Baby baths. Laundry facilities. Motorhome services. Well-equipped campers' kitchen. Excellent shop. Self-service restaurant with takeaway (all year). General room with tables and chairs, TV, drinks machines, and amusements. Playgrounds and covered play area. Excursions and some entertainment in high season. Mountain bike hire. ATM. Drying room. Ski store. Free shuttle bus in winter. Internet point. WiFi throughout (free).

Key Features

 Book Online

 Open All Year

 Pets Accepted

 Disabled Facilities

 Play Area

 Bar/Restaurant

 Skiing

 Bike Hire

Scan me for more information.

Alan Rogers Code: CH9425
83 accommodations
92 pitches
GPS: 46.67999, 7.81728
Post Code: CH-3800

Interlaken, Bern

www.alanrogers.com/ch9425
info@camping-alpenblick.ch
Tel: +41 33 822 77 57
www.camping-alpenblick.ch

Open (Touring Pitches):
All year.

Camping Alpenblick

Alpenblick is an all-year site in a stunning setting, located at the heart of the Bernese Oberland just 100 metres from the beautiful Lake Thun. A Swiss chalet-style building houses the reception, shop and bar/restaurant that is very popular with campers and locals alike (try the 'schnitzelbrot' and dine on the terrace in good weather). There are around 100 touring pitches and a further 80 residential pitches. The touring pitches are mostly grassy and level, with moderate shade, and all have 10/16A electrical connections and some good hardstanding pitches are available for motorhomes.

Campers can take advantage of a special tourist card with many benefits, including free local bus transport. This is a superb area for cycling and walking, with trails taking you through magnificent scenery all around the lake. The lake is very popular for all manner of watersports, and cruisers depart from a point very close to Alpenblick. The views everywhere are majestic.

Sanitary block with hot showers, some washbasins in cubicles and a family shower room. Facilities for disabled visitors. Laundry facilities. Shop (Seasonal) with daily delivery of bread. Bar, restaurant and takeaway (all year). Bar and barbecue for socialising and events. Playground. Boules. Basketball. WiFi throughout (charged).

Key Features

 Open All Year

 Pets Accepted

 Disabled Facilities

 Beach Access

 Play Area

 Bar/Restaurant

Scan me for more information.

Alan Rogers Code: FL7580
70 accommodations
80 pitches
GPS: 47.08570, 9.52590
Post Code: FL-9495

Triesen, Liechtenstein

www.alanrogers.com/fl7580
info@campingtriesen.li
Tel: +423 392 26 88
www.campingtriesen.li

Open (Touring Pitches):
All year.

Camping Mittagspitze

Camping Mittagspitze is attractively and quietly situated for visiting Liechtenstein. Set on a hillside, it has all the scenic mountain views one could wish for. Extensive grassy terraces on a steep slope provide unmarked but level pitches, and electricity connections (6A) are available. Trees provide some shade, mainly along the terrace edges. About 80 touring pitches are available, with the remainder of the site given over to seasonal pitches.

The on-site restaurant "Zur Alten Eiche" (The Old Oak) serves high-quality, seasonal, local dishes and has an extensive wine menu. The terrace and beer garden can be enjoyed in the summer. The surrounding mountain scenery of the local area is well worth exploring - pick up one of the marked trails, some passing the campsite entrance. The Liechtenstein capital, Vaduz, is around 10 minutes drive away, with the Swiss border less than 5km away. It's worth noting that the campsite has Swiss-style power sockets, so an adaptor will be required if you have a CEE or Euro connector.

Two good quality sanitary blocks provide all the usual facilities. Washing machine, dryer and ironing. Shop, bar and takeaway (seasonal; bread to order). Restaurant (March - December). Small swimming pool and paddling pool (seasonal), not heated but very popular in summer. Playground. TV room.

Key Features

 Open All Year

 Pets Accepted

 Swimming Pool

 Play Area

 Bar/Restaurant

 Fishing

Scan me for
more information.

Austria & Czech Republic Map

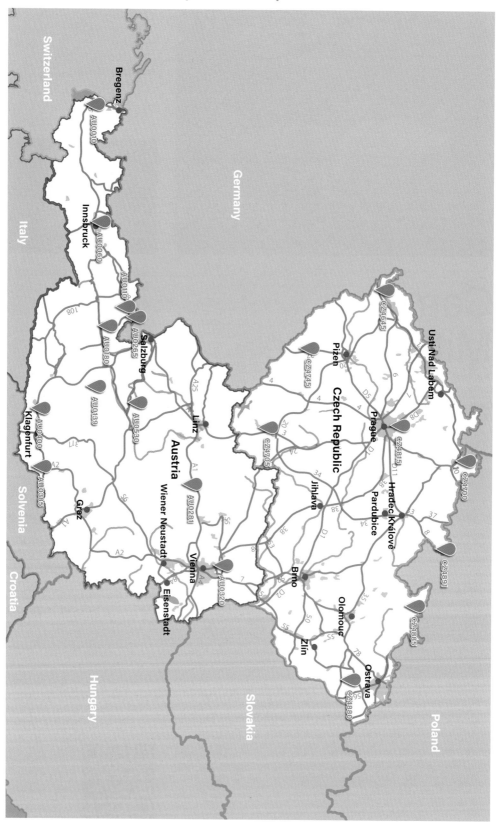

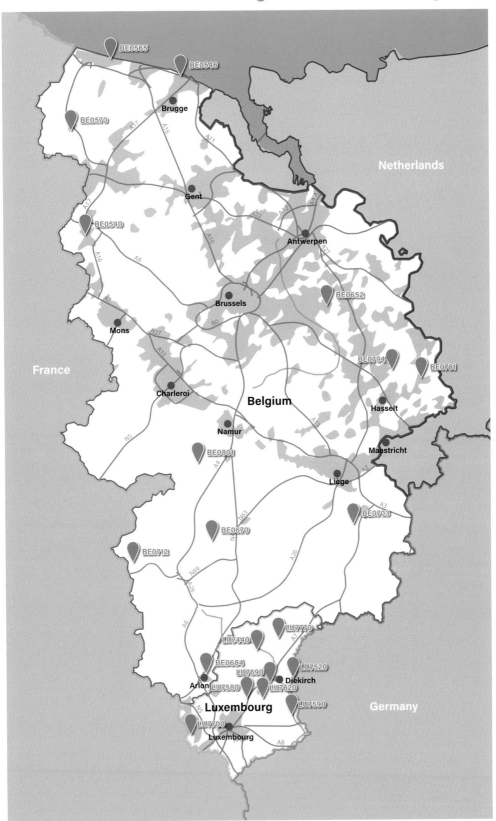

Croatia & Solvenia Map

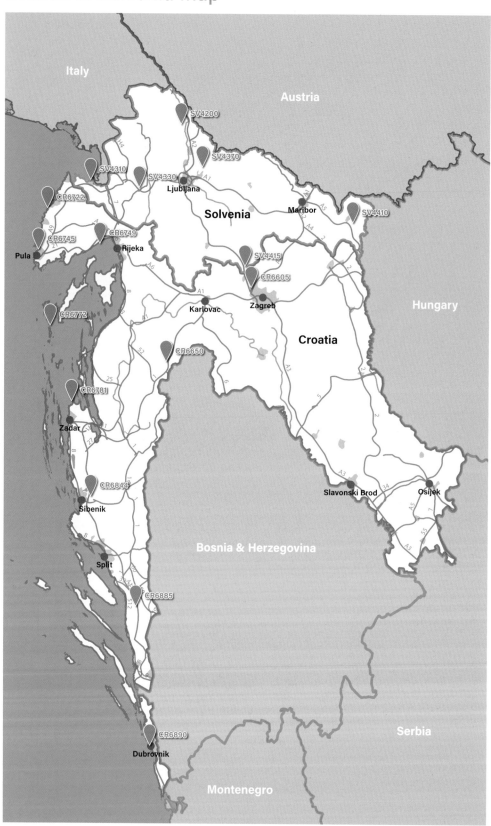

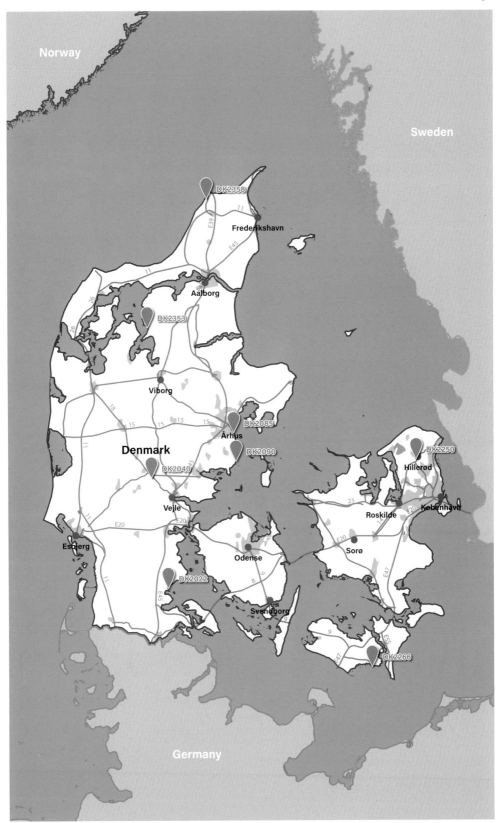

West France Map

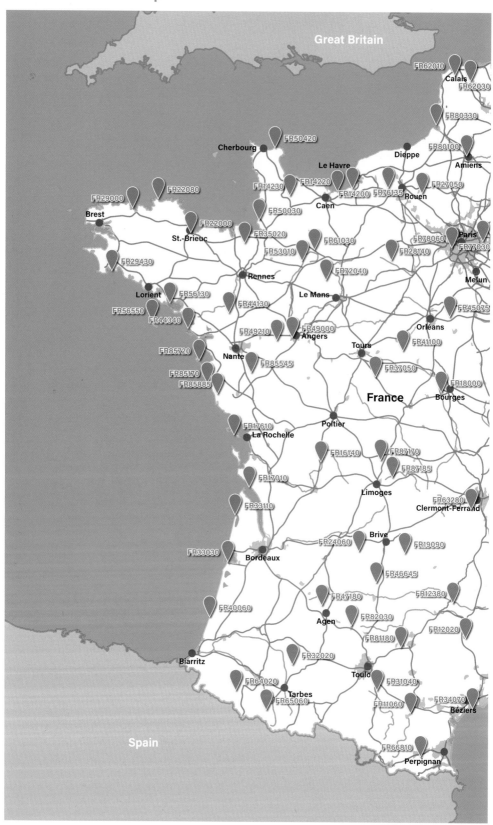

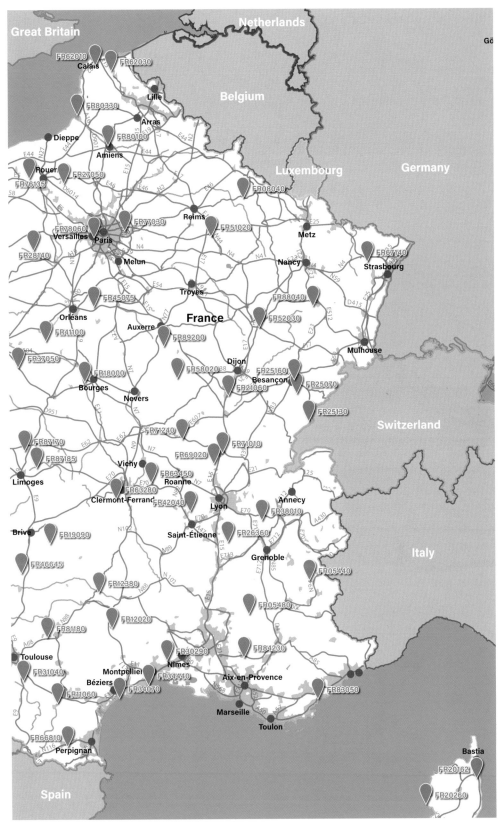

France Languedoc & Spain Catalunya Map

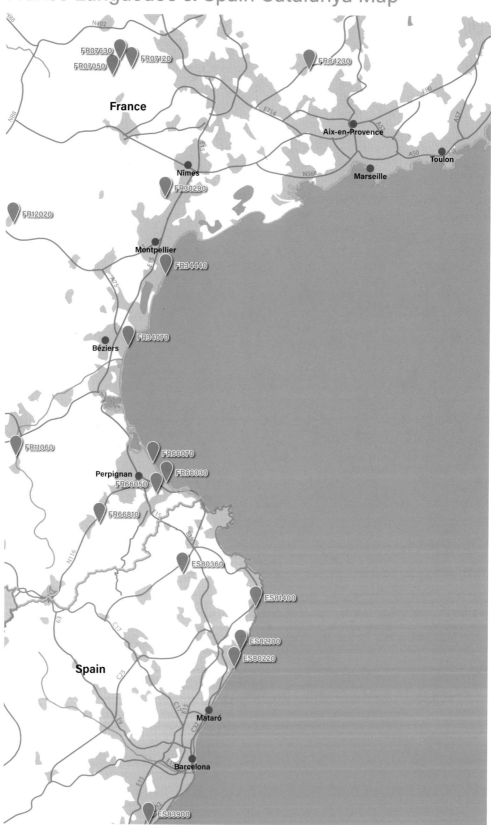

France

FR07630
FR07050
FR07120

FR84230

Aix-en-Provence

Toulon

Nîmes

Marseille

FR30290

FR12020

Montpellier

FR34440

FR34070

Béziers

FR11060

FR66070

Perpignan

FR66030

FR66050

FR66810

ES80360

ES81400

ES82100

ES80220

Spain

Mataró

Barcelona

ES83900

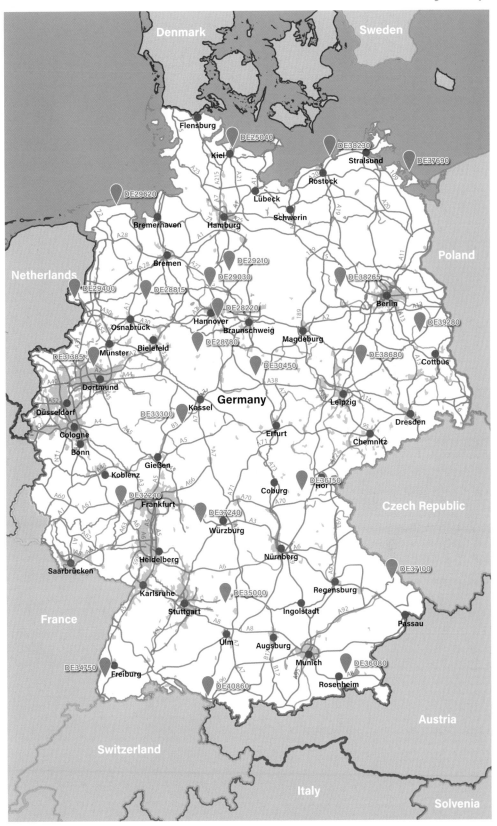

Great Britain & Ireland Map

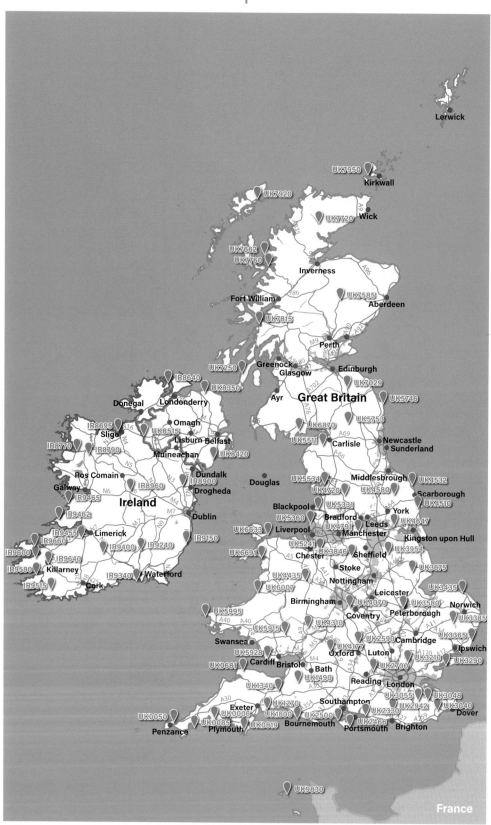

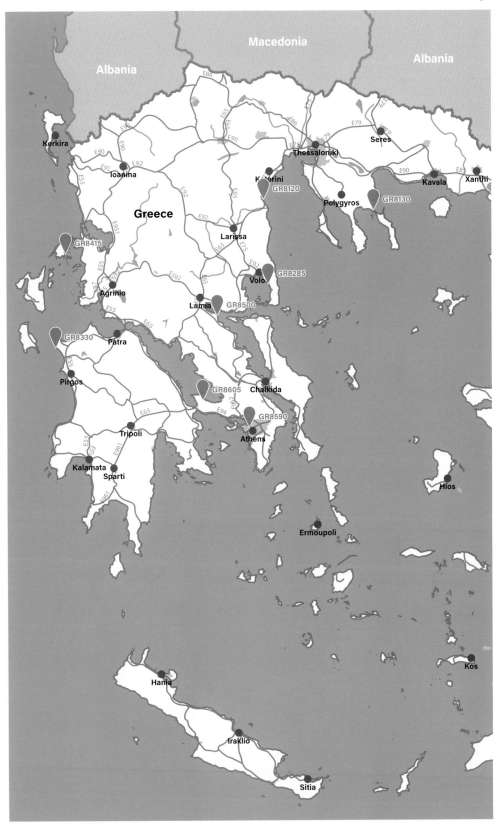

Italy Map

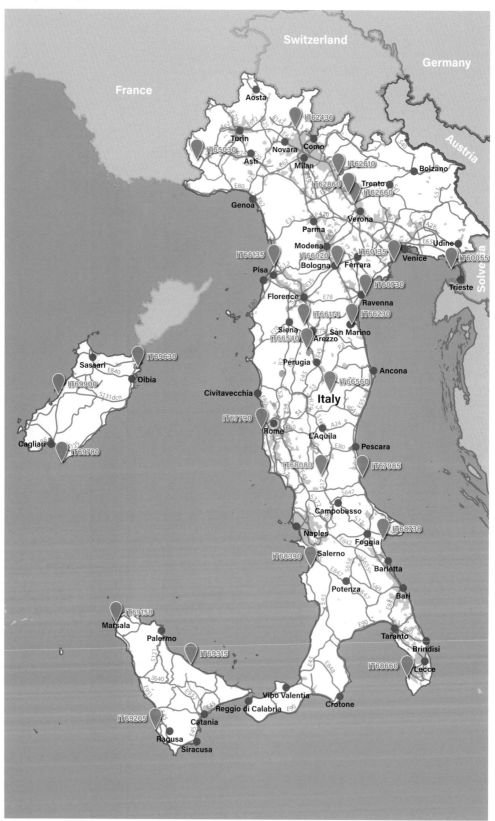

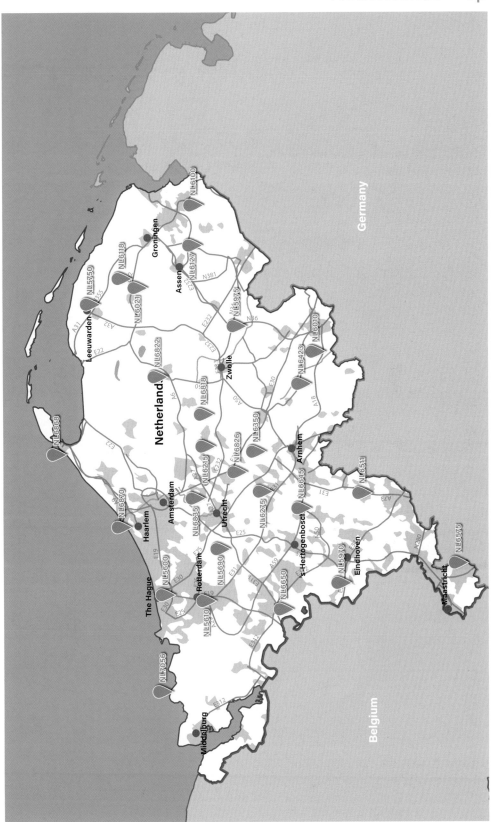

Portugal & Spain Map

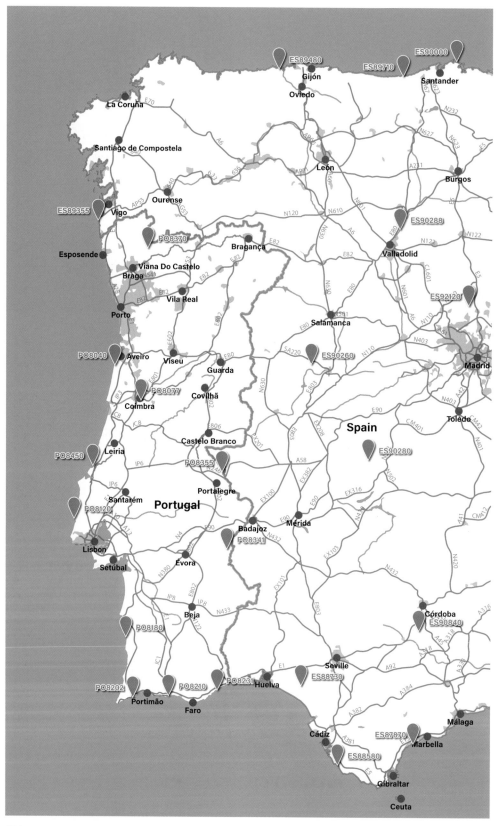

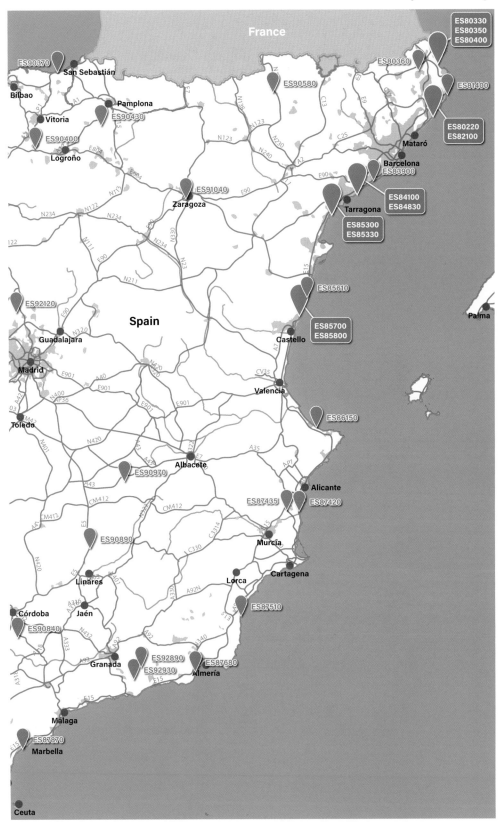

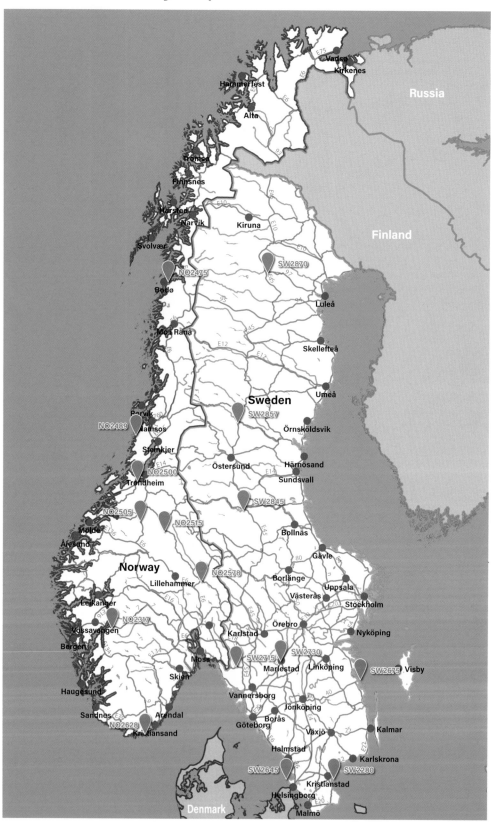

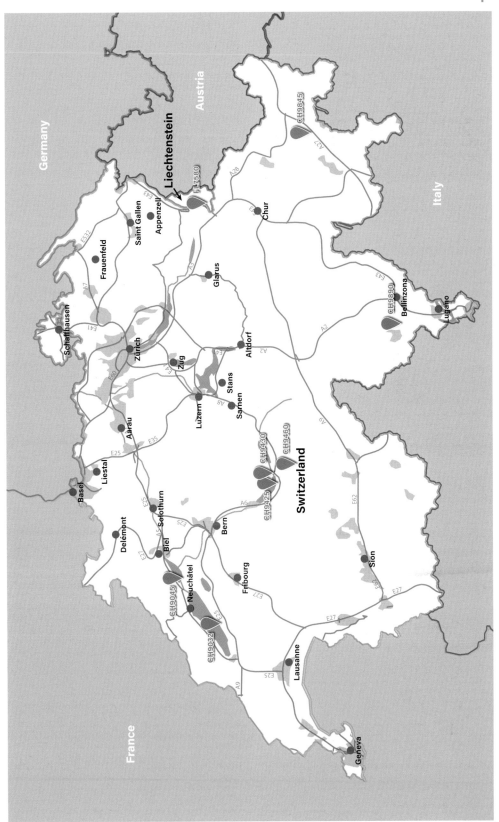

Index By Location

Index By Alan Rogers Code & Name